Dancing with Dictators

To Carol,
all the best,
Luis
10/'17

DANCING with DICTATORS

A Family's Journey from Pre-Castro Cuba to Exile in the Turbulent Sixties

• A MEMOIR •

LUIS SANTEIRO

ISBN 978-0-692-90528-9
Library of Congress Control Number: 2017911086
Printed in the United States of America

Book design by Victoria Hartman

This book may be ordered from www.amazon.com

To the memory of my parents

Author's Note

All the events in this book are factual. Wherever I have created scenes with dialogue, it has only been to further bring to life on the page the personalities of these characters, as they still live on in my memory.

Various early readers suggested that I include a family tree, but I decided that a genealogical diagram would be too intricate and might end up becoming just a list of meaningless names. Therefore I have opted for these brief descriptions, à la Russian novel, which can be referred back to should any confusion arise. In some cases, I have included both the paternal and maternal last names, or the maiden name and married one, as is the custom in Spanish culture.

MY IMMEDIATE FAMILY

Luis Santeiro Crusellas: My father. He was also known as Luisito to many of his friends. To make a distinction, I was often called Luis Manuel, or Luisma.

Nenita Grau Machado de Santeiro: My mother. Baptized Maria de los Angeles, she was always known as Nenita, which basically means "little girl." She found this increasingly incongruous as she grew older.

Maria Mercedes (also called **Mequi**), **Gerardo**, **Francisco**, and **Carlos:** My siblings. I was the eldest child, with a nine-year difference between Carlos and me.

Lourdes: Daughter of my father's uncle Ramón, from his third marriage. She came to live with us at age thirteen, after both her parents had died. A year older than me, she became another sister.

MY PATERNAL SIDE

Abuela (Mercedes Crusellas de Santeiro): My grandmother, who ruled the roost at our house in Havana. She became a widow shortly before I was born, and remained in semi-mourning ever after.

Ramón Antonio Crusellas: My theatrical uncle, and also my godfather. He was actually the son of my father's uncle Ramón, from his first marriage, which made him Lourdes' much older half-brother. After his mother's death, when Ramón Antonio was only five, my grandmother took him under her wing, and he became like another son.

Tiana (Ana Maria Crusellas): Daughter of my grandmother's sister, Otilia. Her father died before Tiana had even been born, so to help her widowed sister, Abuela took charge of her also, supposedly temporarily, then ended up keeping her.

Marietta: My father's uncle Ramón's second wife. A former Zarzuela and Music Hall performer, Marietta remained an integral part of our family, even after Tio Ramón divorced her to marry Lourdes' mother.

MY MATERNAL SIDE

Mimamá (Laudelina Machado de Grau): My grandmother. She was known as Nena to all the adults (which thus turned her daughter into Nenita). Oldest daughter of former Cuban president Gerardo Machado, she wore hats her entire life, even during the twenty-four years that she remained in Cuba after the triumph of the revolution.

Papín (Baldomero Grau): My grandfather. A lawyer by profession, he wrote essays and poetry and fought with my mother to try to save my foreskin. He also loved to place bets at the dog track.

Mamá Elvira (Elvira Machado de Machado): My great-grandmother. A former *Mambisa*, or freedom fighter, during Cuba's War of Independence, she was the widow of President Machado, who had also been her cousin.

Tia Babi (Angela Elvira Machado de Obregón): My grandmother's saner sister, she was married to José Emilio Obregón. Tia Babi had a unique sense of style, which she somehow managed to retain even while shoveling coal into the house furnace during the family's "second exile".

Mari: My "aunt" and godmother. The daughter of Tia Babi and José Emilio, Mari was actually my mother's first cousin, but having been raised under the same roof, she was like a younger sister to my mother. Mari had a deep voice and a flair for over-dramatization. She loved being compared to Audrey Hepburn.

Andres Arellano: Mari's husband. Handsome but slightly deranged, he had charmed Mari with his good looks but impressed nobody else in the family at all. His entering our ranks had been no cause for celebration.

Tia Berta (Berta Machado de Sanchez): My grandmother's more unconventional sister, the one whose eccentricities the family would try to sweep under the rug. She had married Rafael Jorge Sanchez, whom I never knew. According to some, he was a perfect match only in the respect that he was even crazier than she was.

Lugi: Tia Berta's "bewitched" daughter. Her medical condition was never properly diagnosed, as Tia Berta saw no need, believing that

Lugi would one day snap out of her "enchantment," just like Sleeping Beauty.

Maria Regueros: The Machados' housekeeper. With the family for decades, both in Cuba and the U.S., she knew more about each household member than they did themselves.

Prologue

"The day your great-grandfather became president, the people of Havana poured out into the streets to celebrate."

My *bisabuelo* Gerardo Machado, who was president of Cuba from 1925 to 1933, had died almost a decade before I was born, but from my mother's stories and the photo she kept on her desk, the one of him signing his inauguration decree, I felt as if I'd known him. The fancy pen he was using, and the fact that he was missing a finger on his left hand, had always intrigued me.

"He lost it while fighting in our War of Independence, during which he became the youngest general."

She had adored Papá Gerardito, her maternal grandfather, and wanted me, if not to love, at least to admire him.

Sometimes while Mami was telling me these old stories I would stare out of her bedroom windows. From the ones that faced the garden I could look down upon the Spanish-tiled fountain with the naked girl statue. And if I leaned out of the ones facing her balcony, I could see the royal palms that line the entrance to the Hotel Nacional, and beyond it the Caribbean ocean pounding El Malecón—the seaside boulevard.

"Luis Manuel, did you *want* to hear the story or not?"

"*Sí, sí*. Keep going."

"I had awakened earlier that morning because of the noise from the crowd that had gathered outside our house. Peeking through the shutters I could see the neighborhood kids inspecting the black limousine that was waiting to take Papá Gerardito to the presidential palace. The men who had come to wish him well were all in their best white-twill suits and Panama hats. The women, in their cotton-print dresses, were fanning themselves or holding up parasols as shields against the hot Cuban sun.

"Amada, my *manejadora*, who had taken care of me since I was a baby, sprinkled an extra dose of violet water into the tub before she bathed me. Then she helped me put on the beautiful powder-blue dress that Mamá's seamstress had designed for the occasion. It had these puff-sleeves that made me feel very grown up and a big starched silk bow at the waist. Amada always clipped my bangs so that they would make a perfect straight line over my eyebrows, and then she twirled a brush to make my hair bob up at the back.

"I was waiting at the foot of the stairs when Papá Gerardito came down, wearing his black silk tails and pinstripe pants. He stopped at the door to wipe his glasses—the round tortoiseshell ones that he always wore. Then he asked me if I would like to ride in the official car with him, but the crowd intimidated me, so I said no. I was really hoping he would insist, but instead he turned and walked out. On the biggest day of his life he rode alone. The rest of the family—your great-grandmother Mamá Elvira, Tia Babi, all of us—followed him in the motorcade.

"All along the way the balconies were decorated with palm fronds and paper flags, and as he passed by, cheering crowds showered their new president with flowers and confetti. Then the moment he reached the palace, a military band broke into our national anthem, and everybody sang along. Upstairs, in the hall of mirrors, another orchestra was playing Cuban music: *sones*, *danzones*, *boleros*. Papá Gerardito had a reputation for being quite a good dancer, so women were already lining up for a chance to show themselves off with him. But when he saw me walk in, he turned toward me instead and held out his hand.

"'Just do it the way I taught you, *mi amor*,' he whispered. Then with every eye in the room upon us, he reached down and gently started leading me. 'Think of that little square tile that we're tracing with our feet—right, then back, then left, then front again.'

"His voice was so reassuring that I was able to follow him perfectly. Right, back, left, then front again. And I even did it while turning. Soon he had to move on to the wives of senators and ambassadors, who were growing impatient. But by the time he left me, I was happy again.

"Our country should be very grateful to your great-grandfather. Half the things you see on this island today were built during his administration: El Capitolio, the capitol building; the central highway, the Prado Boulevard. You should feel very proud."

It was important for my mother that all her children hear these stories from her. But it was especially so for me, who was the eldest, and likely to soon start hearing other versions.

The first time this happened was in third grade, during a recess. A classmate brought to school an old issue of *Bohemia*, a popular illustrated weekly that specialized in lurid news.

"Look what I found in my *tio*'s garage."

On a brittle and yellowed page was a picture of my *bisabuelo*, looking a bit older than he did in my mother's photograph. He was wearing a rumpled white suit and carrying a bag as he headed up the steps of a small airplane. "The Flight of the Beast," screamed the caption in Spanish. With my heart beating faster I read on.

> El General Gerardo Machado, the donkey with claws, the tyrant who has caused the biggest bloodshed this country has seen since our War of Independence, has finally fled our shores—along with the rest of his parasitic clan. The bag that we see him carrying, as he makes his cowardly escape, is stuffed with millions of pesos, stolen from our already-depleted national treasury. May the vile monster soon encounter the painful end that he so deserves.

I could feel my face turning red. "Bah! That's just a cheap trashy magazine," was all I could manage to say. But when I got home I rushed straight up to my mother's room.

"Why would someone want to call Papá Gerardito a monster?"

"*Ay, mijo.* When you reach a very high position, like he did, there are always people ready to say terrible things about you—jealous, ungrateful people. Your great-grandfather faced plenty of those. Don't ever believe their malicious lies."

1

The house that I was born in was like an Advent calendar, endless doors with surprising things behind each of them. It was built by my father's maternal grandfather, Ramón Crusellas, who came to Cuba in the 1870s from the town of Artés, in Cataluña, to take over his aging uncle's candle-making business. With the rise of gaslight and decline of candle sales, he switched over to making soap and perfume, and by the turn of the century he had a highly successful company manufacturing products well known across the entire island.

The house was in El Vedado, the fashionable district of the World War I era. It sat right on the corner of N Street and 21st Street, but to the family the house was always "La Calle Ene," as if the entire street had been our personal property. Ramón Crusellas, however, barely got to enjoy his beaux-arts creation. He was dead within a few months of its completion. An often-told family story claimed that his little black Pomeranian followed the hearse all the way to his grave, at the Colón cemetery, then died of grief shortly afterwards.

Deaths in the Crusellas family always seemed to have some extra dramatic spin, and two more of them occurred barely a year before I was born. Ramón Antonio, my theatrical uncle and godfather, who was still single and lived on the first floor amid hundreds of classical record albums that he always played at top volume, had told me about those.

"Mamaíta, your great-grandmother, had been suffering from breast cancer and seemed to be near the end. But one night a friend invited me to a Toque de Santo. That's a Santería celebration where they initiate a *babalao*, a priest of the religion. Not that I believe in those things, but I love the rituals, with all the drumming and dancing, and always someone falling into a hysterical trance. I had had it with the death-watch that your grandmother had imposed, so I snuck out for a couple hours of something more uplifting.

"The *toque* was being held in one of those ancient buildings of La Habana Vieja, three floors crowded with small apartments all facing an inner courtyard. The drums were already in high gear when this *mulata*, all draped in white, tapped me on the shoulder. "Señor Crusel-las, *el babalao* wants to see you," she pointed to a nearby room where a wizened old man, all in white too, sat on a rocking chair, smoking a fat cigar. As I approached, he started having convulsions. At first I figured it was part of a very impressive act, but then the convulsions stopped and blood started to trickle down a corner of his tobacco-stained lips. It gave me chills. With eyes wide open he stared at me and said, 'Go home, *muchacho*. Go home right now.'

"Instantly I thought of Mamaíta, and rushed back home. But when I got there nothing had changed. I decided that the *babalao* had sensed I was there for my amusement and found a clever way to get rid of me.

"The next day, while we were having lunch, your grandfather—Tio Manolo, to me—suddenly excused himself and rushed out. This was highly atypical of him, so when he didn't return after a few minutes, I went looking for him. I heard coughing coming from the guest bath-room beneath the stairs, so I peeked in and found him bent over by the toilet. "Are you all right, Tio?" I asked. When he turned to me, there was blood trickling down one corner of his mouth, exactly the same as I had seen on the *babalao*. Right away I called your father and we rushed him to the hospital, but by that evening he was dead."

He then added another detail that seemed irrelevant to me at the time.

"Shortly after Tio Manolo died, his long-time secretary, Mericia, entered a cloistered convent."

I should explain that Ramón Antonio wasn't exactly my uncle. His father, Ramón, was the brother of Mercedes, my paternal grandmother. Abuela, as I called her, had taken Ramón Antonio under her protective wing when his mother, also named Mercedes, died during the 1918 influenza epidemic. It was actually Ramón Antonio's father who had first fallen gravely ill, but his mother, who was very devout, prayed to every saint in the canon offering her own life to God in exchange for her husband's recovery. A few days later he was up and about and *she* was dead. Thanks to her answered prayers, Ramón Antonio's father lived on to enjoy two more wives and dozens of mistresses. Years later, when his first wife's body was exhumed to place the bones in the Crusellas crypt's ossuary, it was discovered that she had not decomposed at all. Instantly, the family canonized her as our own personal saint, "Santa Mercedes." But I digress.

Ramón Antonio also told me that after the death of my grandfather, Abuela had an emotional breakdown. The family's doctor, a Rasputin of sorts, had to be called in. Abuela was devoted to him, despite the fact that he had very likely precipitated her husband's death by giving him a laxative for what turned out to be a bleeding ulcer. His ministrations had also left her with a desiccated right-hand middle finger, after a minor infection from a rose thorn, which made it seem as if she was eternally making a vulgar sign. "Rasputin" had even caused the big scar on my father's left butt cheek, the result of a badly administered injection. And when my Tia Ana gave birth to her only child, Ramoncito, he had allowed her to remain in painful labor for more than twenty-four hours, finally extracting the baby with a forceps, which left Ramoncito with a half-paralyzed arm. But Abuela could see no relation between these events.

Rasputin's tranquilizing shots were not very effective for Abuela, but since her mother, Mamaíta, was still agonizing from cancer, Abuela retained just enough control to keep her mother from discovering the tragic news of my grandfather's death. Ramón Antonio described how Abuela would be wailing down a hallway one minute then make an instant transition as she entered her mother's sick room. "Sarah Bernhardt had nothing on Tia Mercedita."

Mamaíta finally died a few days later. Her death was foretold by her sister, Monona, who was on a ship en route to Havana from La Coruña. Tia Monona, the *living* family saint, had lost three teenage sons fighting for the *Franquistas* during the Spanish Civil War, and possessed the gift, or perhaps the curse, of seeing a light flash by her whenever a loved one died. This time the light flashed prematurely, for her condolence telegram, from aboard the ship, arrived almost an hour before Mamaíta breathed her last.

Another resident of La Calle Ene was my Tia Ana, already briefly mentioned, although she also was not really my aunt. Her father, Abuela's brother-in-law, had died from a mysterious disease that he contracted while doing an engineering project on the Havana aqueduct system. My great-aunt, Tia Otilia, was eight months pregnant at the time, so when her daughter was born, already a semi-orphan, Abuela took over the baby's upbringing to give her widowed sister time to grieve. But when Tia Otilia stopped grieving and remarried a couple of years later, Abuela refused to give up her niece.

Motivated by pity for the fatherless girl, everyone spoiled Tiana, as we later called her, from the moment she was born. She herself told me how if Abuela and Abuelo Manolo were heading out for the evening, but she decided that she'd rather they stay, she would feign sudden blindness, and they would remain by her side. Sometimes she would claim that she was a dog, and a plate would be set for her underneath the dining room table. When she married Tio Paco, at age twenty, a whole new wing was added to the house. It was big enough for them to sleep several rooms apart, once their relationship soured.

While hanging around the servants' quarters one day I overheard two of them gossiping about the *mulata* that Tio Paco was keeping in a little apartment somewhere in the old section of town. And while I didn't fully understand why he was keeping her, I sensed that it was not out of charity.

According to Ramón Antonio, Tiana had had a love affair of her own. I overheard him telling the story to one of his friends.

"His name was Adolfito, and he adored her. Whenever we went to the opera, of which he was a board member, he would stand there, transfixed, staring at Ana. He was unhappily married too, but apparently found a place where they could meet, and would call her to arrange their trysts when he managed to escape his wife. Somehow Tia Mercedita got wind of it, probably through one of the servants. So she installed a telephone extension in the basement and charged a maid to sit there and eavesdrop on their conversations. Once she had irrefutable proof, she confronted Ana and told her that if she did not put an end to the relationship immediately and return to Paco, she would go to court and take over legal custody of Ramoncito. Poor Ana had no choice but to end the affair, and probably her one chance to be happy, for there was nothing back home for her to return to."

This was the scenario that my mother, "Nenita" Grau Machado entered into when she married my father, Luis Santeiro Crusellas, just six months after the double-death. The family was still in mourning, which my Abuela would remain in for the rest of her life. The grand wedding that had once been planned now became an intimate eleven A.M. affair, and the honeymoon, originally scheduled for Europe, was switched to a secluded resort in Sea Island, Georgia—a more appropriate destination for a son in mourning. Then ten days later, Abuela, still emotionally fragile, joined the newlyweds at the posh, but teetotaling and staid, Homestead Hotel, in West Virginia—with Tiana in tow. Many years later Mami still held a grudge over this intrusion and often reminded Papi of it.

2

In August of 1933, Sumner Welles, President Roosevelt's ambassador to Cuba, gave my *bisabuelo* Gerardo Machado a twenty-four-hour ultimatum to leave the country. Despite the fact that the United States was responsible for his removal from office and for the chaos that ensued, the family still sought refuge within our great northern neighbor, just as Cuban political exiles had done throughout our history. My mother was ten days short of her twelfth birthday the night of their abrupt departure. She had told me that story too.

"We had been summering with Mamá Elvira, your great-grandmother, at our beach house in Varadero. I was getting ready for bed when the news arrived from Havana. The reports were conflicting. Some said that Papá Gerardito had already fled the country, others that he had fallen into the hands of the opposition—a possibility that we prayed would not be true. Without a second thought, Mamá Elvira told Captain Morejón, who was in change of the men guarding us, to drive her back to Havana, but Morejón replied that it was impossible. Roads were likely to be blocked, and our cars were too conspicuous. He did not tell her that thousands had already taken over the streets to loot and burn. Mobs were dragging members of the administration out of their homes, ready to tear them to pieces. But the captain assured us that Papá Gerardito was safe, and that the presidential yacht was already waiting for us about a kilometer off the coast. I asked him about Mimamá and Papín, your grandparents, who were in Havana also, and Morejón told me not to worry. There were still enough loyal guards to ensure their safety.

"Mamá Elvira and Tia Babi ran upstairs to wake up Mari and Fifi, my little cousins, and told their *manejadoras* to pack just a few basic things. Meanwhile, María Regueros, our cook, raced around the kitchen throwing together a basket of food for our journey. She had been with us forever, and there was no question that she herself would be coming along.

"There wasn't a single star in the sky that night, and the darkness made the sound of the breaking waves more frightening. Even the usually gentle waters of Varadero seemed to be in turmoil.

"As our little group descended the back porch stairs that led to the sand, we could barely see where we were stepping. I was old enough to realize that I should be as quick and unobtrusive as possible, but Mari and Fifi could sense the tension and began to whimper and cry. Then our neighbors started coming out to gawk from all the nearby porches. I wondered how word could have spread so quickly. I had known all these people my whole life. Their children had been my playmates, right on this beach, every summer since I could remember. But now they just stared in silence as we passed by them, perhaps afraid to incriminate themselves by saying a kind word of farewell. And despite trying to hold my head up high, their cold gazes made me feel ashamed.

"A large rowboat was waiting at the end of our pier, but it kept rocking, and the two sailors straddling it could barely hold it still long enough for us to climb aboard. After Mamá Elvira, Tia Babi, and myself were safely seated, Morejón scooped up Mari and Fifi, then swung them into the arms of the sailors. Now only María Regueros remained. She stood there pondering how to maneuver her ample rear into the boat. Without waiting for her to decide, Morejón took a deep breath, poked his head under one of her arms then slowly lowered her toward us with the greatest possible decorum.

"The ride to high seas to meet the presidential yacht seemed endless. Hard as the sailors rowed they seemed to make very slow progress. As the lights along the beach grew dimmer, Morejón grabbed a flashlight and scanned the black expanse ahead, but he could see nothing.

"'*Ay, Virgencita!*' María Regueros crossed herself.

"'María, *por Dios!* You're making the girls more nervous.' Tia Babi put her arms around Mari and Fifi. Then Fifi started to get seasick. And I sensed that the sailors were starting to get nervous too.

"'They said one kilometer. We've gone almost two. Where are they?'

"'*Shh!*' Morejón told everyone to keep quiet, and cupped a hand around his ear. We remained dead silent for a moment . . . then heard a faint voice.

"'*Aqui estamos!*' It called out from the darkness. 'Over here!'

"A blurry gray patch came into view

"'*Gracias, Señor!*' María Regueros praised Heaven.

"But the waves had grown bigger, and our bobbing rowboat wouldn't remain alongside the larger craft long enough to unload us. A sailor on the yacht kept trying to toss a rope to Morejón, who, determined to grab it, almost fell overboard.

"'*Virgen Santísima!*' María crossed herself again.

"Finally, a sailor succeeded in grasping the rope and tied us up to the yacht. The waves kept thrusting us against it and making a horrible creaking sound. Then something fell from above, uncoiling as it approached. It was a rope ladder.

"'What are we supposed to do with that?' Tia Babi stared at Morejón.

"'Don't worry, Señora. I'll be right behind all of you.'

"I had never known my grandmother or aunt to be the least bit athletic, and I held my breath as I watched each of them climb, convinced that they would fall into the dark water and never be seen again. But to my amazement, they did rather well.

"When Maria Regueros' turn came, I started to pray. But with Morejón and one of the sailors pushing from either side, María rose too, until the men above grabbed hold of her and the massive bottom disappeared over the railing. Then it was time for us girls.

"Morejón held his hand out to me. 'You first, *preciosa*.'

"I liked to think of myself as grown up, and this was the time to prove it. I took hold of the ladder and stepped on the first rung . . . just as a big wave whacked the rowboat and knocked me back down. I froze, and all of Morejón's coaxing was now useless.

"'Throw her up to us!' someone shouted.

"I could see the ambivalence in Morejón's eyes.

"'Go ahead! Wait for a wave. We'll catch her!'

"I was not exactly slim at the time, but after a moment's hesitation Morejón picked me up. As we waited for a wave I could see that he was being blinded by sweat and salt water. He would have to rely on his sense of timing, and hope for the best. Our boat rose further. He took a deep breath, then gave me the heave-ho. Up with a shriek I went. A second later four arms caught me in mid-air and pulled me to safety.

"With regained confidence, Morejón reached for Mari, who kicked and screamed all the way. Then he picked up Fifi.

"'No, please! Don't throw the baby!' Tia Babi pleaded.

"For a second Morejón considered climbing with her, then decided that was even more risky. Ignoring Tia Babi's pleas, he waited for another big wave, then tossed up what looked like a small sack of potatoes.

"Watching helplessly from above, we all held our breath. But Fifi too was caught like a fly ball.

"Any thoughts of hoisting the rowboat had by now been abandoned. Captain Morejón and the two sailors struggled their own way up the swaying rope ladder, then the presidential yacht sailed off.

"Halfway through our turbulent crossing we met up with another ship, which was carrying your grandparents. With her typical Joan of Arc spirit, Mamá had been the very last family member to leave the palace, and she almost got trapped by the mob.

"All night long the ship tossed and swayed. But exhausted from the ordeal, Mari, Fifi, and I all slept soundly, huddled against each other on the presidential bed. I did not wake up again until we had safely moored in Key West."

My mother did not return to Cuba for the next seven years, which the family spent in New York City and ever after referred to as "the first exile." Thirteen relatives, plus a few political hangers-on, had piled into a townhouse on Manhattan's Upper East Side. Despite all accusations about the stolen millions, their finances were tight. Many letters had been exchanged with Cuba in attempts to reclaim any confiscated property that they could sell—but to no avail. Still, this had been a happy time for my mother. She enjoyed a freedom that she had never known while living in the presidential palace. For the first time, she attended a regular school instead of having in-palace tutoring. She made friends whom she could meet for lunch at Nedick's or the Automat, without a bodyguard, then go to Radio City to catch the latest movie, or even stand in line outside the Paramount Theater for a chance to swoon over the newest teen idol, Frank Sinatra.

It wasn't until after Papá Gerardito's death, in 1939, that Papín, my maternal grandfather, decided that enough years and subsequent Cuban presidents had gone by. It was time to go back and test the waters.

As they boarded the plane to Havana, Papín said to my mother, "There may be some people, even old friends, who will want to avoid us—for political reasons. It's probably best if you do not greet anyone until they first greet you."

But much to the contrary, my mother found the warmest of receptions and open doors everywhere. She was the new face in town, a pretty one, and after being in New York all these years, she was considered somewhat exotic.

"My hair was long, which was the latest fashion, like Hedy Lamarr's and Brenda Frazier's, the debutante of the decade. Most of the girls in Havana were still wearing theirs short. I also knew all the lyrics to songs like "Let's Do It," and "Anything Goes," which were considered quite risqué back then."

She had no lack of young men asking her out, and to the shock of some older matrons, was allowed to go unchaperoned.

"But I had one image stuck in my head, one person that I was anxious to run into once again. I had first seen him at the *feria ganadera*, a kind of state fair. I was sitting with my family in the presidential box, watching a dressage competition, when this group riding the most handsome horses entered the ring. I heard someone say they were from the Finca Crusellas. Among them was this boy, a few years older than me. He was riding a white Arab stallion, and had the most beautiful blue eyes I had ever seen. I had never forgotten him. He was your father."

• 3 •

For an only child born with a silver soupspoon in his mouth, my father had turned out miraculously well. And while praise for one's own father might come off as biased or self-serving, compliments about his character came from all directions—friends, colleagues, employees, even from an old Irish lady. She had sent a little note to my mother upon learning of her engagement, penned in the most beautiful handwriting, in purple ink.

Dear Nenita,

Although I do not know you personally, I hope you will pardon the liberty I am taking in writing you a few words on this occasion. I have known Luis since he was a little boy of eight. I have witnessed his behavior as an ideal son, and I have no doubt but that he will make an ideal husband, for he is everything that is good and noble. In my estimation he is perfection personified, so you are indeed fortunate in your choice. I wish I could enumerate all his good qualities but I dare not for he is so modest—and dislikes praise, so you will have to take the rest for granted.

Please accept this little bouquet, filled with sincerest congratulations, from Luis' English teacher.

With my warmest regards,

Nora O'Connor

My father lived by one motto: "If you have nothing good to say about someone, don't say anything." Perhaps this was the reason that he told so few stories, and when he did, they somehow lacked the intriguing details of those told by Ramón Antonio.

"Your *tio* has a very overactive imagination," Papi would say, stopping me halfway whenever I tried to relay some family tale that I had just heard. "That never happened, certainly not the way he says, so don't repeat it."

If my father had one flaw, perhaps it was in trying to please both parties whenever two people he loved found themselves at odds.

"Take care of your mother." Those were the last words Abuelo Manolo had said to him before being wheeled off to the operating table. They had created a heightened sense of responsibility toward Abuela that often left my mother feeling that she was taking second place. Not that Abuela wanted anything but happiness for the newlyweds. She had even given my mother her former suite of rooms and moved to another corner of the house. What Abuela would not do was loosen her grip on the household reins. She kept full control over everything, from the planning of dinner menus to overseeing the dozen or more servants. This left my mother with nothing to do but sleep till noon and play canasta. And then there was Tiana, who did not relish seeing someone else taking over her former place of prominence.

Confronted with all this, my mother soon limited her regular sphere of operation. Except for mealtimes, when she would join the rest of the family in the dining room, she mostly kept to her bedroom, her huge two-tiered walk-in closet, and her pink marble bathroom. This is where my memory of those days places her most, either getting a massage when I came home from school at midday, for our two-hour lunch break, or smoking by a window as she stared toward the horizon dreaming of her own home.

But oblivious to the frictions that existed between the diverse personalities living under our extended family roof, to me, La Calle Ene was a safe mini-universe with about twenty different people to whom I could turn, depending on my needs at any specific moment.

Ruling the roost at the servants' end was Rosalina, our *ama de llaves*, or keeper of the keys. I don't remember anyone ever saying her last name. She was simply Rosalina, a thin, accordion-skinned old lady who had emigrated from Galicia in her youth and had worked for the family since before my father's birth. She was not too popular with the rest of the staff, who saw her as a tightwad and a stool pigeon who would readily report to grandmother any behavior that displeased her. She was deadly loyal to Abuela, as Abuela was to her.

I once overheard other servants complain that she served them days-old *café*. She would also boil milk and skim off the cream for my grandmother, leaving everyone else with the watery remains. Rosalina was not someone that I would ever turn to for comfort, but she did have the keys to every closet and cabinet in the house. I would often find her opening one of them, either to look for something or to organize things. Whenever I did, I would put on hold whatever I was about to do and stick around to see what curious wonders were stored within.

There was a slanted-ceiling closet under the main stairway that was like an Aladdin's cave, with every Gallé vase, porcelain figurine, and Tiffany lampshade that had fallen out of fashion. In the cellar hallway that led to the female servants' rooms, there was also a big old armoire that was packed with old magazines and photo albums. Some of these went back to when Abuela was a girl. I remember a photo of her at a *carnaval* ball wearing a Spanish outfit with a huge *peineta* holding up her *mantilla*, and another one in which she had rings on every single finger, like a Gypsy. It was a revelation to find that Abuela, whom I had only known in black and white, could ever have worn such fanciful things, much less been so young.

One day I came upon Rosalina rummaging through a big storage closet inside the garage. It was dark and dusty, but in one corner, half-covered by a heavy yellowed cloth, I discovered a life-size bronze sculpture of a peacock sitting on the rim of a well. The peacock's tail was made of colored crystals, underneath which was an electric light-bulb socket. The trellis above the well had a twisting grapevine, with clusters of green and purple crystal grapes that could also light up from inside. I thought this was the most beautiful thing I had ever seen, and I could picture what it would look like all dusted off and with those colored crystals glowing. "Why is this hidden in here?" I asked Rosalina. "I have no idea. Ask your Abuela." When I did, she seemed to have forgotten that it even existed. "Oh, *that* thing! Your *bisabuelo* bought it at the Paris Exposition of 1900. It sat on an Andalusian-style patio we once had, until everyone got sick of it."

"Well, I love it. Can I put it in my room?" Abuela laughed and said that I could. Yet whenever I asked when someone was going to move it up there, I was given some procrastinating excuse. My peacock remained in its dusty corner.

Forming a matching set with Rosalina, but more like a cruet of oil and vinegar, was Candelaria—or Canda, as everyone knew her. She was a *mulata*, and nobody was sure how old she was, not even she herself. She *did* know that she was born before 1886, because that was when slaves were liberated in Cuba, and one of her oldest memories was of her mother telling her that they were free. Canda had also been with the family for decades. She was hired to take care of Tiana's son, Ramoncito, shortly after her long painful labor. Canda had traveled with them to The States on various occasions, and she had never forgotten the many times she was dying to pee but couldn't find a bathroom that wasn't marked "Whites Only." Before coming to us she had worked for the Duquesne family, descendants of a French marquee. With "El Marqués" she had even gone to Paris, where she felt people had been much nicer to her. "A few of them came up to me and ran a finger across my skin, to see if the color rubbed off. But there were many others who said I was very beautiful." Because of her age, Canda no longer worked, but since she had no other relatives she simply remained with us.

One never knew where one might run into Canda. Sometimes she sat on a little bench near the garage, where the sun shone all morning long. Sometimes I found her in the garden, by our playroom, where there was a tangled jasmine vine. She collected the little blossoms to make jasmine tea. She knew about all kinds of plants and the illnesses that they could cure. She also knew about the African gods of Santería and what kind of flower each of them preferred. When I was little, Canda would sit beside me and sing old songs that we could both clap to. Some of them also sounded very African. "*Bururú barará como etá Miguel. Bururú!*" Years later I would find her singing the exact same songs to my younger brothers.

Reigning over the kitchen was Pedro, our chef, who was as dark as a moonless night and wore impeccable white uniforms, with a toque. You did not barge into his domain unless you were invited to taste something. Pedro could make just about anything, from traditional Cuban dishes to sophisticated French ones. Some of it I loved, other things became a nightmare for me when they appeared at the dinner table, like brain fritters. My grandmother loved those, so they were served frequently. We were supposed to eat whatever was on the menu, but I had found a clever way to avoid anything that I considered disgusting.

From age seven or eight we got to eat with the adults, and we were expected to behave properly, which included knowing how to serve ourselves when Humberto came to us with a tray. It also meant not interrupting conversations unless we were included. But since dinner was usually served at eight, we were allowed to come downstairs in our pajamas and robes. Fortuitously, robes have big loose pockets, perfect for sliding morsels of unwanted food into—morsels I could then unload in the back of some seldom used drawer. But once a week, usually when my parents went out, we were allowed to make our own menu requests. I would invariably ask for *malanga* fritters, which Pedro excelled at. My sister, Maria Mercedes, whom we also called Mequi, would ask for *fanguito*, or mud, a low-end version of chocolate mousse. My brother Gerardo loved floating islands, which Pedro garnished with lava-like caramel. Even though we had no volcanoes, I would pretend that the floating island on my plate was Cuba, then devour it province by province. Pedro also had an assistant, who was called a *pinche*. But for some reason, these changed far too frequently for me to remember any of them.

Humberto, who served the table and also acted as a sort of Cuban version of a butler, loved to gossip and was fascinated by Havana society. He read the social pages daily, knew who everybody was, and sometimes also what went on in their private lives. At five o'clock each afternoon he would slip on his white gloves ready to open the door to whoever happened to pay a visit to Abuela that day, and he always greeted them effusively. Whenever a major party was being given anywhere in the city, and his dinnertime services weren't needed because the family was attending, he would sneak off and stand outside the hosts' residence to watch the guests arrive. The following morning, while serving breakfast, he would regale my mother with his personal report.

"La Señorita Alina looked stunning last night. That green dress was a perfect contrast for her auburn hair. *Ay*, but la Señora Silvia should never wear a long skirt. It made her look like a midget."

Abuela often reprimanded Humberto for not being where he should have been, or for being where he shouldn't. "This is my last warning," she would tell him. "I guess it is," he'd reply, "Because I quit!" He had already tossed off his gloves on various occasions, but then always returned when whoever replaced him also quit after only a few days of dealing with Abuela.

But my most vivid memory of Humberto happened on the day that Christine Jorgensen, the famous Danish ex-sailor turned female by an operation, arrived in Havana to perform at a nearby nightclub. Her pending arrival had been big news for weeks, and even though I assumed that his becoming a woman just meant he had put on lipstick and a dress, that seemed shocking enough to me.

Humberto, who had the investigative skills of a secret agent, had gotten wind that Miss Jorgensen would be staying at an apartment building right across the street from us. He also found out the time of her scheduled arrival and sneaked off to get a closer glimpse. All the other servants were dying of curiosity too, and along with the rest of us, gathered on the second-floor balcony that faced Christine's building. As her car pulled up, I could see Humberto pushing his way through the crowd of gawkers and reporters. Then, just as Christine stepped out, smiling at the clicking cameras, he walked toward the rear of the car, and when the driver took out the luggage, grabbed two suitcases from him and headed into the building right behind Miss Jorgensen.

"If I hadn't known about it I would never have suspected he was ever a man," he stated, when he later gave us a full report in the downstairs pantry. "Even his voice was like a woman's." When Abuela came in and caught me listening she ordered me to go outside and play. "This is not the kind of thing a child should be listening to," she scowled at Humberto, who wasn't even aware that I'd been spying. The other servants quickly vanished, but as I walked away I could hear Abuela asking, "So did you really talk to her?"

Another indispensable person in La Calle Ene was Carmen, our laundress. Her laundry room was like a laboratory, stocked with the various instruments she would use depending on the kind of garment being washed.

On washboards over two big sinks she scrubbed the more soiled items, always using Jabón Candado, the family-produced laundry soap. She used a long stick to stir the garments she assigned to a huge tin tub filled with boiling water. If she was washing white clothes or linens, she also added *añil*, a blue die that amazingly made whites whiter. Unfortunately, she tended to be overly generous with *almidón*, starch, which made my school uniform pants so stiff they could stand up on their own. Putting these on each morning entailed prying apart each pant leg with my foot, which was like inserting myself into cardboard. Arriving at school with clothes so perfectly starched and ironed made me feel self-conscious. It took about half the day for my pants to start bending at the knee and my shirt collar to stop scraping the nape of my neck.

Drying the clothes was another major production. My grandmother wouldn't dream of having a clothesline anywhere that she could see it, so, as in many Havana houses, the clotheslines were strung across our flat rooftop, or *asotea*. Every day Carmen would pile her wicker baskets of wet washing into the elevator, then ride up to the top, where there was enough room to dry the clothes of an entire army. Rows of sheets and undergarments would soon be flapping in the ocean breeze, and if Carmen didn't pin them down fast enough, they would sometimes fly away.

One issue made Carmen a bit wary about these trips to the rooftop. The *asotea* was also a favorite place for Ramón Antonio and his theater friends to sit in the sun and rehearse a play, often in the nude. Not that having Carmen hanging up clothes nearby bothered *them* one bit, but Carmen let it be known that she did not feel comfortable with the situation. It was former Hollywood tough guy George Raft who, without knowing it, came to Carmen's rescue. The high-rise Capri hotel had just gone up across the street, and Mr. Raft was managing the casino. His name had helped make the hotel instantly popular, and the nudist group suddenly found it was not very relaxing to be stared at by twenty floors of tourists. The rooftop sunbathing finally came to an end.

There were many others working for the family whose jobs were equally indispensable.

There was Raymundo, the gardener, and Machito, whom Abuela always referred to by his *more proper* last name, Cruz. His job was to bathe the dogs, wash the cars, hose down the terraces and walkways, and just about any other odd chore that came up. There was also Teolindo, our night watchman, whom I always heard about and believed to be my *pretty Tio* but never got to see. That's because he started work after my bedtime and was gone by the time I got up. His starting time also coincided with *el cañonazo de las nueve*, a nightly nine P.M. cannon blast from La Cabaña fortress, which could be heard all over the city and people would often set their watches to. This ritual went back to when Havana was still a walled city; the *cañonazo* signaled the closing of the gates. Abuela remembered when as a young girl she heard a huge explosion. "Isn't it a little early for *el cañonazo?*" she thought, then heard her father say, "Well, they finally blew up the Maine!"

Perhaps my favorite member of La Calle Ene's staff was José. He had been my Abuelo's chauffeur until his death, then later became my mother's. Like Rosalina, José had emigrated from Spain, still spoke with a Castilian *zeta*, and called cars *coches*, instead of the more typical Cuban word, *máquina*. Some said that he had been on the Republican side during the Spanish Civil War and had had to flee after the triumph of Franco. If so, it was ironic that he had ended up working for our family, since my great-grandmother had been a staunch *Franquista*; she even received the medal of Isabel La Católica for all the money she contributed toward the reconstruction once the war ended. The photo that Franco signed and dedicated to her still sat in the library, right next to those of beloved family members now dead and gone, which made me assume that he was yet another *tio*.

I normally rode the number thirteen school bus, or *guagua trece*, a twice-daily trip that took forever, because after picking me up in El Vedado we would meander all through old Havana picking up other students. But sometimes, if José was not busy at the end of my lunch break, he would offer to drive me back for the afternoon session. Along the way we would listen to a popular radio show, *Mamá Cusa*, about a funny meddlesome old woman, played by a male actor. If we arrived before the show was over, José would park in the shade, about a block away from the main school gate, so that I wouldn't miss the ending. On days when he happened to be driving Abuela's eight-passenger town car, which looked to me like a big old hearse, I would beg him to let me get out and walk the rest of the way, too embarrassed to have my classmates see me arrive in such an ostentatious vehicle. José would always agree, but then remain there, keeping an eye on me until I was safely inside the gates.

Abuela also had her own chauffeur, although these too changed frequently. Whenever she hired a new one, she would give a most important instruction, "Never, under any circumstances, drive me past the Colón Cemetery." Although she kept many photographs of her dead loved ones, she did not want to see or be reminded of their actual resting place. My father, however, would take us there often, and I had grown to enjoy these visits. It felt more or less the same as stopping by to see any of our living relatives. While Papi went around putting flowers over the various tombs, I would ask him about the people in them. What did he die of? What was she like? What relation are they to me? I loved to hear about our Santa Mercedes, whose body was still perfectly intact in there. I was also somehow proud of the fact that our statue was not just another wimpy angel or soulful-looking Virgin. It was a woman, leaning in sorrow over a fading marble bouquet, with its petals dripping down. But what intrigued me most was that she had one breast poking out from the folds of her robe. Papi told me that Ramón Crusellas, the *bisabuelo* who built our house, and whose faithful Pomeranian had followed him to the cemetery, had bought it in Italy. His cameo was also carved into the side of the monument, and he looked rather pleased.

The most intriguing thing about these visits, however, was watching the people who came to ask favors or give thanks to La Milagrosa, the *miraculous* lady buried across the way. She was said to help women who had trouble conceiving become pregnant. This was a bit ironic, since she herself died in childbirth and had been buried with the baby at her feet. But years later, when the coffin was opened so their remains could be transferred to the ossuary, the baby was found clutched in her embrace. The statue above the grave was of a mother holding her baby in representation of that. Women would line up to touch the figure, then walk away without turning their backs to it. For some reason this had become part of the ritual, walking backwards all the way down the road, perhaps hoping that the longer they walked that way the better chances they would have of being blessed with a miraculous pregnancy.

• • •

Without a doubt, the most important staff members with regards to us children were Telma, Mercedes, and Delia, our *manejadoras*. I refrain from calling them nannies because they were nothing like Mary Poppins, who would give her wards spoonfuls of sugar. In fact, even though we lived in the land of sugarcane, Delia seemed to relish giving us a spoonful of Milk of Magnesia every Saturday morning.

Each of these women was in charge of a different child, and there was no love lost among them. Telma, who took care of my sister, Mequi, was by far the nicest. She had a son named Chuchi, who was a couple of years older than me. He lived with Telma's mother somewhere in La Habana Vieja, but she would often bring him by, and we'd spend hours playing together.

Mercedes first looked after my brother Gerardo, and a few years later after Carlos, who was the youngest. She was also quite nice, as long as you didn't mess with *her niño*. If she got wind of the slightest trouble between Gerardo and me, she would rush to his defense like an angry mother hen. Mercedes also had a sneaky way of pinching the underside of your upper arm, where even if the pinch left a bruise, our parents were not likely to see it. Her nephew was the great Afro-Cuban musician Miguelito Valdes, of whom she was very proud.

My *manejadora*, and later my brother Francisco's, was Delia, whose emotions often ran out of control. Most of her coworkers felt she had a few screws missing. Whenever she had a disagreement with the other *manejadoras* or if my father reprimanded her, she would go crying to my mother. I think that Mami felt sorry for Delia, and she became strangely over-protective of her.

Delia was thin and curveless, which to Cuban men was next to a sacrilege. There seems never to have been anyone special in her life, but she frequently fell in love with the male protagonist of her latest favorite *telenovela*. Since we lived just a block away from CMQ, the main TV station, she would drag me there often in hopes of catching a glimpse, and sometimes cornering, whomever she was obsessed with at the moment. I enjoyed these little excursions because while Delia scouted for her prey, I could stay at the CMQ record store and listen to albums, or I could watch the reporters of Radio Reloj giving their round-the-clock updates in their fishbowl newsroom. Right across from them was the Radio Centro barbershop, where many of the station's performers got their haircuts. Delia loved taking me there too, because she was likely to run into one of them, stuck in a barber chair and unable to escape her. To my misfortune, she one day developed an unrequited crush on Willy, the head barber. From then on she would take me for a weekly haircut, and for the many months that this obsession lasted, I was practically bald.

There were two popular children's shows produced at CMQ, *Gabi, Fofó, y Miliki* and *El Viejito Chichí*. The first one had a circus theme with a live children's audience sitting around a center ring. Gabi, the straight man, would play a saxophone while his brothers, Fofó and Miliki, got up to all sorts of clownish mischief. Mequi and I were front-row regulars. But for some odd reason, one day Gabi decided to announce that the children of the station's dear friend, Luis Santeiro, were in the audience. Half-blinded by spotlights, he turned to the stands and asked that we raise our hands. We were both too shy to identify ourselves, but without missing a beat, a group of rambunctious older kids in the back row jumped up waving their arms and shouting, "It's me! Me! Me!" I took their claim quite literally, and that night when my father came home I felt very angry toward him for having had all these illegitimate children that we knew nothing about.

El Viejito Chichí, or Little Old Chichí, had puppets in his show, with a continuing story that I thought was far more interesting than he was. But our visits to his program came to an abrupt ending. The one rule that we were always reminded of before the show went on the air live was that we needed to keep very quiet—unless Chichí addressed us directly. Mequi, who was two years younger, had done a pretty good job of behaving until the afternoon when the kid sitting next to her suddenly pulled out a cookie. As he was about to take a bite, she suddenly snatched it away, which resulted in an all-out fight that disrupted the story *El Viejito* was trying to amuse us with. He did his best to continue as if nothing was happening, but the moment that they stopped for a commercial, a production assistant lifted my kicking and screaming sister and quickly whisked her out of the studio. I sat there, mortified, trying to act as if I had no idea who that brat was.

Dissatisfied with her unproductive chasing after *telenovela* stars, Delia decided to become a star-maker herself. I got a bit suspicious one morning as she was dressing me, because she had picked out a rather fancy outfit, and so far as I knew there was nothing special on the agenda, besides another of our regular visits to CMQ. But then once we got there she whisked me into an elevator and took me up to a floor where we had never been before. It was the production office of a weekly amateur hour.

"This boy can sing. You *have* to have him on your show," she insisted as she accosted the producer. Then she turned to me and commanded, "Sing, Luis Manuel!"

Afraid to disobey, I broke into the first song that came to my head, an upbeat rumba. "*La múcura está en el suelo y mamá no puedo con ella . . .*"

Appropriately, it was about a kid who drops and breaks a heavy water jug, which gets him into deep trouble. The producer's face registered patient desperation, but out of sympathy, he waited until I had finished the entire song. He then patted my head and said that I did indeed have a very nice voice. I did not, however, make it onto the program. Frustrated with my audition failure, Delia turned her star-making efforts toward my brother Francisco, who soon afterwards, to the surprise of the entire family, starred in a Bosco chocolate milk commercial. "*Mmmm! Delicioso!*"

CMQ was quite a big part of all our lives. Crusellas, the family company, sponsored a variety show as well as various *telenovelas*, some of which my uncle Ramón Antonio directed. He would bring actors over to rehearse at La Calle Ene, and after the roof became too exposed, their sessions moved to the front terrace. Passersby would often stop at the sound of their loud emoting, convinced that someone was about to get killed.

Perhaps due to the family's involvement, Abuela started watching the *telenovelas* that she herself sponsored, and she became as addicted to them as Delia was. She took to popping by Ramón Antonio's rehearsals and inviting the actors to have lunch with her, then plying them with questions about their characters. "When is Alejandro going to realize that his wife Dinorah is not really crippled?" "Estrellita is already pregnant by him, isn't she?" "And what about Tano? He wasn't really killed in that hurricane, was he? He's too handsome to die so soon." But perhaps the most interesting lunch of all happened on the day that Ramón Antonio showed up with Marlon Brando. He had met the actor in New York, invited him to Havana, and was now serving as his nocturnal guide to its seamier side. Abuela had not seen any of Brando's films and was not particularly impressed by his conversational talents. Brando, on the other hand, was not impressed by Abuela, and later commented to Ramón Antonio that his aunt was much too stiff and formal.

CMQ also became the scene of a dramatic event in the revolution's fight against Batista, one that was closely experienced by my sister, Mequi. The *revolucionarios* had laid out an intricate plot for attacking the presidential palace and assassinating the dictator. At the same time, another group was to break into the TV station and take over Radio Reloj, to announce his demise. The hope was that the news would send joyful Habaneros into the streets and create total chaos. The first group managed to break into the palace and shoot their way almost up to Batista's inner sanctum. In the process, both the attackers and the defending military guards suffered losses, but finally the rebels were defeated. Meanwhile, unaware of this, the second group had also managed to take over the station and was already spreading the news of a victory. Within minutes, Batista's police arrived and another shootout was underway.

It was late afternoon, and my sister's school bus was about to drop her off. She was the last remaining student. As they reached the corner of 21st and M Street, they could hear the shooting. There were patrol cars everywhere, and people were running hysterically or lying flat on the sidewalk, hoping to dodge the flying bullets. Upon seeing the chaotic scene, the monitor who always accompanied the bus driver told Mequi that they were taking her back to the school. The thought of going all the way back to El Country, over a half-hour away, was not an option that my sister found acceptable.

"I don't care what's going on. I'm getting off."

She started arguing with the monitor, until the driver, eager to get himself out of danger's way, just opened the door and let Mequi out.

She ran as fast as she could toward our house, only to find that, for fear that the disruption might somehow spill into our yard, the front gate had been locked. Mequi tossed her book bag over it then began the precarious climb. Everyone in the house had been avoiding the windows, fearing a stray bullet, so nobody learned of Mequi's plight until she managed to make it safely inside.

With the realization that our neighboring TV station was a valuable target for the revolutionaries, our appearances in the audience of *Gabi, Fofó, y Miliki*, and *El Viejito Chichí* also came to an end.

Humans were not the only species that lived in La Calle Ene. There was a nasty parrot, which despite being played records designed for teaching her species to sing opera arias and spout witty phrases, could only say *puta* and *maricón*, nasty words that a disgruntled servant had taught her. There were also two flying squirrels that I had bought at my favorite pet shop; disappointingly, they turned out to be nocturnal and very boring. Every September, I would bring back a new batch of baby sea turtles that I collected on moonlit nights in Varadero, as they crawled from their nests to the ocean. I would have to keep adding salt whenever I changed their water, which soon became tiresome. Someone would eventually convince me that it was time to set them free. José would then drive me to the Malecón sea wall and ease me down to the spiky coral rock below so that I could gently place the tiny turtles into the waves.

We also had dogs, lots of them, which, not to be outdone by the dramatic family deaths, kept staging their own theatrical mishaps. The most pampered of all were Lord and Lady, my father's prized Dalmatians. They had been given to him by Abuelo Manolo shortly before he died, which made them extra special legacies. Lord was a beautiful specimen and had won Best in Show on more than one occasion. He loved being on display and would proudly let judges measure his tail or inspect his teeth. Outside of competition, however, he was quick to irritate and likely to bite anyone who came too close, except my father. The popularity of Dalmatians had caused them to be over-bred, and just like overly intermarried European monarchs, they had developed problematic quirks. To my father's dismay, his beloved Lord began to go insane. After he snapped at me on a couple of occasions, it became necessary to confine him within one of the second-floor terraces. Then one day, hearing my father's voice down below, and desperate to go to him, he jumped right over the balustrade and barely missed landing on Papi's head. Alas, after limping around for just a few days, Lord went on to live for a few more mentally deranged years.

The total opposite by nature was Ramón Antonio's sweet and chubby terrier, Mike. Whenever he wasn't trailing behind my uncle, he could be found lying down by the kitchen window, where he was likely to have a scrap of food or two tossed out at him. After one of my uncle's rooftop sunbathing sessions, Ramón Antonio opened the elevator door to head back downstairs when suddenly Mike rushed on ahead of him. Unfortunately, due to some strange malfunction, the elevator was not there. Poor Mike went flying down four whole flights, landing with a thud that Ramón Antonio heard from way above. Hysterical, he rushed down the stairs, convinced that he was about to find a Mike pancake, but miraculously, he had just broken some bones. Mike too went on to live a few more years, although with a pronounced limp that had the beat of a slow rumba.

Our house was quite crowded, and not just with the living. Photos of my dead ancestors were prominently displayed in various rooms, making their presence still feel quite real. And Delia, besides being borderline insane, was also an *espiritista*, gifted with a sixth sense that had her running into spirits at every turn. She had lectured Mequi and me about the grave importance of the light surrounding these manifestations.

"Last night, when I went down to the pantry to get your brother Francisco's milk bottle, I felt one of them following me. Whoever it was did not fully materialize, like many of the others, but I could clearly see the bright white glow. You must never be afraid when their light is white. That always means it's someone letting you know they're watching over you, or trying to warn you of some potential danger. It's only when they're in darkness that you need to worry. Those are the spirits that want to harm you, or have been sent by someone who's giving you *mal de ojo*, the evil eye."

These stories had resulted in our becoming scared of our own shadows, and we avoided being left alone in any room of the house, especially after nightfall. But Delia wasn't the only one who had seen spirits in La Calle Ene. My father and uncle had also had a memorable encounter. Ramón Antonio told me that story too, and this was one time when Papi did not accuse him of being overly imaginative.

"I must have been eight or nine when it happened, which means your father was six or seven. We had adjoining rooms and would leave the door in-between open to keep each other company and talk ourselves to sleep. The grownups would all still be downstairs, and even our *manejadoras* would disappear after putting us to bed. It was just the two of us. So this one night, we're chattering away, as usual, when suddenly, right in the middle of a sentence, your father went dead silent. I called out, 'Luis, are you asleep? Luis . . . ?'"

"I wasn't asleep," Papi interrupted. "I had just seen this . . . figure glide into my room . . . a woman, with a long dark veil that covered most of her. For a moment I thought it was someone playing an unfunny joke, trying to scare us, but there were no footstep sounds. No sounds at all, not even breathing. It was as if she was floating. I could hear Ramón Antonio calling but I didn't dare say a word. I pulled the sheet right up to my nose, praying that she would vanish, but she just stayed there at the foot of my bed, staring, as if trying to see who I was. Then finally she turned around and glided toward Ramón Antonio's room."

"I was starting to get up and make sure your father was okay," Ramón Antonio took over again. "Then I saw her coming through the door, and quick as I could I jumped back into bed and covered my head . . . which I instantly realized was really stupid because now I couldn't see what she was doing, and that was even more frightening."

"So then," said Papi, "*I* started calling out, 'Ramón . . . Ramón Antonio? Are you all right?' But now he wouldn't answer me."

"I couldn't. I was petrified. But I finally got the courage to lower the sheet and take a peek, and there she still was, staring at me. Only the strangest thing happened. I suddenly stopped feeling scared. I couldn't see her face under that veil, yet it felt as if she was smiling and meant me no harm at all. She hovered there for another moment. Then, as if content with what she had seen, she turned around and floated right out the balcony, and you know how high that is. You also know I'm not a big believer in the afterlife, but what your father and I saw that night, and we definitely saw it, was no living being."

"I've always thought it might have been your mother," my father said to Ramón Antonio, "coming to make sure you were okay."

"Possibly. Our very own Santa Mercedes. But whoever she was," Ramón Antonio assured me once more, "she was real."

They never saw her again, although many years later, when Mequi slept in that same room, she swore she saw a similar dark-veiled lady glide up to the foot of her bed, then float out the balcony. She refused to spend one more night there and had to be moved elsewhere.

There were a few other people who also lived in La Calle Ene for temporary spells. There was Mercedita la Americana, given that nickname because she was born in Tampa, and also had to be differentiated from all the other Mercedeses. She was the daughter of my great-grandmother Mamaíta's youngest brother, who had vanished for years, then was suddenly rediscovered working as a short-order cook in Ybor City. Abuela convinced him that she could offer the girl a more promising future and brought her to live in Havana, where Mercedita soon became a part of the social set. Then there was Nena, whose last name I can't remember. She was a friend of Abuela's who often came by in the afternoon to chitchat and crochet together. One day she fell ill and was taken to a guest room. Rasputin was called in, and it turned out to be nothing serious, but somehow Nena never left again, except feet first, when she died a few years later. And most importantly, there was Marietta, who didn't actually live with us, but was a constant presence. She was Abuela's brother's second wife, whom he had divorced a few years earlier in order to marry his third one.

Marietta had red hair, which in our Cuban world was highly unusual. She had been born in Spain and could sing and play guitar with lots of *salero*, which means something like charm or élan. It was never ever mentioned, but I had also heard from Ramón Antonio that Marietta, his former stepmother, had once been a stage performer. She had toured Latin America with a Zarzuela troupe, then wound up in Havana with her sister, doing a variety act called *La Mascota y La Negra*. Marietta was La Mascota, which means the "mascot" or "pet," and her sister was "the dark one." My great-uncle Ramón, the inveterate womanizer, had fallen head over heels for her, but unlike his many other passing conquests, this one seemed to stick.

When the family learned that he was planning to marry a music hall temptress, they were horrified. Then when they realized that Ramón intended to go through with it no matter what they thought, they hired men to go around the entire city collecting every single magazine in which Marietta and her sister had been featured. They also made the sister sign a contract agreeing to never again perform in Cuba. Intimidated by her new in-laws, Marietta herself never uttered another word about her perfoming past, but her quick-wittedness and charm were things that could never be swept under the rug. She was funny and lively and always the center of any reunion of which she was a part.

When my great-uncle left Marietta, my grandmother took her side. But she was unable to stay away long from her beloved brother and kept on meddling in his new life, especially after he became a father again at age sixty. Tio Ramón's much younger wife, also named Mercedes, referred to her as *la bruja*, the witch, and would never come anywhere near La Calle Ene. It was only after Mercedes was killed, when a jeep driven by one of Fidel's *milicianos* ran a red light and crashed into her car, that our cousin Lourdes, who was twelve at the time, began to spend time with us, much to Marietta's dismay.

Though barely a year older than me, Lourdes was far more mature and sophisticated. She could play piano, speak French, and pass herself off as old enough to get into movies that you had to be over fifteen to see, like *Pillow Talk* and *Peyton Place*.

One afternoon, after seeing a more child-appropriate Disney film, Mequi and I were at the popular restaurant El Carmelo with Lourdes and Mademoiselle, her French tutor. Suddenly Tio Ramón, her father, walked in with a curvy young blond on his arm. I recognized her as one of the secondary stars in one of our sponsored *telenovelas*. Seeing us, Tio Ramón instantly came over to say hello. Lourdes got up to give her father a kiss but totally ignored the actress. Almost in a whisper, Tio Ramón said to her, "Don't you say hello to the *señorita*?" To which Lourdes replied, "*Yo no saludo a putas*"—"I do not greet whores." Mequi and I shrank down into our seats and braced for a big scene. Even Mademoiselle seemed at a total loss for words. But Tio Ramón just took his lady friend by the arm again, turned around, and headed to the farthest possible table.

• 4 •

Perhaps my favorite time of the year was the *carnavales* season, which led up to Lent. For weeks there would be a slew of children's costume parties, for which we dressed up in a variety of exotic outfits, most of them from different Spanish regions. Abuela would bring these in her traveling trunks, among the myriad other things that she brought back from her European trips. It was as if carnival time gave her license to showcase our Iberian roots. I had a Gallego, or Galician, costume, which included a triangular felt hat with pompons, long white underwear that ballooned from under a shorter set of pants, and the traditional Galician bagpipe, or *gaita*. I also had a toreador's *traje de luces*, or suit of lights, covered with glittery sequins stitched on with gold and silver thread. My sister, Mequi, often got dolled up as a Sevillana, with a multi-ruffled long skirt in the classic polka dot pattern, and a tall *peineta* to help hold up the flowers in her hair. But her favorite was the Lagarterana costume, from the province of Toledo. It had a dress and apron trimmed with lace and completely covered with embroidered flowers in every color of the rainbow. Carnival was also the period during which we were most photographed, so that there would be keepsakes of us looking adorable. A glance through any family photo album would make one believe that we spent our entire lives in fancy dress.

During these pre-Lent weekend afternoons, there would also be *paseos de carnaval*, a promenade of floats, open-back trucks, and convertibles, all loaded with revelers in every kind of imaginative getup. The route made a continuous loop from the Malecón seaside avenue, up the Paseo del Prado, past the Capitolio building, and then back again. My siblings, cousins, and I would ride atop the back seat of my father's convertible, while our mothers held on to our legs so that we would not slide overboard. But since the parading traffic moved so slowly, I would sometimes escape them for a moment to pelt the passengers of nearby vehicles with fistfuls of confetti.

On *carnaval* evenings there would also be *comparsas*, which consisted of large parading dance groups, each with a specific theme, not unlike the *scuolas di samba* of Brazil. Our parents often took part in one of these at the Country Club. One year their theme was the Stone Age. A couple of hair and makeup experts from CMQ came over to our house to do up some members of the group. I stood nearby fascinated as they glued on thick bushy eyebrows and warts onto the men's faces, strung animal bones from the women's hair, and, as a finishing touch, placed little plastic ticks and lice all over everyone's body. Soon, the entire house was overrun by frightful-looking creatures sipping cocktails, but to me they were still far less scary than any of our resident ghosts.

After all the fun of *carnaval*, however, we paid for it with the doldrums of Lent, those long forty days before Easter when it seemed as if anything enjoyable was taboo, and all that Pedro cooked was fish with little bones that kept sticking in my throat. At the La Salle school, which I attended, it was all about making little sacrifices in emulation of Jesus, who had sacrificed so much more for us. The school choir, which I was a part of, even stopped rehearsing, as this was definitely no time for singing, not even religious music. We were also urged to give up things that we loved, like having a Coca-Cola during recess, and to make frequent visits up to the chapel. It was during one of these visits, with my friend Otto Garcia, that something happened that was to mark my life.

Our school chapel was large and dark, except in the late afternoon when sunlight poured in through the west windows. This being Lent, all the saint statues and crucifixes were covered with purple cloth, which gave the place an added eeriness. We knelt to say a quick Hail

Mary, so that we could add one more notch to our chapel-visits tally sheet. I was about to get up to leave when Otto yanked me back. "Did you see that?"

"See what?"

"The Christ figure, on the main altar. It just moved, under the purple cloth."

At first I thought he was pulling my leg, then realized that he was dead serious. We had just been shown the movie about Bernadette and had seen how all the adults and priests had called her a liar for saying that The Virgin had appeared to her, so I figured that I should at least give Otto's claim more of a chance. I knelt back down and stared at the crucifix. A pigeon cooed somewhere up in the eaves, but I saw nothing. Then suddenly Otto's body straightened, and he started to nod as if agreeing to some silent request.

"What is it now?"

"He would like for you to see Him also, but you're being too doubtful. You must *want* to see Him, with all your heart."

I knew that the church was supposed to be the home of The Lord, but the thought of His actually being there, watching us, sent a shiver up my spine. Preferring not to see anything, I closed my eyes and bowed my head in prayer. "Lord, I am *really* not worthy . . ." Then loud footsteps startled me, and I started running out the center aisle as fast as I could. "Wait! Don't leave me!" Otto ran after me, as if suddenly scared too. But then back in the playground, he couldn't resist telling some classmates what he had just seen, or perhaps imagined. Only by now his experience had grown even bigger: Christ had shifted on the cross. A heavenly voice had echoed through the chapel. A ray of light had shone down from Heaven. And the worst of it was that when someone asked me if all this was true, I answered "Uh-huh."

The word soon spread throughout the schoolyard, and since our minds had already been pumped with spiritual talk and miracle movies, an apparition did not seem like such an oddity. Perhaps the time had finally come for a heavenly visit in Havana—better yet, in our own school. When classes let out, instead of heading home or starting up the usual ball games, dozens of students rushed up to the chapel. I felt guilty for being partly responsible, but I figured that it would all soon blow over. The following morning, however, I had barely crossed the school gate when I realized how mistaken I'd been.

"*He* was one of the first to see it!" some kid shouted, pointing at me. Overnight, the miraculous events had multiplied, just like the loaves and fishes. Someone had seen The Virgin trying to uncrucify Jesus. Everyone present had seen his own guardian angel. Saint Lazarus' dogs had barked! Shortly before lunch, the vice principal gathered the whole student body to make an announcement. "I want everyone to put a stop to these ridiculous stories about our school chapel. Nothing, I repeat, nothing, has taken place there." But rather than stopping it, this only made even more students head on up to satisfy their curiosity. By day's end, miracles were rampant. Christ had multiplied the *sandwichitos*. One third-grader had been able to feed seven kids out of his little lunch bag.

Our principal was a fearsome presence. His baldheaded and black-robed figure was something you did not want to encounter along any corridor. When angered, his voice was like that of a high-pitched wrathful god, and now he was stepping right into our classroom, standing just a few feet from my own desk.

"I used to have trouble understanding what causes man to be so stubborn, but now I am old and have finally accepted that we are simply imperfect creatures. In my long life I have also encountered situations such as the one that has been taking place in our chapel, and I am well acquainted with the one responsible. He is here among us."

Oh, God. Poor Otto, I thought.

"His name is Lucifer. Beelzebub. Legion." With each word, he gave my desk a jolting whack with the cord that hung from the waist of his habit. "My house is a house of prayer, and you have turned it into a den of thieves. You have helped him make a mockery of our most holy sanctuary. And in doing so, you have committed a grave mortal sin, which I trust you will go to confess."

I was never so relieved to hear blame put on the Devil.

The school chapel was instantly closed and remained so for the rest of Lent. No further mention was made of the incident, but for years I carried a deep guilt. I had allowed myself to become the Devil's tool, and then, afraid of identifying myself, had not confessed the sin, which meant that it was never forgiven. By going to communion afterwards, I had committed an even graver one, a sacrilege. I was no longer a member of the Good Shepherd's flock. Satan had triumphed. My soul now belonged to him.

IF LENT WAS boring, Semana Santa—Holy Week—was frightening. All TV shows were cancelled, and the only thing one could watch was some priest reading Easter Week scripture. The radio was pretty much the same. And for Cubans to go without any music was truly a major sacrifice. Then there were the processions with those life-size bleeding Christs with awful wigs, bent over under the weight of the cross. His pitiful look truly made you feel guilty for every least sin you had ever committed, which we were told were like a slap to His face after having died for us. And as if all of this wasn't bad enough, we had our own resident *espiritista*, Delia, to make the horrors even more vivid. She would tell us that from three P.M. on Good Friday, which was the hour of Christ's death, until His resurrection on Easter Sunday, the Devil had completely free rein and might pop up anywhere. She described him as *El Resbaloso*, "the Slippery One," who could grab you by the toes and drag you right out of your bed if you were bad. I could picture his oily skin and the long sharp claws, ready to attack. I saw him lurking behind every door and mango tree, which made me stick very close to an adult for those entire two days. *El Resbaloso* certainly assured Delia of our perfect behavior.

Easter Sunday, with its chocolate eggs and dime-store bunnies was always a welcome breath of fresh air. Those American symbols of Resurrection were not so widespread in Cuba, but my mother always made sure to have enough of them for organizing an Easter egg hunt. These would be held in La Finca San Luis, the family farm, where we spent Semana Santa and where there were plenty of flowerbeds in which to hide our prizes. Rafaelito, the son of one of the caretakers, who often came to play with us, was fascinated by these exotic items and would offer to make trades with me—a malted milk egg for a shiny mica rock, or a windup hopping rabbit for a fallen mockingbird nest that he had found. In Wajay, the nearby town, the poultry shop also sold dyed baby chicks. We were each allowed to get just one, so I would have a hard time deciding what color chick to pick. It was very important that we all choose a different color, so that when one of them died, often from an excessively loving squeeze, there would be no doubt as to who was now chickless.

La Finca was my father's greatest passion, hopefully after my mother. There he could indulge in his two favorite endeavors, horseback riding and landscaping. A double row of royal palms ushered you into a tropical paradise of fruit trees such as *mameyes*, *guanábanas*, *zapotes*, *caimitos*, *mangos*, and *tamarindos*. There were also giant banyan trees with nooks and crannies that we turned into secret hideouts. We would swing from their hanging roots like little Tarzans, or slide down them pretending to be firemen. The house itself, which everyone referred to as *el chalet*, was covered with flowering vines that almost hid it completely.

There was jasmine and *galán de noche*, or ladies' man of the night, which gave the evening air a strong sweet scent. We would always try to keep an eye on the night-blooming cereus buds because they only bloomed for one night. These were the biggest flowers I had ever seen. Abuela called them *Espuma de Santa Teresa*, "Saint Theresa's foam," although to me the petals looked more like long white goose feathers, with a gradual hint of yellow toward the pistils.

Nighttime at La Finca was magical, with all the green-glowing *cocuyos* flying around, but it also had its downside. We had to sleep inside *mosquiteros*, mosquito nets, and not just because of mosquitos. There were far more undesirable creatures, like scorpions and *arañas peludas*, big hairy tarantulas that were supposedly not poisonous, but could still scare the hell out of you. There were also zigzagging bats, which people said could get tangled up in your hair. We would see them making nosedives into the pool for a quick sip. But the pool area seemed to attract more than just bats. Delia claimed to have seen ghosts there too, one of them with a fat belly and always carrying a newspaper. She also saw a white-gowned lady who climbed our water tower nightly, then hanged herself. Her visions made us stay safely inside from sunset to dawn.

Another strange nighttime threat was something that the locals called *el sereno*. It was supposedly some strange miasma in the nighttime air that could make you sick, sometimes even fatally. The *campesinos* would try to avoid going out at night also, and when they had to, they covered their nose and mouth with a handkerchief, or at least with their own hand.

At the far end of La Finca was *la caballeriza*, the stables, where my father kept his beloved horses. They had wonderful names like Cubanidad, Tacloban, and Bali, while the ones that we children rode had less poetic ones—Panchita and Trés Patines ("Three Skates"). Either Papi or Tomás, the stable master, would take us riding along the alleys of the neighboring sugarcane mill, El Central Toledo. On these little excursions, we would come across the thatched-roof huts, called *bohios*, where *guajiro* families lived. They always invited us in for a *cafecito*, and would feel slighted if we didn't accept. The women used an old sock or stocking for dripping the water through the coffee grinds, and to those of us who didn't drink *café*, they sometimes offered *guarapo*, squeezed sugar cane juice that I found far too sweet. The insides of these *bohios* were immaculately clean, but what struck me most was that even though the floors were made of packed down dirt, they would sweep them as if they were tile or marble. The adults were much too proud to accept money, but before continuing on our way, Papi always gave each of their kids a few coins.

There were many different animals in La Finca, but there was one in particular that held a place of honor. It was a mule named Koloso, which just sat in his own stable doing nothing. The family was extremely grateful to him, for he had saved their lives.

Some years back, they had been traveling through Spain and stopped one evening at a country inn. Tiana had been in a languid mood, and to tone down the bright light of her bedside lamp, she draped a silk scarf over it. In the middle of the night, while everyone slept, the scarf caught fire, and it quickly started to spread. Koloso, who was in a nearby field, began to bray, which woke up everyone just in time. In gratitude, the family purchased Koloso from its owner and shipped him on a long sea voyage to Cuba. There were some who thought that Koloso might have been better off if he had kept quiet.

• 5 •

I would hate to give the impression that my mother's side of the family was any less picturesque or eccentric. Closest to us were our maternal *abuelos*, Nena Machado and Baldomero Grau, whom we called Papín and Mimamá. They lived in the Country Club section, in the very first house of that suburban district. It had originally been the home of its American developer and was a sprawling property with a separate building for doing laundry and also two garages. One of these had an unusually high ceiling because it had been built to store construction trucks. The other one didn't even have room for a car because it was jam-packed with the empty wooden boxes of the cigars that Papín smoked constantly, as well as the big round cardboard boxes in which part of Mimamá's vast hat collection was stored. Although hats were no longer in fashion, she never stepped out the door without one on. Even indoors she wore short beaded veils that draped over her forehead. During the final days of Batista, the *revolucionarios* planted a bomb in the Havana Vieja Woolworth, and a couple of people died in the explosion. Since my grandmother shopped in that district almost daily, my mother called the store to ask if one of the corpses happened to be wearing a hat.

Almost every Sunday we would go with our *manejadoras* to visit Papín and Mimamá. We also stayed with them whenever our parents traveled abroad. Their maid, Albina, thought that I was too skinny, and she would try to fatten me with *meriendas* of Malta Hatuey, a sickeningly rich malt she mixed with a few dollops of condensed milk.

In his old age, Papín had taken to feeding stray cats, and the grounds were teeming with dozens of feral ones. They also had Junior, a Boston terrier that Mimamá had once fallen on and almost crushed. After he died, she took to wearing a black and white striped hat that made it seem as if she had stuffed Junior and was now wearing him on her head. For a while, there was also a pig that Mimamá bought to fatten for Noche Buena but then became too fond of to have it killed. Perhaps out of gratitude, the pig made its home right outside Mimamá's bedroom window, where his oinking became a nightly lullaby.

Papín was president of Havana's Theater Guild; he also wrote essays and poems. He had written a letter to me shortly after I was born. It was meant for me to read when I grew up, but I came across it prematurely. In it he described the fight that he had with my mother when he found out that I was about to be circumcised. He said that when it came to these matters "one should always try to add, but never subtract." He wanted me to know that he fought valiantly to try to save my foreskin.

Papín loved going to the dog races and would often take me with him, although I don't remember him ever winning. He would also take me to Havana's Coney Island, which was not far from their house. One day I convinced him to let me go into a traveling sideshow that was visiting for a few weeks. The main poster showed a woman in a bikini with a question mark over her private parts. I think that Papín was too busy lighting a cigar to notice that detail. We were sitting in the front row, and the show was about to begin when the manager suddenly rushed in shouting, "Hold the curtain! There's a kid in the house." We were politely escorted out, so I remained forever curious about what that question mark was hiding.

Without question, the most eccentric maternal relative of all was Mimamá's sister, Tia Berta. She was into the occult and was prone to making decisions according to the recommendations of Santería priests, something that the rest of the family avoided talking about.

She often showed up at people's doors with messages from the other side, like the one she brought to my staunchly Catholic Grau great aunts, Margot and Eva.

"I was at this . . . *gathering* last night, when suddenly we were contacted by someone who seemed terribly eager for me to tell you these words . . . 'The other world exists.'"

This completely freaked out Margot and Eva, for those were the exact four words they had secretly agreed with their now-deceased brother, Tio Juan, that the first one of them to die would do their best to send back.

Tia Berta had a daughter named Lugi, who was politely referred to as . . . *different*. Lugi spoke a language of her own, which was only spoken fluently by my aunt and godmother, Mari. But Mari had recently married and moved to a sugar mill in the province of Las Villas, where her husband, Andres, was working. Her departure had left Lugi feeling isolated.

Tia Berta had never accepted that there was anything wrong with Lugi, at least nothing that *espiritistas* and *santeros* could not cure. According to one *babalao*, Lugi had been born perfectly normal. Her problems were the result of a cursed flower bouquet that an enemy of Papá Gerardito had tossed one day into the palace automobile that baby Lugi was riding in. Tia Berta started to take part in unorthodox rituals in order to rid Lugi of her bewitchment, but so far none of them had succeeded.

But the undisputed matriarch of our maternal branch was my *bisabuela*, Elvira Machado y Machado, widow of the former president. We often went to visit her at La Finca Nenita, the farm that they had named for my mother. After their abrupt departure in 1933, mobs had looted the presidential palace as well as the homes of other members of the government. The farm had not been spared. An angry crowd had burned down the house and killed most of the animals, which included a collection of rare birds, and even an ocelot. The house still remained in ruins, but Mamá Elvira had had a modest bungalow built right across from it and would spend many afternoons rocking on the porch along with a lady companion. I would wander through the maze of fallen walls, which were now overgrown with banyan tree roots, and play jungle explorer. Papá Gerardito's old bathroom, still partly covered in turquoise tiles, became my hidden treasure room. I once asked Mamá Elvira what had happened to the house, and she said that a big hurricane had knocked it down. The farm also had many half-destroyed cages, and I would try to envision the animals that once lived inside them.

A long fountain with a bridge crossing in the middle still stood under two giant ficus trees, which over the years had filled it with their fallen leaves. These piles of dried leaves reached above my knee. I would jump in and wade through them, pretending that the crackling sound was being made by quicksand about to engulf me. One day a *campesino* caught me in the midst of my fantasy and started shouting, "*Muchacho*, get out of there! That's full of *escorpiones* and *arañas peludas*!" Scorpions and tarantulas? I couldn't jump out fast enough. That was the last time I ever played in the leaf-filled fountain.

The only thing that Mamá Elvira had had restored was the large strawberry patch, which Papá Gerardito had been proud of. Walking slowly, but holding herself very erect, she would sometimes accompany us as we went row by row filling wicker baskets with the big fat berries. Mami had told us that Mamá Elvira had been born in a very modest house, in a town called Camajuaní, in the province of Santa Clara. During the War of Independence, she would ride through the countryside bringing food and other supplies to her husband and his troop of Cuban freedom fighters. On more than one occasion she had also carried a wounded patriot back from a battlefield for medical treatment. It was hard for me to imagine this slim old lady ever having done any of that. Perhaps it was those memories that she thought about while rocking herself in front of the ruins.

• 6 •

I was eleven when the revolution triumphed, on January 1st of 1959, and my multi-layered cocoon began to fray. I had started to wish that we lived in a place where one could go to the movies without worrying that a bomb might explode and catapult a body part onto the seat next to you. I had read about that in *Bohemia*. It showed a close-up of the hand that flew halfway across the auditorium during a Cantinflas film. They said those things were over now that Batista had fled and the revolutionaries had nothing to rebel against. But it was more than that. *La Revolución* had also given rise to passions that felt divisive and confusing to me. My parents tried to avoid talking politics in front of us, for fear of who we might repeat their words to, but I knew that they had no great love for Fidel and his longhaired *barbudos*, despite all those rosaries draped around their necks. Even the servants were now at odds with each other.

"The days of that *vieja* upstairs telling me I don't know how to mop floors are coming to an end."

"Then if I were you I'd start worrying, 'cause your job will come to an end too . . . and then what if she was right?"

Almost every day Rosalina would have to stop an argument before the knives started flying. But by far the most devoted *Fidelista* of all was Delia, my *manejadora*, who had now shifted her telenovela star crushes to Fidel himself, papering her entire room with his photos.

"*Mua! Mua!*" she would go around kissing them. She had also hung up a popular sign on her bedroom door that said, "*Fidel, esta es tu casa*"—this is your house—even though the home she was offering him wasn't hers to give.

Things had also changed at my school. Suddenly classmates with whom I had been friends for years and who had come to my saint's day parties at La Finca were not so friendly anymore. One of them even took to calling me *latifundista*, the newly popular term applied to owners of the large plantations or cattle estates that *La Revolución* had started to confiscate—although our farm hardly qualified as that.

One day my friend Yohel proudly described how he and his father had taken baseball bats and joined a mob knocking down parking meters, an act encouraged by our new leaders because these were symbols of our former dictator's greed. My father had not been amused when I told him this. He said it was vandalism and that everyone who participated in things like that should be put in jail. Yohel and I continued to be friends, but now there was something unspoken that made our relationship more cautious. Yet I myself could not help getting a little caught up in the revolutionary spirit. When my best friend, Johnny, whose mother was Canadian, got me upset over some insignificant disagreement, I scowled at him and spit out the words, "*No queremos productos Americanos*," "We don't want American products," another phrase that Fidel had popularized. And when the American partners of our family's company came to La Finca for lunch one Sunday, I felt a surge of patriotic fervor and let the air out of all their car tires, something that my father made me deeply regret soon afterwards. But despite my minor attempts at revolutionary behavior, one morning, shortly after the Christmas break, something happened in class that made it finally clear I did not belong to this new order.

The La Salle brothers, who taught us, took vows of chastity and poverty, but every Christmas season my mother insisted on sending them some useful, non-materialistic gift. Since the family was in the perfumery business, this seemed like an ideal choice. So each year she would ask my father to ship the good brothers a huge box of Crusellas' own of Hiel de Vaca soap and Kolonia 1800 cologne. One this particular day, Brother Antonio, our fifth-grade teacher, perhaps also moved by revolutionary zeal, swept into the classroom and without once glancing at me directly, started to rail about "these arrogant millionaires who apparently think us religious people stink and keep sending us soap." Everyone, of course, knew exactly to whom he was referring, and taunts of "arrogant millionaire" soon joined those of "*latifundista.*"

"Why did you have to send them soap?" I yelled at my mother when she came with our chauffeur José to pick me up.

"*Ay, mijo.* I really thought they would appreciate being saved a necessary expense."

During the two months I had spent the previous summer learning English at Chimney Rock Camp, in North Carolina, I had discovered a world of carefree anonymity. For eight whole weeks no one had called me *latifundista* or even suggested that my great-grandfather threw his enemies into shark tanks and ate sautéed human brains for breakfast. But better yet, the novelty stores that sold wonderful things like baseball caps with deer antlers and key chains with petrified moose turds had seduced me. During one excursion into town, two of my cabin mates had bought Ant Farms, then one week later received real live ants over the mail. But the company that sold these would not send ants to Cuba, which in my eyes made my country a second-rate place. I didn't care anymore if we lived in a big beautiful home or had a *finca* with horses and a mule that had saved the family. Only up North would I be able to have one with ants.

The revolution was rapidly bringing about major changes that were not making my family very happy. No matter how much our parents tried to keep all this from us, it was impossible not to sense it. The new government kept confiscating more private property and carrying out other actions that undermined the democratic process. Papi was coming home from work each day with further bits of bad news. Then came the televised trials of dozens of men accused of being enemies of the revolution. These were held at the major sports arena. I was not supposed to be watching, but every TV set in the house was tuned to them, so they were hard to avoid. Whenever a defendant tried to deny a charge or say anything that might save their skins, the crowd would drown them out with shouts of "*Paredón! Paredón!*" referring to the prison wall in front of which those condemned would be executed. At one point, Fidel himself appeared to personally vilify one of the accused, who had been presenting a too powerful self-defense. Unable to watch any more, my mother had stormed out of the room.

Another development worrying our parents was the indoctrination program that was already being implemented. By official decree entire schools, mine included, were bussed to the military base to hear Fidel speak. I had stood in the midday heat, along with my classmates, for what seemed like an eternity as our long-winded *comandante* went on and on about things that I neither understood nor cared about. Feeling close to passing out, a few of us escaped our ranks to search for water but could find none. Still, I had come home waving a red and black flag of the revolution and showing everyone a souvenir photo of Fidel with a white dove of peace perched on his shoulder. Not wanting to antagonize Delia, Mami allowed me to put it on top of my dresser. But then even more alarming news arrived. The government was about to pass a law called Patria Potestad, which basically meant that children would become property of the state. That was when my parents realized they needed to make a quick decision about our future.

I had been looking up "manatees" in the encyclopedia when Mami and Papi came upstairs to talk to us. These mammals had fascinated me ever since I learned that they breast-fed their young, just like human mothers, and may have been the original inspiration for mermaids. Still believing that everything was possible, I had once asked Santa to bring me one as a pet—a wish that was never granted. Mequi and Gerardo were lying on their bellies, laughing like seal pups as they watched an episode of *Mamá Cusa*, which was now being aired on TV. Papi turned off our portable Zenith, which brought on a chorus of complaints. But the look on his face quickly ended that.

"We're leaving for Miami in the morning." He sounded very casual. "You will be going to school there."

I jumped up and said, "Yay! I can get an Ant Farm!"

Seeing my enthusiastic reaction, the others became excited too. "Are we flying or taking the ferry?" "Will we need scarves and earmuffs?" "Will there be snow?"

Papi avoided giving us the most important bit of information. They planned to leave us there and return to Cuba. He was convinced, however, that the present situation could not last much longer. The Americans would never sit idly by and let Fidel continue to trample over all their interests. Throughout the half-century of our republic they had stepped in whenever anything displeased them. So it was simply a matter of waiting out the passing storm.

• 7 •

Going in and out of the country was still not a major problem, so long as you had no political involvement and weren't caught trying to take out anything of value. Suitcases were carefully inspected, and sometimes your clothes and private parts too. Papi carried his golf clubs, to give the impression that we were just off on a quick holiday.

Within a few days of our arrival, Hurricane Donna hit Miami head on; our motel lost electric power, and the entire main floor flooded. To us, it was a fun adventure wandering through darkened hallways scaring people, then cooking hot dogs on a Sterno, and afterwards driving through floodwater that reached the door of our rental car. This was the last fun that we would have for quite some time.

My image of American schools came strictly from Hollywood movies. I had pictured quaint ivy-covered buildings and bike rides to a nearby malt shop where a jukebox played and everyone danced rock and roll. The last thing I had envisioned were the crenellated prison-like walls surrounding the Miami Military Academy.

"I'm so sorry, *mijos*." Papi apologized to Gerardo and me as we drove into the campus. "But it's the only boys boarding school in Miami, and we want you to be as close to us as possible." When they hugged and kissed us goodbye, I broke away quickly, afraid to burst into tears in front of the older cadet who was waiting to help us carry our duffel bags to the dormitories. "And please, look after your brother!" Mami shouted to me as they headed back to their rental car. Gerardo was only nine years old and spoke very little English.

The only tangible things that now tied us to our parents were the

Superman and Scrooge McDuck comics that they had bought us after our special farewell lunch, but those were confiscated the minute we walked into our barracks.

"A" barracks housed fifty boys, all seventh- and eighth-graders, from exotic sounding places like Cincinnati and Tegucigalpa. Many of them, I soon discovered, were the troubled offspring of rich Latin Americans, some of them related to past or soon-to-be-deposed leaders. Among them was Romualdo Ramirez, the loud, pot-bellied bully in the neighboring bunk, who boasted about his distant kinship to Trujillo, longtime master of Santo Domingo. There were also quite a few Jewish boys, whose parents seemed to be either divorcing or starting up new relationships. Such was the case of Robbie Gershenoff, my bunkmate. His mom was off to Europe with her fiancé for a pre-wedding trial, but had promised to be back before his Bar Mitzvah. It had made the arrival of that day the main goal of Robbie's life.

"You're much farther away from home than I am," Robbie said as we unpacked, "So you get to choose. Top bunk or bottom?"

"Top," I replied in my accented English, hoping that being able to peer out through the high louvered window would make me feel less imprisoned.

Each night, during study period, Robbie would wrap long black straps around his arms, and tie what looked like a wooden toy block over his forehead. He would then memorize passages from a worn-out book, mumbling them over and over in a language that sounded very strange. Robbie explained that it was Hebrew. This was all totally new to me, since my only prior knowledge about Jews was that they did not go to Heaven because they weren't baptized. It was hard to imagine how Robbie, who was so kind and patiently explained any English words that I didn't understand, would not be rewarded by all-merciful God for his exemplary Christian behavior.

"Do you have indoor bathrooms in Cuba? Had you ever seen TV before you came here?"

He did tend to ask the silliest questions, which made me realize that my Cubanness was as foreign to Robbie as his Jewishness was to me. I simply kept nodding yes to everything, though I wanted to say, "Of course we have bathrooms, with bidets. And we even got our first color TV channel last year."

From the very first day I wanted to blend in and not be looked at as some odd creature, but I had the one undeniable characteristic that in this group branded me as a foreigner—pubic hair. Even the older *Americanos* in "A" barracks, those on the verge of fourteen, still had high-pitched voices and silky smooth skin, while we Latins already spoke an octave lower and were starting to grow a fuzz on our chin and upper lip. A couple of *Caribeños* even had acne, which relegated them to a category of their very own—perverts.

At bath time there were only ten showers for fifty cadets to fight over. The longer it took you to grab one, the less time you had left of the half hour allotted for bathing, spit-polishing shoes, shining buckles and brass buttons, tying your tie, throwing on your dress blues, and running down for evening flag formation. Every day the tension mounted—until it erupted into an all-out war. The hairless banded together against the pubescent, sneering at our emerging curlicues as if we had some kind of contagious disease. My voice was also beginning to change, and some of the looks I got made me feel as if something awful was happening to me. A demon had entered my body and was oozing out of my groin and armpits, perhaps in punishment for my earlier sacrilege.

Each evening before lights out, doddering old Captain Wilson, the night watchman, limped around the barracks counting heads. The process took forever, as smart-ass cadets, taking advantage of the Captain's shaky memory, tried to trip him up.

"Goodnight, Captain! Don't let the bedbugs bite."

"How many hours do you sleep, Cap—seven, eight, nine?"

"Goddammit!" He'd lose his count, and everyone would roar for making the old man swear.

"Ah, ah, ah! No foul language!"

Captain Wilson leered as he limped back to the beginning and started counting all over again. When he was finally finished he would sigh with relief, turn off the lights, then declare his revenge. "Anyone who says one more word will find himself running 'round that parade ground till sunrise!"

"Taps" would soon start playing. That lonely bugle sound, coming from some undetermined place, probably a record player, made me long for my parents and La Calle Ene. If I felt like I was about to cry, I would press my face against the pillow so no one would hear. Sometimes I stayed awake for hours staring at the Apache Motel across the street. Its teepee-shaped roof and colorful Indian designs were so much more like The United States I had always pictured.

From my bed, I could see the red vacancy sign flashing on and off. It shone upon a posse of plaster Indians who lurked behind bushes, ready to attack a horse-drawn covered wagon. A cute blond girl with a checkered bonnet poked her head out through a slit in the canvas top, her mouth wide open with fright. I tried to imagine what else was inside that wagon. The girl's mother was probably cooking dinner, still unaware of what was about to befall them. Perhaps her father was playing "Oh! Susanna!" on a banjo.

If I pressed my nose really close to the window screen, I could also see the Apache Motel pool, which was open until ten o'clock, a whole hour past our "A" barracks lights-out. There would always be some lucky kid running around chasing another kid. Sometimes they'd do cannonball dives, which made big noisy splashes.

"Keep it the fuck down out there!" some brave cadet would eventually shout, making Lieutenant Tinoco erupt.

"Whoever said that better shut their trap . . . if you know what's good for you!" Tinoco, the supposedly mature and responsible barracks supervisor, was an eighteen-year-old senior. One morning I accidentally bumped into him as I stepped out of a toilet stall.

"Watch it, *pendejo!*" He was from Ecuador, and the word *pendejo* was obviously used differently there. To us it meant pubic hair. But then maybe that's exactly what he saw me as. "Where are you from?" When I said Cuba he sneered. "Oh, God. Not another one. I hate you *Cubanos'* guts—a bunch of troublemakers. You better watch it, or I'll have your ass on a spit."

After my eight weeks at Chimney Rock Camp, my vocabulary was adequate, but sometimes even words I thought I knew would make no sense. "Trap," for instance, made me think of those funny contraptions Elmer Fudd was always setting out to catch Bugs Bunny, or as we called him in Spanish, *El Conejito Bogs*. Did someone actually have a trap in the barracks that Tinoco wanted them to shut? As for the "ass on a spit," all I could picture was someone slipping on a puddle of saliva. Not understanding isolated words frustrated me, but not half as much as trying to make sense of entire instruction-filled lectures. The words melted into one another until the language that I thought I sort of knew became unintelligible gibberish.

As a Spanish saying goes, "*No hay mal que por bien no venga.*" Basically, every misfortune brings along a blessing. And it was in the midst of verbal confusion that something dawned on me. If I was having such a hard time, what was it like for Gerardo, who didn't even have the benefit of those eight weeks in a summer camp? Thus began my campaign for trying to get us both out of this hellhole.

Every night after dinner, while other cadets did their homework, and Robbie mumbled in Hebrew, I began to write letters—to anyone who might have some influence over my mother and father. I wrote to both of our *abuelas*, who I knew were not very happy with their decision. I wrote to my godfather, Ramón Antonio, who so loved dramatic stories, and to Mari, my godmother, who also possessed a theatrical touch. I wrote to Miss O'Connor, who had taught English to two generations of our family, and to José, our chauffeur. I wrote to Telma, Mercedes, and Delia, our *manejadoras*. Perhaps Delia's contacts in the other world could finally turn out to be useful. I wrote until the bottom side of my left hand, all smeared with ink, started to cramp up. And I will say with all modesty, that my letters were masterpieces of heartbreak.

> *Queridos Mami y Papi,*
>
> I am studying hard, like you told me to, and getting better with my English every day. I am even learning some Hebrew. Did you know Adonai means God? You will be happy to know that I pray to Him every night, so that he will get us out of this horrible place very soon. Not so much for my sake, but for poor Gerardo, who is much too young to be suffering like he is. He cries all the time, which doesn't help much, since crying is the worst thing one can do in military school. I hear there is a mean lieutenant in his barracks who spanks the kids with a metal dustpan. They even took away the Superman and Scrooge McDuck comic books you bought him on our last day of freedom. Every time I have seen the poor kid since you abandoned him, he has been in tears. . . .

The truth was that separated by age into different dormitories, the only time I ever saw my brother was when our platoons marched past each other. Even then, a quick glance was the most I could catch of him, for we had to look straight ahead while marching, unless we wanted to risk a whack on the head from our platoon leader. This had already happened to me twice while trying to get Gerardo's attention.

I had no idea of the bull's-eye effect that my letters were having. I only heard about it many years later, when my mother described how Papi, after coming home with each day's bad news, would sit on the terrace to read them—and cry. All I knew at the time was that I wasn't hearing what I wanted. "We're coming to get you and will all be together again." So I kept on writing.

Querida Mamá Elvira,

Como estás? I am fine, except for not sleeping too well, worrying about poor Gerardo. . . .

I was convinced that my *bisabuela* would react. Gerardo had had the honor of being named after her late husband and ex-president, Gerardo Machado. Surely she would not sit idly by while her beloved husband's namesake was tortured on foreign soil. But I also knew that one could never have enough ammunition.

Querida Mari,

My birthday is coming up. But there is only one gift I want this year—to be together with all of you. . . ." "Querido Ramón Antonio, They call this a school, but they won't even let us play music. Didn't you once tell me that there could be no real culture without it? . . ." "Querida Delia, I really miss Pedro's *arroz con picadillo*. The food here has worms. By the way, I'm sorry I laughed when you said you had seen Saint Atanasio. You're so lucky to be able to see your dead loved ones. I can't even see my living ones.

Twice a day, after lunch and dinner, we were allowed to use the pay phone outside the mess hall. But it was strictly forbidden to do so until you had finished your entire meal. This meant that unless you wolfed it down, by the time you finished, there was a line winding half way around the building—and I was a slow chewer. I would watch some lucky cadet chatting away and wish that I could hear my parents' voices. Although even if I'd managed to get to the phone, calling Cuba was totally out of the question. The only person I could try to reach was my sister Mequi, or Lourdes, who were both at a nearby boarding school run by the Sisters of the Assumption. Papi had told me to check in on them from time to time. But as head of the family in exile, I felt like a complete failure. I was sure that by now they figured I had forgotten them. I hadn't exchanged a single word with any of my siblings since the day that we had all been left in our schools—and suddenly I felt an intense need to do so.

One morning I woke up determined to succeed. The moment the lunch bell rang I bolted out my classroom and ran to the mess hall as fast as I could. To my amazement, I was one of the first in the cafeteria line. Feigning a stomachache, I asked to be served as little food as possible. This way I could smear things around my plate and make it seem like I was done. It would mean going hungry until dinnertime, but it was worth it. Within seconds I was sliding my tray down the dirty-dish chute and making tracks for the phone. Two kids were already ahead of me. As I waited, I dug into my pocket for Mequi and Lourdes' school number. I had kept it with me since the first day, for it gave me a false sense of proximity. When my turn finally came I inserted a dime into the slot and dialed, then counted three rings before a gruff voice answered.

"Assumption Academy."

I figured it must be a nun. "May I please speak to María Mercedes Santeiro, or Lourdes Crusellas?"

"Who's calling?" The voice became even gruffer. It was definitely a nun.

"It's, uh . . . their brother."

There was a pause. "Sorry. Our students are not allowed to receive calls from men."

"Men? But . . ."

The line went dead. This was the first time I had been called a man, at least for real. Papi was always saying things like, "You're a man now, so start acting like one." But that was just something fathers said. For God's sake, I was only twelve. Even the motto on our uniform T-shirt spelled it out: "Boys today, men tomorrow." But maybe the nun had sensed that I had pubic hair. Whatever the case, I was not about to give up. I reached into my pocket for another dime, but then the kids behind me started to yell.

"Hey, *Cubano!* One call per person. *Comprende?*"

That afternoon, in Science class, I got extra homework for staring out the window while Captain Manley drew the digestive tract. In English, I made everyone roar for answering "Yes, Ma'am" when Captain Brundage asked, "Are you with us, Private Santeiro?" And at soccer practice, when the ball rolled right through my legs into the goal box, I was called a dumb spic and told to go back to Cuba. If only I could.

That evening, shortly after lights-out, Romualdo Ramirez's bunk started squeaking.

"Are you jackin' off, you pervert?" Robbie whispered.

"What, jealous you got nothing to do it with?"

Though he was only twelve and a half, Romualdo had assured everyone that he was already producing enough *leche* to impregnate an entire cowherd.

"I can cum just as much as you, shithead," Robbie shot back, shockingly dropping his Bar Mitzvah boy aura. Then our bunk started squeaking too.

"Shut your goddamn traps!" Lieutenant Tinoco shouted from across the barracks. But then suddenly I felt my penis starting to get rock hard. Just about anything could make it that way these days—even manatees' breasts. It caught me totally off-guard but I couldn't stop myself from joining the action. It's as if my body demanded some kind of payback for all the shit it was going through. The squeaking became even louder.

Now it was Robbie's turn to be startled. "What the hell you doin' up there, man?" Cut it out! Tinoco's gonna kill us."

Romualdo's voice cracked in the dark, "What's the matter, Pipi Boy? Scared we'll find out what a fake you are?"

Then the bunk on our other side started rattling too. It wasn't clear whether those boys were horseplaying or entering the competition, but Robbie wished that he had kept his trap shut and had gone on rehearsing his Hebrew.

"Come on, guys. We'll all get into real trouble."

By now I had become oblivious to the world around me . . . until my covers were abruptly stripped away and I was blinded by a flashlight.

"All right, you clowns! I warned you!" It was Lieutenant Tinoco. "Outta bed and in front of your bunks. On the double!" He bellowed loud enough to be heard at the Apache Motel.

Romualdo, Robbie, and the kids from the third bunk all hopped out and struck rigid attention poses. But I held back.

"Move it, *Cubano!*" He waved a broomstick at me. "Or I'll shove this thing up your ass like a roasting spit!"

I finally dragged myself over, still clutching my pillow in front of me. I tried to push reality away by thinking about the elusive meaning of "spit," but my image of a saliva puddle was about to evaporate.

"What's with that goddamn pillow?" Tinoco came closer, but I just stood there, frozen, holding on tight to it.

"Get rid of that fucking thing!" He yanked the pillow away, exposing my erection, which was poking right out of my pajama bottom.

"Well, well, well! What have we here?" Tinoco grinned.

I stole quick glances to my left and right. Surely I wasn't the only one in this predicament. But there were no telltale bulges under any of my partners-in-crime's pajamas. They were the very picture of innocence. I alone thrust forth at full mast.

Tinoco spared me the embarrassment of turning on the overhead lights, but every cadet around leaned out of their bunk to catch a closer glimpse. Then we heard footsteps, and saw another flashlight approaching.

"What's all the commotion?" Captain Wilson had returned.

I thanked God for the old man's unsteady pulse, which kept his light beam from focusing. "*Padre nuestro . . .*" I started to pray, "I promise to say a thousand rosaries if you make this thing go down." But my erection was still not shrinking fast enough. Then just as the Captain was only a few feet away, Tinoco decided to be merciful.

"All right you schmucks, back into bed!" He told the Captain that it was only a couple of smartasses, yackety-yacking like old biddies. But my relief did not last long. The moment Captain Wilson left, Tinoco crept up and whispered in my ear, "Don't think I'm letting you off this easy, *Cubano pendejo*. I'll deal with you tomorrow."

For half the night I lay awake sweating and wondering what horrible punishment Lieutenant Tinoco might have in store for me. I stared across the street at the Apache's blinking vacancy sign, wishing I was inside that covered wagon with the little blond girl, about to be scalped. At least such a death would be quicker.

To my surprise the following morning Tinoco said nothing about the incident as he marched our platoon to flag-raising formation. I began to feel that the entire affair was behind me. It had all been an idle threat on Tinoco's part to put some fear into me. The day went by without a single hitch—until the flag-lowering ceremony.

This was the most important daily event at the academy. About the only excuse for missing it was being in the infirmary with ptomaine poisoning. General Sampson, the top man himself, carried out a strict inspection. Our uniform brass buttons had to be sparkling, our shoes spit-shine polished, ties perfectly knotted and hanging exactly one half inch above a glittering belt buckle. Fingernails had better be clean, and every hair on our head plastered into place with the help of Brylcreem or Vitalis.

While waiting for everyone else to arrive, platoon leaders had fun with their mini troops, honing our marching skills with new drills. Sometimes we sang call-and-response verses that helped us keep in step. Lieutenant Tinoco had a favorite, which he made us sing whenever he felt particularly cheerful.

I got a girl in Pensacola . . . Honey! Honey! . . .
I got a girl in Pensacola . . . Babe! Babe! . . .
I got a girl in Pensacola, her tits give me Pepsi Cola . . .
Honey, oh babe, be mine!
Stamp with your left, your right, your left!

I enjoyed singing these ditties because they made me feel like I was learning *real* English, not the formal one I had studied with Miss O'Connor in Cuba, but the one that true natives spoke. Although I did find it a bit ironic that Tinoco, who had made me feel so sinful the prior evening, should now be filling our heads with images of Pepsi-dispensing *tetas*.

Another thing that I had grown fond of was the tune the bugle played as the flag came down. I had come to associate it with food, for the moment the ceremony was over, platoon leaders sprang their cadets into double time, trying to be the first to reach the mess hall. Lieutenant Tinoco was a pro at getting our group there ahead of everyone. This time, however, he made us stand still, letting all the others march on by. When cadets started grumbling, Tinoco shouted, "Shut your traps!" Then with a smirk he announced, "We're going to hear a little pre-dinner confession tonight."

Confession, to me, was something that you needed a priest for, and maybe a church. But Tinoco's tone was ominously similar to the one he'd used when threatening me the prior evening. My hands began to sweat. Then I heard him call my name.

"Private Santeiro, will you please come forward?"

My mind raced in every direction, except the one I seemed to be headed on.

"What's wrong, Private Santeiro? Has your little hobby made you deaf?"

"Excuse me?"

"I guess it has," he grinned, and the entire platoon laughed, except for my bunkmate Robbie.

My legs began to quiver, even before hearing Tinoco's next order.

"I want you to tell your platoonmates what you were up to last night."

For once I hoped that I hadn't understood correctly.

"I repeat," the lieutenant said slowly, "What . . . were . . . you . . . doing . . . last night?"

There was no way I could say it. "Uh, nothing, sir."

"Nothing!" Tinoco shouted into my ear. "Are you implying I imagined things, Private? Because I most definitely remember seeing something . . . poking right out of your pajamas." There were more giggles. "Shut your traps!" he yelled, then turned back to me. "I'll ask you one last time. What were you doing last night, Private Santeiro?" The platoon had stopped laughing. "I'm waiting."

I took a deep breath then mumbled, "I . . . was touching myself."

"What was that? I couldn't hear you. Maybe I'm going deaf too."

"I said, I was . . . touching myself."

"Touching yourself?" Tinoco shouted as if for the whole school to hear, and then repeated with cynical emphasis, "*Touching* yourself?"

I could see other platoons staring as they marched by.

"We call it masturbating, Private. Add that to your vocabulary. Or if you prefer, jacking off, beating your meat, pulling your porker."

I prayed that he would stop, but Tinoco wasn't quite through yet. He leaned over and put his nose right up to mine. "Is that the kind of thing parents teach their kids down in Cuba?"

My face was already red with shame, the mention of my parents made it more so, but with rage. "No. It's not." I replied defiantly, expecting something worse to happen. But then his tone turned cynically sweet. "All right. Now I think you should thank me."

"Excuse me?"

"For the free English lesson."

I figured he was joking, and forced a tentative smile.

"Wipe that stupid smirk off!" he shouted. "Go on. Thank me."

I hesitated, then with a cracking voice said, "Thank you."

"Thank you, what?"

"Thank you, Lieutenant Tinoco . . . sir."

"You're welcome . . . Private Santeiro. Now get back in line. On the double!"

I rejoined the ranks with my heart beating triple time and my eyes glued to the ground.

"Now let that be a lesson to the rest of you. Next one I catch beating their meat will not get off this easy."

I wondered what he could possibly do that was any worse—short of an execution.

Dinner was franks and beans, my favorite American food, but this time every forkful made me gag. I slid my half-full dinner tray down the cafeteria chute and headed back to the barracks, ready to outdo myself with letter writing. I had already composed one in my head. I would tell my parents how poor Gerardo had been humiliated in front of everyone, and broken down in a torrent of tears. Then as I reached my bunk I noticed Romualdo Ramirez, lurking by his locker and quickly turning away to hide something. But my mind was too cluttered to care about what Little Trujillo was up to.

"You saw it, didn't you?"

"What?"

"Don't act dumb. You know what I mean." He had picked the wrong day to bully me.

"Lay off me, *schmuck!*" I was startled by my brand new word.

"Listen, *maricón* . . ." Romualdo raised a fist and spit out the worst insult that one Latin male can fling at another. So I shoved him away, hard. He then reached into his uniform and pulled out a pocketknife, which he poked into my chin. "If anyone says something's missing, you better keep your mouth shut. Or I swear I'll kill you, *cabrón*."

"Go ahead. Kill me, *schmuck*." The word felt even better the second time.

Having had his bluff called, Romualdo just stood there unsure of what to do next. Then, as in Old Testament days, when God kept popping up at crucial moments, we heard the most fearful voice on campus.

"Private Santeiro!"

I turned and saw Colonel Sampson, standing a few feet away. Romualdo's knife vanished with supersonic speed. When I looked again, *Leche*-man was diligently spit-polishing a shoe.

"Hello, Colonel Sampson. Gotta keep these nice and shiny!"

Ignoring him, Sampson called me over. "Private, I need you to come with me."

My heart sank. Tinoco had told on me, and I was about to get expelled. All this trouble, just for . . . pulling my porker. But why hadn't the Colonel asked me to pack things up? Maybe they weren't even letting me take my uniforms, for being a disgrace to the institution. So many nights I had dreamt of getting out this place, but never like this, in total dishonor—a black mark to my family's reputation.

Colonel Sampson strutted beside me in total silence. I wanted to say something that might make him feel kindlier, but I couldn't get up the courage. Our walk lasted long enough for me to create a dozen scenarios about my imminent fate. I visualized many possibilities, except the one that I encountered when we reached the administration building.

My mother and father were standing there, next to each other, both looking incredibly glorious to me. Mami was in a knit suit, the kind she usually wore when going to New York or Europe. Papi was in a tweed jacket. Even in the dead of winter nobody dressed like that in Miami. It was as if they had meant to travel farther, then gotten off the plane before their destination.

I was so focused on them that I didn't even notice Gerardo, already standing beside them. He was clutching Mami's hand as if nothing could ever make him let go again. This was the moment I had longed for since the day I watched their rental car pull away and stared until it vanished from view. I wanted to run to them, but stopped myself.

Could they have been summoned because of my jerk off? I checked their faces again for signs of anger or disappointment, but all I saw was their loving smiles.

"Here's your other one," the Colonel ruffled my hair as if such warm gestures had been an everyday occurrence. "Wish all our kids were like these two."

It had been less than three months since I had seen my parents, yet they looked different to me. Even their voices didn't sound quite the way I remembered. I had always been so proud of their fluent English. But now, as they thanked Colonel Sampson, I could detect accents. Their grammar was perfect, but their words were too precise. They didn't tumble into one another in the way real Americans spoke. It occurred to me that they probably didn't even know everyday expressions, like *schmuck* or *shithead.*

"How long will you be staying?" the Colonel asked.

"Until the situation down there changes," Papi replied.

I couldn't believe what I was hearing. They had come to stay.

Not *giving a shit* anymore about what Colonel Sampson thought, I ran to my parents and dove into their embrace.

Francisco and Carlos, my youngest brothers, were waiting in the car. This time Papi had rented the least expensive model that Hertz had available. It didn't even have a radio. As we drove past the Apache Motel, I glanced at the besieged covered wagon. The little blond girl was still poking her head out; from up close, she looked even more scared. I wished I could rescue her. Then we turned into Biscayne Boulevard and I realized that I had never seen the other side of the wagon. All those nights that I had lain awake wondering what was inside it, I never suspected that a little dog was poking its fuzzy head out too, barking for help as arrows pierced the canvas. This discovery made me wonder whether Indians scalped dogs.

There were so many things I wanted to ask. But all I said was, "Where are we going now?"

"To pick up Mequi and Lourdes at their school. Then to our motel."

Gerardo wanted to know if it had a swimming pool, and if we were going to live there.

"Until we find a house to rent."

He asked if *that* would have a pool. Papi looked at us through the rear-view mirror. "You probably haven't heard yet. Fidel confiscated the company."

"Luis, *por favor* . . ." Mami interrupted.

"I think they should know." Papi looked at us again. "That will change again, of course, but no one can say when."

"So we *won't* have a pool," Gerardo said.

"Maybe we will," Mami jumped in before Papi could say anything more.

I couldn't have cared less about a pool, or even if we had lost everything. At the moment, I was even grateful to Fidel for having sent me my parents.

Little else was said as we continued toward Mequi's and Lourdes' school. It was already getting dark, and I sat back to enjoy the bright neon lights along the boulevard. There was a somersaulting clown over the welcome sign of the Frolic Motel and a green olive popping in and out of the Martini glass at the Wet Spot Lounge. Then as we entered downtown, we all rubbernecked toward the huge Coppertone billboard with the playful puppy tugging at the little girl's bathing suit. The puppy kept bouncing up and down, exposing her snow-white *culito*. *This* was the America that I had dreamed of. After months imprisoned at the Academy, I was finally free—at least for a few days.

The nuns were already waiting for us. Papi had barely finished parking when two of them floated out of the main building escorting Mequi and Lourdes. In their flowing black habits the nuns reminded me of vultures carefully guarding their next meal.

"They must be back by Sunday at five," said one of the nuns, seemingly intent on dampening our reunion.

"We lost everything, didn't we?" was the first thing Mequi said when she got in the car.

"What a lovely greeting!" Mami smirked.

"I know we did. My friend Helen's parents arrived yesterday, because Fidel took all *their* things. She said if you showed up it meant you lost everything too."

I saw Mami and Papi exchange a look.

"It's true, *mija*. Fidel confiscated a lot people's things," Papi said with a smile, as if to make it sound less catastrophic, then he stressed one point again, "But not for long."

✦ 8 ✦

The disaster that had befallen my parents was still not talked about in the days or weeks to come, at least not in front of us. Perhaps they did it to protect us, or maybe to avoid reliving the pain. It would take a long while before bits and pieces of the story began to trickle out of my mother.

"We were both in bed, recovering from the Asian flu. We had fallen asleep when the phone rang around seven P.M. and woke us up. It was your father's dear friend Rogelio, calling to say that Fidel was about to speak. Why anyone would think we needed to hear one more word that man had to say was beyond me. But something told us that perhaps we should. So I dragged myself out of bed and turned on the portable Zenith, which your father wheeled into our room after we left you in Miami. The Revolution's anthem was already playing.

"'Onward fellow Cubans, our country shall reward your heroism!' Such a catchy tune. If only it had stood for something we believed in.

"'*Compañeros!*' Fidel began. Then he announced, after denying it for almost two years, that his was indeed a Marxist revolution and he was about to read a list of companies that *La Revolución* was nationalizing. We lay there, like mummies, as he called out almost every well-known Cuban firm. After he said each name, the crowd would shout out, '*Se llamaba!*'—'So it was once called.' Then we heard him say, 'Crusellas y Compañía.'

"We continued to lie there, already drained by the Asian flu, unable to move or say one word. It was as if our minds could not process what we had just heard or the immensity of it. With one quick statement, everything that your father's family had worked for, honestly, for three generations, had been wiped out.

"I finally got up again and told Luis that I was calling our friend Mario Franca to book us a flight to Miami first thing in the morning. But your father looked at me like I was crazy.

"'Why? We're not criminals who need to escape.'

"His ability to remain calm under the worst circumstances had always infuriated me. He just lay there, staring at the ceiling for a long time, and then he fell asleep, which made me think that he was either abnormal or totally irresponsible. I had to take two spoonfuls of Benadryl and still hardly slept. But when I woke up in the morning he was already putting on his tie, as if it were just another regular day. I begged him not to go to Crusellas. I knew that showing up at the factory would only cause more trouble. But there was no stopping him."

What happened next was one story that my father did share with us in detail, one that he very much wanted us to hear—and remember.

"Of course I knew there would be trouble. But I needed to see it with my own two eyes to be convinced of what I had heard over the television.

"I drove along the same route that I had taken every morning of my working life, but suddenly everything looked different. All the familiar sights that I had taken for granted now felt precious and endangered. I kept flooring the accelerator, anxious to get there and yet dreading it. I wondered how Fidel intended to carry out these takeovers. Whoever was placed at the helm would need guidance and instruction, neither of which I was about to provide. All I knew was that I couldn't allow three generations of hard work to come to an end without at least some show of resistance.

"There was a young *miliciano* posted at the main gate. He told me that this was no longer my property and that I was not allowed in. But I sped on past him, quickly parked the car, and headed toward my office. Then I heard someone else shout, 'Somebody stop him, *coño!*' Two men started chasing after me, but I decided it was too demeaning to act like a trespasser in what I still considered legally mine. So I stopped and turned to face them. 'Yes, gentlemen?'

"'You have to leave the building, *compañero*.'

"'We're obeying orders,' the second man said, sounding apologetic. He had been one of our longtime employees—a loyal one, I had thought.

"'Whose orders?'

"'The revolution's. This company now belongs to the people.'

"'But it still has my family's name outside.'

"'That will soon be gone too. Along with your family.'

"Disregarding them, I turned and kept going.

"'Look here, *compañero* . . . Do you understand Spanish? This is no longer yours. Get out!'

"They followed me all the way to my office, where I started gathering the picture frames with family photos. 'The company may not be mine, but these few things still are.'

"They stood and watched me cram the frames into an empty box, then escorted me back out in silence. I sat inside the car for a moment, catching my breath and letting the adrenaline wind down. Then I noticed an engraved inscription on one of the picture frames: 'To our beloved Luisito, from your ever-grateful staff. Navidad 1958.'

"Two days later, they froze our bank account and safe deposit boxes, without giving us any reason or explanation. We were called in for an inventory. Your mother, your Abuela, and I had to sit for hours in a stifling vault as two representatives of the new government went through every single item. They mocked us for an antique baby rattle that was among the jewelry and also for other items that they considered decadent—gold cufflinks, tie clips. One of them held a diamond necklace up to his head, as if it were a tiara, and said something like, 'My, my. Look at this. Royalty!'

"As we walked out of the bank I turned to your mother and said, 'Okay, Nenita. I think it's time to leave.'"

My mother eventually told the story of that last day:

"There was so much to do in such a short time, which in a way was a blessing. We couldn't stop to think about what was happening to us. We had decided not to tell any of our friends, although many had already left and others were also in the process. One was afraid of saying anything that might incriminate either yourself or someone else. So I just called your *abuelos* and asked them to come over, without explaining why.

"Then there were also the servants to deal with. Your father took whatever money we still had in the house and distributed it among them. Luckily Canda and Rosalina were already living in a home for the elderly, and we asked Mercedes and Delia to remain in the house for the moment. But there was nothing we could do about the others. We had lost our source of income. Now it was up to Fidel's communist state to look after them.

"Afterwards Delia came into my room. She was very sad and asked why we were leaving. She said that Fidel was a good man and everything would turn out fine in the end. I didn't want to argue, and told her that we felt it would be best for the children.

"Mamá and Papá arrived while we were packing, and I gave them the news. They understood, of course. I told them that I hoped they would follow us once we were settled, but Mamá replied that we already had enough responsibility with all of you and your Abuela Mercedita, who was also coming with us. The last thing they wanted was to be an added burden. Then, you know my mother, she saw my small suitcase and started telling me that I should also take this, and that, and the other thing.

"'Definitely take at least one hat.'

"'Mamá!' I stopped her. This is not like our other exile. 'We'll be back in a few weeks. Besides, Miami's not New York. We won't need any winter clothes, or hats.'

"Still, saying goodbye to them was heartbreaking.

"Your father had warned me not to try to sneak anything out. He was afraid that if they caught us doing so, they might stop us from leaving. We were already taking the portable Zenith, which folded up to look like a suitcase, and once again he was carrying his decoy golf clubs. But then just as José pulled up with the car and we were about to head out, I saw the gold picture frames with our wedding photographs and all of your first communion ones, and without saying anything I slipped them into my suitcase.

"While waiting in the long line to go through customs I saw that not only were they opening luggage but also taking some people into small booths to do more thorough inspections. I began to wish that I'd listened to your father. 'Luis is going to kill me,' I thought, and I pictured the two of us in La Cabaña prison, with all of you stranded in Miami. But then when our turn came they hardly even looked at us. Now I was furious with myself, for not having snuck away more valuables.

"We were finally seated on the airplane, praying as I counted the seconds to take off, when a *miliciano* came aboard and said that there were two people who needed to get off for further document inspection. I froze. But the names they called out were those of our friends, Sonny and Cuca Mendoza.

"The rest of us remained in that sweltering plane for another hour and a half. But luckily, Cuca and Sonny finally returned, looking very pale but relieved. After we were in the air, Cuca came by my seat and said, 'Until today, I had no idea how tough American dollars are.' She had hidden a hundred-dollar bill in her powder case. Afraid that they would find it, she quickly slipped it into her mouth as they were being led off the plane, and chewed with desperation until she was finally able to swallow it.

"I had felt naively optimistic the prior evening, but now, as I watched the Cuban shoreline with its royal palms vanish in the distance, I sensed that I would never again return to my country."

• 9 •

One of our first outings in Miami, between lunch at Walgreens and seeing Disney's *Swiss Family Robinson*, was a visit to the grave of our ex-president *bisabuelo* at Woodlawn Park Cemetery. His final resting place was a marble niche in the maze-like mausoleum.

As we wandered through the corridors looking for him, carillon chimes began to play an *Ave Maria*. Mami said that it had been years since her last visit. For us children it was a first. When we reached our destination, she bowed her head and made a sign of the cross, gesturing for us to do the same. After allowing her a moment of introspection, I whispered, "Why was Papá Gerardito buried in Miami?"

"It was the nearest place to Cuba."

"Didn't he want to be buried there?" Gerardo asked.

"Very much so."

"Then why wasn't he?"

"He couldn't be, *mi amor*."

"Why not?"

My mother was about to explain but then stopped. "I'll tell you some other time."

"Oh, who cares where you're buried," Mequi said. "When you die you're not here anymore. You're up in Heaven. If you were good."

"You're quite right, *mija*."

A middle-aged couple had just approached. As the man bowed his head toward Papá Gerardito's niche, the woman turned to Mami.

"My husband wanted to pay his respects to the General."

Hearing this, the man looked over. "If he had still been around,

Fidel would not be there today. All those bombs and strikes that brought him down . . . it was already the communists at work." He turned back to the niche and said, "I apologize, *mi General*."

We were starting to leave when the woman pointed to a fat red rose in a bud vase, and asked, "Excuse me. But would you happen to know who sent him that flower?"

"No, I don't," Mami replied.

"*Ay*, too bad. I was hoping you might. The guard told us there's a fresh one every day."

"Really?" Mami seemed surprised.

The woman leaned closer, trying to keep us from hearing. "The rumor is . . . they're sent by a former mistress. He was quite a lady's man, you know."

No longer in the mood for prayer, Mami quickly ushered us out.

When they began searching for a house to rent, Mami decided that we should definitely get one with a swimming pool. While this sounded extravagant under the circumstances, she had her reasons. Now that we could no longer afford *manejadoras*, cooks, or chauffeurs, a pool would help keep us out of her way while she embarked on her new adventures in domesticity.

With all his Cuban assets gone, Papi's entire capital consisted of some cash that he had sent to a U.S. bank to buy new machinery for the company. The purchase had kept getting delayed, something for which he now felt very grateful. It was not a huge amount, but still far more than most of his newly exiled friends had to their names.

Projecting that Fidel might last six months, a year at most, Papi worked out a budget for our living expenses. He soon found out, however, that the figure he had given the real estate broker only afforded cookie-cutter homes in nondescript neighborhoods, none of them with a pool. He may have come down in the world, but he wasn't quite ready to settle for that, at least not yet. He sat down again and reworked the budget. It became a little less frugal on the housing end, and more so in every other respect. Our year in boarding schools had already been paid for, and our younger siblings would be going to parochial ones. But Papi still felt confident that our exile would not last long. By next summer we would be bathing in the glorious turquoise waters of Varadero again, looking upon this as a sad but brief interlude.

After seeing endless houses, Mami finally found one she loved. It was in Coral Gables, facing a golf course. She joked to Papi that they could pretend it was the Havana Country Club. The place came furnished in a mish-mash of old wooden furniture that the owners had brought down from Massachusetts. Mami also liked their aura of solidity.

To help sway any lingering doubts, the realtor pointed out that the street the house was on had almost no traffic, and the biggest potential danger to kids was being hit by a golf ball. She then showed us the *pièce de résistance*—an oversize screened-in pool that took up the entire backyard.

Without giving Papi a chance to haggle, Mami turned to the agent. "How soon could we move in?"

"Soon as you sign the lease." The realtor held out a pen, which Papi, after a moment of hesitation, finally reached for.

The following day we arrived, crammed into our brand-new aqua-and-white Chevy Biscayne. Afraid to inherit someone else's headaches, Papi had decided against buying a used car. He justified the added expense by making sure the model he got included no frills, which meant no air conditioning or even a radio.

The move was a simple one, since all we had was one bag per person, plus the portable Zenith TV and Papi's golf clubs, which he now might get a chance to use after all.

Our "temporary" home had three bedrooms, but there were nine of us. One room would be Mami and Papi's, the second one for Abuela, Mequi, and Lourdes, and the third for Gerardo, Francisco, Carlos, and myself. Since there were only two small beds in ours, the first thing we did was go to Sears to buy a couple of bunks, which the salesman promised to have delivered immediately. There was also a tiny space by the kitchen, which the realtor called the maid's room. A maid was not within Papi's budget, but that room was soon filled by Renecito, the son of Papi's good friend René Scull. He and his wife Maria had become active in the *contra-revolución*, and after having been exposed by someone, they had sought asylum in the Brazilian embassy.

Within minutes of arriving we all put on our bathing suits and ran out to test our new pool. Mami began to unpack, and said she would call us when dinner was ready. But the hours passed, our fingers and toes crinkled up like bleached prunes, and still she wasn't calling.

"Isn't dinner ready yet?" "I'm starved."

Mami had completely forgotten that making dinner was now also her responsibility.

Years later, she would look back at the confusion of this day with fondness.

"I rushed to the kitchen hoping that God would grant me a miracle and make Pedro, our former chef, materialize. But all I found in the pantry were four cans of something called 'SpaghettiOs' which the previous tenants had left behind. Hoping that those would be enough for everyone, I read the directions, which simply said, 'Heat and serve.' That sounded encouraging. Then as I searched around for a pot to put the SpaghettiOs into, I realized I had never turned a stove on in my life. But before even getting to that, I had to cross yet another hurdle. The cans needed opening, and I had no idea how to use an opener either. After failing to figure it out I did the only thing I could think of. I yelled out, 'Luiiiiiis!'"

Papi had been in what the realtor referred to as the Florida room, taking possession of the Mexican desk with hand-painted flower splotches. He had carefully sorted all his receipts, and put them into different pigeonholes according to their urgency. He also labeled the striped notebook that he had bought on discount at Walgreens to record all our expenses. Fidel's *milicianos* had kicked him out of his office, but here he was, setting up a new one to manage his much reduced empire. It was the only thing he could do at the moment to feel a bit useful. Though suddenly, Mami had another chore to test his worth.

"*Que va!* I don't understand these American inventions," he muttered as he fiddled, unsuccessfully, with the can opener.

"Then we'll have to go out to dinner." Mami now felt off the hook.

"Ooh no! We have rented a house, for which I'm paying plenty. So we're eating in."

I got into our new Chevy with them and we drove to a grocery store that we had seen on our way over. Papi had been impressed by the cleverness of its name, which also advertised their business hours, "7-Eleven!" A half-hour later we returned with two stuffed bags of groceries, every item in them fulfilling Mami's requirements: easy to prepare and no need for a can opener.

Our first dinner in our new, "temporary" home was a pepperoni pizza, which was also the first thing that Mami had ever heated. Abuela remarked how we seemed to enjoy this meal far more than any fancy menu that Pedro had ever prepared. Afterwards, Mami and Papi did the dishes together, another novel experience.

When I went into their room to say goodnight, I found them moving the night table out of the way so that they could push their twin beds together. They had always shared the same bed and were doing their best to improvise a joined one.

"There! Now it's even wider than the one in Cuba," Papi smiled.

In the morning, when we burst in again, I noticed that the beds appeared to have drifted apart during the night. The sheet they had used to unify them now sagged like a collapsed tent, and they were both tightly nestled into the same twin.

"What's for breakfast?" Gerardo asked.

Papi looked at Abuelo Manolo's brass carriage clock, the only memento he had risked sneaking past Cuban customs. It was barely seven A.M.

Mami, who had always slept till noon, dragged herself up without any idea of what she was going to serve us.

We had just been in our new home a few days when there was a call from Havana. It was Mercedes, one of our *manejadoras* who had remained in the house, to let us know that it had been confiscated. Two revolution officials had knocked at the door in the middle of the night. When Delia opened, they informed her that she had one hour to get out. Mercedes quickly got back into bed and pretended to be very ill, but they burst into her room and ordered her to quickly pack up her things and leave.

Two days later, there was another call, this one from Mario Mena, who administered La Finca. The exact same thing had happened there, except that he had not even been allowed to take any of his personal possessions.

Our last remaining properties in Cuba were now gone too.

• 10 •

The Machado New York townhouse was in the "silk stocking district" on Manhattan's Upper East Side, a neighborhood where restrained classical façades provided low-key camouflage to opulent interiors. Rockefellers and Biddles had built homes here during the Gilded Age. Looking up toward Fifth Avenue from the front door of 15 East 82nd Street, one could see the steps of the Metropolitan Museum and the imposing columns flanking the main entrance. The houses along the street created a frame for the view that gave the effect of a grand proscenium theater.

When my mother's family first moved in, during their 1933 exile, they had not been particularly welcomed. The last thing nearby residents wanted was a controversial neighbor, whom *Time* Magazine had dubbed "the Mussolini of the Caribbean." But perhaps to their relief, Papá Gerardito had not been able to remain in the house for long. The new Cuban government requested his extradition, and he had unexpectedly been forced to flee. My mother remembered having answered the phone when a still-loyal diplomat from the Cuban consulate had called to give the warning that they were on their way to arrest him. One newspaper claimed that he had escaped disguised in a chef's uniform. Mami said it was just a rumpled twill suit.

For days afterwards, not even the family knew of his whereabouts, and reports of the citywide search for this "number one fugitive" became front-page news. But then time turned notoriety into oblivion, and before long the Machados were just another anonymous family living behind another subdued façade.

The house had been purchased during the height of the depression, when property values were at an all-time low. The previous owners, descendants of Charles James Fox, the famous British parliamentarian, had lost a fortune in the stock market crash and, happy to find a buyer, they had included most of its furnishings in the sale. There had been cloisonné vases, lacquered Chinese chests, and Louis XV chairs. But at the end of their first exile, the Machado family had taken most of their favorite pieces back to Cuba, never imagining that barely a decade later they would lose them to Fidel.

No one had set foot inside the house since 1950. The place had enjoyed neither upkeep nor maintenance. Now the family was returning for a second exile, with no money to pay for the urgently needed repairs.

The New York exile group was headed by my great-grandmother Mamá Elvira, the ex-first lady, already in her nineties but still erect and sharp-minded. Accompanying her was one of her daughters, my *saner* great-aunt, Angela Elvira, whom we called Tia Babi, and her husband, José Emilio. There was also Mari, their daughter, *my* godmother, and Andrés, her husband. Having grown up in the house, Mari was a true New Yorker at heart. She had not enjoyed living in a remote sugar mill, and despite the unfortunate reason for their return, she was glad to be back in her true element. Finally, there was Maria Regueros, who had worked for the family since the presidential palace days. She was the exact same age as Tia Babi, but life had been less kind to her. The inadequate diet that her family had been able to afford when she was a child had resulted in her developing rickets. It had left Maria with slightly bowed legs that had grown more bowed over the years. She now walked with two canes, which made her waddle from side to side like a pendulum.

Mari had often been told that she resembled Audrey Hepburn, though her Caribbean hips were somewhat ampler. It was a comparison that she relished. At times it even seemed as if the Hepburn persona had become part of her psyche. My mother was shocked by her story of their departure, even though she did suspect that Mari had overdramatized it.

"I was not half as fortunate as you, darling," Mari told her. "Mamá had warned me that we might be singled out because of who we were. She said all we needed was some petty official with an old axe to grind. But I told her that too much water had flowed since Papá Gerardito's day. Most of these young guards hadn't even been born, much less had any axes to grind. Still, she made Andres and me promise that we wouldn't attempt anything risky, and I swore on Abuelo's grave that I wouldn't dream of it.

"Mamá Elvira, Mamá, and María Regueros went through customs first. Their papers all seemed in order, so they got waved through to the glass-enclosed waiting room, which really does look like a fish tank—with lots of very unhappy fish. Andres went next. They searched his suitcase, felt his pockets, checked his wallet. But everything was in order too, so they let him join the others. I had insisted on being last, but by now any worries I had had faded. The inspector was about to wave me through too, when God knows what came over him. Suddenly his hand went up and he said, 'Go into that room!'

"I acted like I thought he meant, 'Go to the fish tank,' and started heading there, but he grabbed my arm and turned me toward one of the inspection booths. I could see the others staring through the glass partition with horrified looks. Then this fat-assed *miliciana*, in skin-tight olive-green fatigues that she had to have been painted into, led me in and closed the curtain.

"'Take off your clothes,' she barked.

"'I have nothing to hide.' I stayed cool as a cucumber and took off my shoes and dress.

"'Your bra and slip too.'

"'Excuse me?' Now I was starting to get angry.

"'You heard me. Strip!' she was like a yappy fat-assed Chihuahua.

"So I took off my slip, unhooked my brassiere, then smiled and said,

'As you can see, they aren't large enough to hide anything. Unfortunately.'

"Then she says, 'Now your bloomers.'

"I was outraged. 'Do you have any idea who I am?'

"'No, *compañera*. But I know *I* am the customs officer. So take them off!'

"I turned away trying to think fast. 'I'm afraid I'm . . . in my time of the month,' I said demurely. But she swirled me back toward her. That's when she saw the bulging pouch that I'd stuffed inside them, which must have made me look like a marsupial.

"She leapt toward me and yanked it off. All I could do was stand there, frozen, as jewelry tumbled to the floor like fizzling fireworks.

"'My, my!' the bitch smiled. 'Amazing menstruation you rich *gusanos* have.'

"Then I remembered a bit of advice that someone once gave me, 'When caught red-handed, always deny.' So I put on my most innocent face and said, '*Dios mio!* How did all that get in there?'

"The discovery of my illicit cargo made the other inspector furious for having let the rest of us get by them. They dragged Andres back into another booth, where he was stripped and poked everywhere. But he had nothing. Surprising to say, a slight sense of respect for old age still seemed to survive, because they only frisked the others superficially. Although they did take away the gold saints medals that Mamá always pinned to her bosom. She was ready to kill me. But the important thing, my dear, is that we got out."

According to Mari, Andres had been one of the handsomest young men in Havana. They met after a regatta between the Havana Yacht Club and the Havana Biltmore. And even though his team had lost, he was still in full celebratory mood. Mari had not only liked his looks, she also thought he was one of the most *simpático* human beings she had ever come across. Her parents, Tia Babi and José Emilio, did not share her enthusiasm. They were aware, through the society grapevine, that Andres had a reputation for being a little crazy and prone to overdrinking. On a couple of occasions, his club membership had been temporarily suspended, but Mari defended those infractions as being just silly youthful pranks. There was, however, another reason for the family to feel lukewarm about the budding romance. A couple of Andres' relatives had been among Papá Gerardito's staunchest enemies. One of them was even rumored to have been involved in the planting of a bomb that came close to killing him, had his car not taken a different route on that particular day. But all of her parents' antagonism only made Mari more determined to marry her slightly demented Adonis. And now, Tia Babi was witnessing the offspring of her father's former political foes about to take up residence in his home.

My mother adored her grandmother, Mamá Elvira, and also Tia Babi. She's the one who had curled her hair up into little *moñitos* every school night, read her bedtime stories, and stayed up with her when she was sick. Now, despite there being a tight quota for long-distance conversations in my father's budget, Mami would call New York frequently to see how the family was settling in.

Mari tried to make it all sound like an exciting adventure. "When I walked in through that door, darling, I felt like Howard Carter, clearing my way through cobwebs into Tutankhamen's tomb. But it's nothing that a little dusting and vacuuming can't get back into tip-top shape."

Tia Babi, not wanting to worry Mami either, avoided mentioning that they had forgotten to notify the electric company and spent their first night by candlelight. She also did not tell her about the leak from the roof that had seeped six floors down to the basement, damaging every ceiling and wall along its way, or that the wooden floors had become so dry that they were now like splinter mine fields, nor that cockroaches were forming nightly conga lines in the kitchen. She assured her niece that all was absolutely fine, exactly as she had left it a decade ago, if perhaps with a slight tinge of neglect.

Though I had never been in the house, I had often seen the photographs in my mother's albums and could describe it by heart. The most important rooms were on the second floor. There was a dark wood-paneled library with red brocade wallpaper, then a formal sitting room with stiff-back gilded chairs and a big crystal chandelier. The dining room, with its extra long table, was where everyone who happened to be staying there during the first exile had gathered for meals. It ended in a circular glass-domed conservatory, at the center of which sat a velvet-trimmed pedestal with the cast-iron statue of a Greek slave girl. She was sitting, with her legs to one side, casting someone's fate with animal bones. Her right arm was thrust forward, as if she had just tossed the small vertebrae that lay in front of her.

Mami had told me how Papín had made a playful habit of shaking the statue's hand.

"*Buenas noches*, Señorita. What does fate hold for us today?" Indeed a question that the family might be asking her once more.

Down in the kitchen, the appliances were all remnants from another era. The stove, once a top-of-the-line model, looked like something out of a quaint Edwardian dollhouse. Its thick brass legs were bowed, just like Maria Regueros', and its tapering exhaust pipe rose toward the ceiling like a funnel cloud. There was also an old icebox, the latest advance in cooling at one time, now looking like another museum piece.

There was one last thing that Tia Babi did not mention to my mother, although she would hear about it soon enough. Maria Regueros, who also had her occasional spirit sightings, had kept shivering. When Tia Babi asked if she was coming down with something, Maria replied that she was fine. It was something altogether different.

"We are not alone, Señora Angela Elvira. El General is watching over us."

"I know he is," Tia Babi replied, pointing upward, "from Heaven."

"No, no," Maria Regueros shook her head. "From the sixth floor."

Tia Babi prayed that if her father's spirit was indeed somewhere nearby, he would not be too upset about Andres' presence.

• 11 •

Once a week, my mother would dial the overseas operator and try to place a call to Mimamá and Papín in Havana. Each time they spoke, she would plead with them to come join us, but Mimamá would hedge and say that they were perfectly fine down there, making ends meet with Papín's pension, which had not been taken away. Yet, in coded language she would try to convey that she was safeguarding the few things she had been able to rescue from our house before it was confiscated, and that she planned to hold the fort until we could all return. For the rest of their brief conversation, while my father stood nearby reminding her of the high per-minute cost, Mami would try to exchange pleasantries. She would tell them about her progress in the kitchen or with her driving, now that she no longer had Pedro or José to do those chores. She would also give them updates on how well we were adapting to our new schools, and how quickly our English was improving. They would ask her to send pictures, which she always promised to do. But during one particular conversation, Mimamá could not avoid telling Mami something that greatly disturbed her.

Fidel had decided to change the Cuban currency so as to ensure that there were no secret capitalists left with millions hidden somewhere in their homes. Every neighborhood had been assigned a specific place where one had to go to make this exchange. For Mimamá and Papín, that place turned out to be in our house. They had had to stand in line for hours, waiting for their turn. But then, as if trying to give the experience a positive spin, Mimamá added how this also gave her a chance to poke around and see if any of our furniture or paintings still remained. Mami was not convinced that Mimamá had been completely truthful when she said that it all still looked almost exactly like the day we left. After they hung up, Mami went to her room and did not come back out until it was time to start thinking about dinner.

To cheer herself up, she decided to try out a brand new recipe. It called for a can of Campbell's cream of mushroom soup and one of asparagus, both blended together then poured over a panful of chicken parts. Mami was becoming adventuresome. She was in the process of opening the soup cans, a task that she had now become quite an expert at, when the phone rang again.

"Luisma, my hands are all sticky. Can you see who it is?"

"Darling! It's your godmother. Don't say it! I know I missed your birthday, but we're on exile mode. I promise to make it up to you some day. Is your mother around?"

Mami sensed who it was, and felt in no mood to talk. She made that clear by her facial gesture.

"She's busy cooking."

"Cooking!" Mari said as if I'd mentioned leprosy. "Well, dear. Tell her that our mutual friend, Lillian, reported that that pool of yours is starting to look like the Ganges River during Lunar festival."

I took that as an insult. "It's been hot, and we're the only Cubans who have one."

"Sweetheart, there's miles of free beaches down there. It just smacks to me of refugee mob mentality. I'm sorry, but this Miami exile sounds terribly déclassé."

I was about to ask if she thought she was banished royalty, but then heard screaming coming from the pool in question, and Mami asked me to take over the soup mixing.

"Sorry, Mari, but there's trouble at the Lunar festival. I have to hang up."

Mami ran outside. *"Que pasa?"*

"Francisco won't let me play with his frogman," Carlos whined.

"He's got one too. It's not my fault he broke it."

Our mother was discovering that her two younger kids did not know how to play together. Their *manejadoras* had been highly competitive and were possessive of *their niños'* toys. They had managed to pass on their territorialism, something that Mami was determined to change. As much as she missed having domestic help, she was also finding that she had become indispensable. One day she told Papi how she thought that the exile was bringing us all closer together, and that for once in her life she felt really needed. Papi did not appreciate hearing this. Anything positive said about our present situation seemed to him like a betrayal. From then on, Mami kept her newfound sense of fulfillment all to herself.

Our pool had indeed become a magnet for my parents' rapidly growing number of exiled friends. Some would drop off their older kids while they went off in search of jobs or apartments. Other mothers hung around, letting their younger children turn into prunes in the water while they tried to top each other with stories of loss and departure.

"The back screen door is always open. Feel free to come anytime." Mami welcomed everyone, then usually returned to her ironing, washing, or cooking. Whenever she heard that one of her guests could cook, she would insist that they give her a recipe to add to her expanding repertoire—preferably one easy to make and that did not involve more soup cans. She carefully wrote down these directions on three-by-five cards, then filed them under the initial of the contributor—A: Adelaida's chicken casserole. C: Chachi's ground beef stew. R: Rocio's condensed milk peach cobbler.

The men would stake out their own territory in the living room, sometimes filling it with cigar smoke and always the smell of strong *café*. Unlike their wives, they did not talk of how they got out of Cuba, but about how they intended to get themselves back.

"This country better act fast."

"This country's going to do nothing. Just watch."

"Of course they are. The CIA's already signing up volunteers for the invasion."

"They'll screw it up, like always. Getting rid of Fidel needs to be an inside job."

"By whom, and with what money? Fidel has everything."

"Bah! Fidel is a big windbag."

"Okay, then let's go get rid of him."

"Oh, no. The Americans helped put him in there. Now let *them* take care of their mess."

"*Mira, chico.* The only ones responsible for this mess is us. We sat at the Yacht Club drinking daiquiris, then the minute things got tough, we left."

"What else could we do?"

"Stay and fight like men for what was ours—instead of sitting here waiting for the Americans to bail us out, like cowards."

"Are you saying *I'm* a coward?"

"Señores, *por favor* . . ." Papi would intercede whenever things heated up, which they invariably did.

All the way from the pool I could hear them, ready to come to blows. I wondered why Cubans had to be so loud. I never heard a peep from any of our American neighbors.

"*Niño!* Stop pushing your sister!" one mother would yell.

"Mariana! You're splashing everyone!" another would say even louder.

"Victor! You hit Bebo again and I'm taking you right home!"

I began to wish that they would *all* go home, with their shouting and their tiresome stories of Cuba. But every week kept bringing more exiles, and whenever Papi heard of a friend in need he threw our door wide open. If not quite Lunar Festival, at times our house did resemble a makeshift refugee camp.

It all began with one folding cot, which we Cubans call *pin-pan-pun*, for the sound made by its simple three-step setting up process. Papi had bought this at Sears, fast becoming his favorite store. The first exiled guest to use our *pin-pan-pun* was an old friend of his, once a successful lawyer and now just another penniless refugee without a license to practice his profession. Then came Papi's cousin Carlos, who after unsuccessfully looking for a job in New York and Miami decided to try his luck in Spain. There was Mericia, my late Abuelo's secretary, who had by now left the convent, and Nena Puente, Abuela's cousin, who came out briefly, then decided that she was a burden to her sons and returned to Cuba. Soon there were two *pin-pan-puns*, which came in very handy when friends who were still in Cuba started to send out their children. They were usually being sent to live with relatives who had already moved to places like Chicago or Detroit. It would often take Papi a few days before he could locate these relatives and put their wards on a plane or a bus. The house was endlessly crowded, yet always with a strong sense of camaraderie. Still, there were a couple of instances when Mami *did* try to draw the line.

"*Four* people? Luis, where do you intend to put them?"

"We have the two *pin-pan-puns*, and Silvia's very short. She can fit on the love seat."

"What about her third kid?"

"I'll stop at Sears on my way to the airport and buy a sleeping bag."

One supposedly temporary guest, whose stay kept getting prolonged, was Marietta, my great-uncle Ramón's second wife. "I am only staying until I can sell some jewelry and rent a little apartment," she assured Papi shortly after arriving. Marietta had beautiful jewelry, which Tio Ramón had faithfully given to her after each infidelity. With guileless innocence she had stuffed her crocodile purse with as much of it as she could cram in, and she had been one of the lucky few who made it through Cuban customs without being inspected. But Marietta's arrival presented a strange predicament. We also had Lourdes living with us, who happened to be the daughter of Tio Ramón's *third* wife, the one that he had left Marietta for. For a few days the two of them did their best to skirt around each other politely. But then, their mutual affection for the same man, whom Marietta still adored despite everything, brought them together and they formed an inseparable bond.

Every single one of our guests would soon find a job—as hotel desk clerks, department store sales persons, even as night shift attendants at a Drive-thru Farm Store. No one remained a day longer than they had to, or took advantage of my parents' generosity. And for as long as they were with us, everyone contributed in whatever way they could—ironing, vacuuming, sharing the food rations that they received at the Cuban Refugee Center. We had an endless supply of powdered milk as well as large tins of spam and peanut butter—the latter a new and exotic item to most Cubans. A former dentist, for whom Papi helped translate some legal forms, later thanked him by taking care of all our cavities—in an improvised barber chair that he secretly set up in his garage.

When one set of guests departed, Mami would store the *pin-pan-puns* in our garage, only to drag them back out a day or two later. The house was a never-ending parade of once prominent people now starting over from zero.

We children understood that this was a special period and that we all needed to pull our own weight. We were happy to make our own beds and try to keep our room as neat as possible, even to do the dishes on nights when *our turn* came up. But little by little the sense of communal adventure began to wear thin. The cot-cluttered living room that had once intrigued us became just an annoying obstacle course. Our lives seemed to be consumed by the business of exile, and there wasn't one corner of the house where one could escape it. Abuela's radio was tuned twenty-four hours a day at top volume to a Spanish-language station that ranted non-stop about the imminent demise of Fidel. Papi told us that this gave her hope and that we should be more understanding. And at meal times, even though Mami did her best to avoid the subject, something would always bring the conversation around to the same tiresome theme—Cuba! I was getting sick of it. At least for me, our special period of camaraderie was coming to an end.

• 12 •

Winter had arrived early up in New York, bringing yet another problem—heating bills. The Machado townhouse had fireplaces in almost every room, but the main source of heat still came from the antiquated coal furnace in the basement.

When Andres saw the bill after the first coal delivery, he almost fainted. It caused an argument between him and Tia Babi, who had placed the order. He was even more horrified when he found out that the mountain of black fuel they had dumped into the basement was only a one-month supply. Given their extremely tight finances they needed to find a way to make that shipment last as long as possible, so Andres came up with what he felt was a stroke of brilliance. They would wait until the eleven o'clock weather report each night, then load the furnace accordingly. The only problem with that, they soon found out, was that television meteorologists frequently make mistakes.

My mother could sense that something was very wrong when Tia Babi called her one morning with her teeth chattering. She reluctantly admitted that they had made a slight miscalculation and had spent a somewhat frigid night. But she assured Mami that they had lots of blankets and that Mamá Elvira had been kept warmest of all, with the wonderful fur coat that Mari had found in a fifth-floor closet—probably left behind by some long-ago guest. The lining was a bit moth-eaten, but the rest of it was amazingly preserved. Tia Babi also confessed to having come down with lumbago. Since Maria Regueros' bowlegs kept her from doing certain chores, and Mari and Andres were mostly out and about looking for jobs, the task of stoking the furnace had fallen mostly on her. Before ending the call, not to leave Mami too alarmed, she did add that all the shoveling was also helping her to lose weight.

In the two months since their arrival, unexpected bills had kept piling up, and Fidel seemed nowhere near departing. At first they ignored the leak from the roof, hoping that it might miraculously seal itself back up. But after one heavy rainstorm, three floors of wallpaper buckled and chunks of ceiling plaster collapsed. They finally called in a roofer, whom Tia Babi asked not to do anything before giving her an estimate. After a few pokes around the rooftop, the man came down with a morbid look and told her that it would not be cheap, but that if they didn't do something about it quick, they might wake up one day with the whole house on top of their heads.

Years of seeping water had also damaged the antique electric wiring. Short circuits were daily occurrences. First the lights went out in a hallway, then in one bedroom, then in two. Filled with macho confidence, Andres announced that he himself would do the rewiring. Mari and Tia Babi begged him not to, but he was determined—until an electric shock knocked him off a metal ladder. For days he went around smelling like overcooked hamburger.

An electrician was finally called in. Tia Babi asked him to do only what was absolutely necessary. But after taking one quick look, the man shook his head and told her they were lucky not to have been fried to a crisp, and they found themselves facing yet another unexpected expense. They had all arrived clinging to the fantasy that they could live rent-free, overlooking the small detail that old houses become enormous money drains. One could cut back on groceries or electricity, but collapsing roofs and fire hazards had to be dealt with.

Given the fancy address in which they lived, and the lingering rumors about the millions that Papá Gerardito had fled the country with, some people still assumed that the family had plenty of money outside of Cuba. One day Andres made a most unfortunate remark, "We're going broke here. Whatever happened to all that famous money that

The General supposedly took?" This made Tia Babi livid. She quickly grabbed the phone and called my mother.

"Papá was the most honest president that ungrateful country of ours ever had. And now I have to live with *the enemy* right under my roof."

Mari called a while later to clarify. She felt that her mother had over-reacted. Andres had only been joking. I heard my mother reply that some things were best not joked about.

In typical melodramatic fashion, Mari said that she felt like a Capulet, being punished for having married her handsome Montague. "Two houses divided. As if dealing with a crumbling one wasn't bad enough."

My father kept telling my mother that her family should stop living in the past, sell the house, and be done with their cumbersome white elephant. On this, Mami disagreed. She felt that Mamá Elvira had had enough upheaval in her life, and she hoped they could avoid displacing her yet again. If they could just hold on a little longer, maybe things would finally change in Cuba.

To Andres' credit, as soon as he realized that the exile was becoming prolonged, he did start looking for a job. But he went about it the only way he knew how, by reaching out to family contacts. He went down to a Wall Street firm that specialized in sugar trading. His grandparents had been close to one of its founders. He also went to see a steel manufacturer with whom his father had once had some business dealings. They were all very friendly to him, but in the end, no offers were made. Turned down by every contact he could think of, Andres began to lose confidence.

He was getting a haircut at a barbershop on 86th Street when the barber suggested he go to an employment agency. Andres thanked him, though he had no intention to follow up on the idea. In the world that he came from, people did not do such things. There were old alliances, ties that went back for generations. There was always someone to give a helping hand, if you were ever unlucky enough to need one. Going to an employment agency meant admitting that he knew no one. And if he knew no one, then he was no one.

Mari also began to contact her old Sacred Heart classmates. Most of them came from money, and some had married better still. She was hoping they might give her an interesting lead, or perhaps even know of a specific job that she was suited for, but they too assumed that she was still well off, and Mari was not too eager to dispel that image. They would suggest that they meet at a restaurant for lunch, invariably a fancy one, then when the bill came, say, "Let's go Dutch, shall we?" Mari quickly decided that she needed to find a different technique for her job hunting.

Meanwhile, Tia Babi was having no trouble filling up her days. She had begun to rummage through six floors of rooms and closets that had become overstuffed over the years, and was determined to take advantage of this "temporary" exile to clear out some of the accumulation. The items that she was unearthing weren't only the family's, but also those of bygone friends and political associates whom they had sheltered during the previous exile. "We're just leaving this trunk here for a few days." "My secretary will come to ship these books back to Havana." It had all remained behind, like unclaimed chapters of other people's lives.

In the afternoons Tia Babi usually sat in Mamá Elvira's room. All bundled up they would recite idiosyncratic prayers to obscure saints, asking them to please help Cuba. Sometimes they also rummaged through the boxes of old clippings that Tia Babi had come across during her house cleaning. Occasionally she would send us ones that she thought we might enjoy. My favorite, from the "Believe It or Not" column in the *Daily Mirror*, had a pen-and-ink sketch of Papá Gerardito. "Gerardo Machado," it said, "was once president of The United States. Cuban presidents may not leave the country during their term of office. To legalize his visit to the U.S., the Cuban Congress extended the borders of Cuba to include The United States."

I asked Mami if I could keep it. She smiled and said, "How I wish you could have shown this to the friend who brought you that horrible article from *Bohemia*."

• 13 •

In Miami, Sears *pin-pan-puns* and the occasional sleeping bag continued to crowd our living room. At mealtimes, friends would often show up in their terminally sputtering vehicles, then shyly but promptly accept when Papi invited them to join us. There were so many comings and goings that one suspicious neighbor reported us for running an illegal flophouse. The policeman who came to investigate happened to be the son of Polish immigrants and was sympathetic to what Cubans were going through. He not only dismissed the complaint, he also wrote a note to the meddlesome neighbor suggesting that she apologize to us for making false accusations. The neighbor never did, but she never again complained.

By the time Mami managed to pull dinner together it was usually near nine P.M. This became a pet peeve of mine, especially after learning that the typical American household ate at six. I might have minded it less if Papi had let us eat in front of the TV, but he insisted on our sitting at the table with the adults, where the conversation might help expand our horizons. Unfortunately, all that the adults continued to talk about was Cuba.

"The invasion should be landing any day now." It always began with some guest.

"We've been hearing that for weeks."

"But it's true this time. I heard it from a friend with CIA connections."

"Oh, please! The CIA has become too scared to do anything."

"Scared of what—Fidel?"

"No. The Russians."

"The Russians are ten thousand miles away!"

"But all they have to do is press that little red button."

I wanted to show Papi that I was listening. "Is that little button really red?"

"Stop asking silly questions and eat."

"It's not a silly question," Mami came to my defense.

"The only thing that's red," said another guest, "is the propaganda that Fidel has brainwashed half the world with."

It killed me to think of all the great TV shows I was missing because of Cuba: *The Twilight Zone*, *Lassie*, *Mr. Ed*. It made me wish that I was an American.

One Saturday my bunkmate, Robbie Gershenoff, invited me over to his house. His mother had broken off her engagement and returned from Europe earlier than expected. Robbie was ecstatic. The Gershenoffs lived on Palm Island, off Miami Beach. Robbie's mother even offered to drive me back, if someone could bring me over. Robbie explained that she hated getting up before noon and wasn't much good until two P.M.

Papi was more than happy to take me. He felt that I was turning into a hermit, and was relieved that I had at least one new friend.

Robbie lived alone with his mother in a house that was twice as big as ours. His room was filled with amazing things: remote control racecars, walkie-talkies, even a real telescope through which he could spy on people in the next island. When I mentioned that our house was *a little* overcrowded, Mrs. Gershenoff, who asked that I call her Rita, said that she would be more than happy to have me move in.

"Does your mother let you eat by the TV?" This was my most important requirement.

The question seemed bizarre to Robbie. "Where else would I?"

Before driving me back, Rita took us to Woolfie's Restaurant for a typical six o'clock American meal. She and Robbie had huge pastrami sandwiches. Since I had never heard of that, I ordered a hamburger.

When I got home I told Gerardo about the telescope and the pastrami, as if I was lecturing on the artifacts and diet habits of aborigines. More than ever, I wished that my family could be a normal all-American one, like the Gershenoffs.

When I told Mami about their move-in invitation, she quickly nixed the idea.

"But why do I have to sit there night after night hearing people talk about the same old thing?"

"Because we're a family, and families eat together. At least ours does."

"Abuela gets to eat in her room, listening to her radio."

"That's different."

"Well, I'm sick and tired of hearing about Cuba."

Mami slammed down the bean can that she was opening. "Luisma, you have to realize that all these people's lives have been turned upside down by what happened down there."

"So? Mine was too," I sassed.

"Not like theirs. Things affect one much harder when you're older."

"But why can't they talk about something else now and then? Why always Cuba?"

"They talk about Cuba . . ." Mami paused, searching for the precise words, "because if they didn't, they would feel they're no longer part of it. And that would be even more painful."

This still didn't make total sense to me, but for the moment at least, I decided to let it go.

NOT HAVING A job was starting to bother my father too, and not just because of our dwindling finances. He had worked at the Crusellas Company since he was eighteen. Despite being an heir to it, his father had made him begin at the very bottom. He had traveled the back roads of the island selling soap and cologne to pharmacies and bodegas. Papi had always been proud of the work ethic that his parents had instilled in him. But now it seemed to be backfiring. Mami kept telling him to stop feeling guilty and try to enjoy having some extra free time to spend with us. She even suggested that he take his famous golf clubs and go play a few holes on the course across the street. Taking her advice, he splurged on the fee one day, but pursuing that little ball around for hours only made him feel more inconsequential.

It was at one of our crowded Sunday lunches, between forkfuls of *picadillo*, that one of the guests dropped an interesting bit of information. The Cuban Refugee Center, he said, needed volunteers. They could barely keep up with the processing of new arrivals. The following morning, as Papi headed to Publix with Mami's grocery list, he suddenly took a detour, drove all the way downtown, and parked near the tower inspired by the Giralda of Seville, where the Cuban Refugee Center was operating. Later he told us what happened.

"It was just nine A.M. and the line already spilled down the front steps and halfway around the block. As I walked past it, people started grumbling.

"'*Oye!* The line starts back there! This is a democracy. We are all equal.'

"'Yes. Equally broke!' Someone joked.

"I was happy to see that my countrymen's sense of humor was still intact. I told them that I worked there, and felt a little guilty for lying, but within minutes it wasn't a lie anymore. The man in charge of volunteers turned out to be a former employee of Crusellas. "Luisito!" He threw his arms around me. And when I told him I had come to see how I could help, he asked if I could start right away. They were desperate for people fluent in English who could help fill out refugee applications and translate for immigration authorities. It all happened so fast that I had no time to call you—until my ten-minute coffee break."

But what concerned my mother most at the moment was the fact that he had totally forgotten about her groceries. "Now we'll have to go shopping and I won't have dinner ready till midnight!"

"You don't need to cook tonight. I'll go to 7-Eleven and get pizzas."

Then she thought of another problem. "If you start working downtown, what do we do about the car? I need it for a million things."

"I'll take a bus."

Papi's willingness to take public transportation finally made her more sympathetic. But what really got to her was the thought of her husband, who had until recently run his own company, now being reduced to taking ten-minute breaks.

"Our lives have certainly changed." From that moment on she was totally supportive, and she never once complained, no matter how late my father came home from his new job.

WORKING UP TO ten hours a day, Papi's spirits never flagged again. He was only helping to fill out blanks on a page, simple data like age and marital status. But to him, each of those forms meant another passport to freedom.

The conversation at our dinner table now shifted from the overall political picture to a far more personal one. Each night Papi brought back new stories.

"I processed this woman today who has four kids, all under seven. She speaks no English and doesn't know a soul here. Immigration is sending them to Ohio." "I translated for this man who's ninety-two. He came to join his son but could not stop crying for having to leave Cuba." "These three little girls arrived alone. Their mother sent them to stay with an uncle, but we can't find him anywhere."

"We still have the *pin-pan-puns* and a sleeping bag," Good Samaritan Mequi said.

"Don't put ideas into your father's head. I'm sure it already crossed his mind."

I felt like an insensitive monster for just wishing that Papi would chew faster, so we could finish dinner in time to catch at least the end of *Twilight Zone*.

I was doing homework while watching *The Tingler*, a spine-chilling Vincent Price classic, on the afternoon that my father came home with news about the big demonstration.

"They want as many of us there as possible so we can get national attention and people start realizing what Fidel is doing. Hurry! We're leaving in five minutes."

I told Papi that I had to study for an exam, but he said that this was far more important. I couldn't believe my bad luck. The Tingler was about to frighten a deaf-mute to death.

"I don't care how important it is. I'm not going."

"Stop contradicting me and get in the car."

I pleaded with my mother, but she was no help. "Do what your father says."

"But why?"

Papi wanted us to witness the event so that the love for our country would stay alive. But he could not express that, and instead just yanked me by one arm. "Because I say so!"

The Tingler was squeezing the mute woman's spinal cord and suffocating her.

I said, "I'm not going."

Now it was Mami who yanked my other arm. "Get into that car immediately!"

When I stepped into the Chevy I found that it was already full. Marietta, Mequi, and Lourdes were in it, so was Pancho Miranda, an old friend of my father's who had arrived recently and still seemed shell-shocked. Then Abuela joined us too, looking like a Grand Duchess heading for the picket line in her black dress and three-strand pearl necklace. I squeezed in further to make room.

As we drove toward downtown, I scrunched way low on the seat and peered at passing cars. Ours was the only one on the road with seven people in it, four of them good-sized adults. I felt that everyone was staring, and I could imagine them thinking—"Refugees!"

Finding a parking space became another ordeal, and Papi was not in a good mood because we were already running late.

"Right there!" Marietta pointed to an empty spot.

I started to explain the meaning of the yellow lines painted across it, and was stunned when Papi pulled in anyway.

"We can't park here," I said. "It's illegal."

"*Ay, hijo.* With all the problems we have, you think I'm going to worry about some yellow paint? It's an empty space. I'm parking."

The others cheered him on.

"But they'll give us a ticket!"

"If they do, we won't pay it," Pancho said, as if forty-eight hours in the U.S. had given him full understanding of its laws.

"The mayor of this city should pay it, for not providing more spaces," Papi said.

I decided to keep my mouth shut.

The stretch of greenery between downtown and Biscayne Bay was known as Bayfront, but Cubans had dubbed it *El Parque de las Palomas*, "Pigeon Park." Perhaps out of solidarity with those wandering birds, they had also chosen this as the unofficial site for all their gatherings.

The open-air bandshell stadium was packed, and dozens of banners bounced up and down as the crowd chanted: "*Cuba sí! Rusia no! . . . Cuba sí! Rusia no!*"

I would have happily stayed in the rear, but Papi insisted on going as close to the front as possible, even though all those rows were packed too.

Then Marietta clasped her hands and shouted, "Carmelina!" She flung herself into the arms of another deposed duchess. "*Dios mio!* What are you doing here?"

"*Ay, mija.* Waiting for Fidel to fall, like everyone else. You need a seat?"

"Yes, but there are seven of us."

"Don't worry, *querida*. Squeeze in."

The entire row scowled as Carmelina pushed to make room for our entourage.

Soon everyone was spotting familiar faces: "Luis!" "Pepe!" "Pancho!" "Rogelio!"

I was mortified by all the kissing and hugging, and by being dragged out of my protective shell for Papi's introductions.

"Emilito, have you met my son? Luis Manuel, get up and shake hands."

"*Dios mio!* He's almost a man!"

Suddenly everyone jumped to their feet, as a scratchy Cuban national anthem began to play. Hundreds of little flags appeared out of nowhere, and voices broke into song: *"Al combate correr Bayameses."* "Onward to battle, people of Bayamo." Bayamo is the town where the Cuban independence movement had been born, in the mid-nineteenth century. I knew that from history class. I knew the rest of the words too, but I refused to join in. Looking around, I could see that I was the only one. I turned to Abuela and to Marietta, who was singing at the top of her lungs, and noticed that their eyes were full of tears. I looked at Papi, and Pancho, and even Lourdes and Mequi, and saw that all of them had become emotional. Then I felt my father's hand reach for mine, and my eyes began to mist up too.

• 14 •

With employment rejections continuing to pile up, Andres had started to drink. He had never been a teetotaler, but his consumption had now increased noticeably. Tia Babi told Mami how she could smell it on him when he came home each evening. She suspected that instead of going to the job interviews he claimed to have gone to, he was spending his afternoons at one of the pubs on 86th Street, throwing away money that they did not have.

Upon hearing that he was still unemployed, his barber now suggested that he should start looking into hotels and restaurants. He assured him that with his good looks and savoir-faire, he was bound to make a wonderful concierge or maître d'. This had only made Andres' faltering self-confidence plummet even further.

Mari was also becoming a bit desperate. Most of her exiled friends were already employed. Those deposed Cuban princesses had set out to conquer New York with their tropical charm and good breeding—and mostly ended up as sales clerks.

"If they can do it, I said to myself, I most certainly can too," she boasted to Mami during one of her calls. "So I put on the Chanel suit that I left Cuba with and strode into Bergdorf Goodman to fill out an application. As you well know, Nena, Mr. Goodman's wife is a fellow Cuban, and longtime friend of Mamá's. But I am not one to drop names in order to get favors. I intend to find a job on my own merits. At least I did, till this snooty bitch in personnel, without even looking at me, says 'Sorry, I'm afraid we're not hiring at the moment. We'll let you know if that changes.' Well, my dear, her nasal tone made me lose it. I said, 'Listen, Mrs. Goodman happens to be a dear old family friend, and she will certainly hear about this!' Then I strutted out thinking, 'Their loss, baby! Screw Bergdorf's!'"

Mari had gone on to fill applications at Bonwit Teller, Saks, Lord & Taylor, B. Altman, Bloomingdale's, and even Ohrbach's and Alexander's, which she considered a big step down. But every one of them already seemed to have a glut of refined Cuban-exile salesladies. She was incensed that they would dare turn down Audrey Hepburn's doppelganger, with the sexier hips.

"And can you imagine," she went on, "the personnel director at Ohrbach's even asked me to sell myself to him! That's the most vulgar thing I ever heard of. I said to him, 'Sorry, but I'm not for sale.' Then I walked right out of there too."

"Now *she's* started drinking too," Tia Babi reported to Mami. "I found a Vodka bottle hidden in her night table." I later heard Mami telling Papi how worried she was.

But lately Tia Babi had been keeping busier than anyone. Besides shoveling coal, and arguing with Andres over her using too much of it, she now spent two afternoons a week volunteering at the International Rescue Donation Center. The items that came in were meant for *all* needy immigrants, but three Cuban volunteers were making sure that the lion's share went to refugees from their own island. Tia Babi's job was to sort the clothes by gender, then neatly fold or hang them. Besides this being a constructive endeavor, it also gave her a chance to get together and gossip with two old friends, both of whom also dressed up for their volunteer work as if they were going for tea at the St. Regis.

Since the center was located in an upscale area, the donations tended to be of very high quality, much of it almost brand-new. One day, her friend Eva held up a button-down Oxford shirt from Saks and observed that it was extra-large, like her husband. Tia Babi got her drift and told her disapprovingly that these items were for charity. But then Eva reminded her that charity begins at home.

"Let's not fool ourselves with these ten-year-old Chanel suits we're wearing. Fidel may not have been able to take away our sense of style, but under this fancy giftwrap, we're now all charity cases too."

Tia Babi had been struck by the comment. Until that moment, she had still not thought of herself in this category. It had taken the much savvier Eva to spell things out. From that day on, whenever she came across an item that she thought might fit anyone in the family, she started to quietly put it aside. Soon we began to receive boxes full of button-down shirts and chino pants from Brooks Brothers, linen blouses from Bonwit Teller, and housedresses from Macy's. These arrivals would create an excitement in our house that was only matched by Christmas.

Mami said that she could always tell if Mari had been drinking when she called, but I couldn't. And even if she had been, it never bothered me because she always had some amusing story to tell.

"Darling, you won't believe what I found yesterday inside a dusty old trunk!" From her tone I assumed that it might be something like the crown jewels. "Two of my favorite childhood dolls—Shirley Temple and Charlie McCarthy. They're collector's items now, you know. I used to play Presidential Palace with them. Charlie would be the president and Shirley his daughter, who always got kidnapped by the opposition. I would tie her up and dangle her, head down, over a tubful of water, until she was rescued at the very last minute. Is your mother around?" Once her story was done she would switch tone on a dime.

"Mari, be frank with me, is everything all right up there?" Mami would try her best to bring her back down to Earth. "Please promise that you'll tell me if I can help in any way."

It annoyed Mari that my mother should sound so magnanimous when she knew that Papi had us practically on ration cards. But rather than argue, she would change the subject. I could usually hear her booming voice from three feet away.

"Darling, what *is* that noise? Don't tell me you're making more *picadillo* for the exiled masses."

Mami explained that she was stapling feathers to an Indian headdress.

"Oh. Are you taking in boarders from that disenfranchised group too?"

My mother had never been artsy-craftsy, but when no one else volunteered as den mother for the Little Flower's Cub Scout troop that Francisco and Carlos had recently joined, she had unwittingly agreed to do so. With Thanksgiving coming up, she had found a book on simple costume making at the Coral Gables Public Library, and she was now following instructions, just as she did with cooking recipes.

"Well, you're getting much too Betsy Ross for me," Mari said. Then before hanging up, she also reported that Maria Regueros had supposedly seen Papá Gerardito. He had flashed across in front of her on the fifth floor landing, wearing a perfectly starched *guayabera*. This last bit of news made Mami laugh.

"I guess that means they must have good laundresses up in Heaven."

A few days later Tia Babi called again to report that Andres' job hunting had now come to a complete stop. She could no longer accuse him of going to the pubs on 86th Street; he was now doing all his drinking right at home. It was time to start seriously praying that Fidel's revolution would end before their money did.

As long as Andres was staying home, Tia Babi decided that she might as well make good use of him. Each morning she started presenting him with new list of chores: light bulbs to change, plaster holes to patch, leg chairs to re-attach. Andres soon began to feel that he had become the Machados' errand boy, and he deeply resented it.

Complaints about the house being too cold would also make his temper flare. He felt these implied that he was solely to blame for limiting the use of heating fuel. He began to avoid his mother-in-law as much as possible and spent most of the day up in his room, sipping vodka while scanning the papers for news about Cuba.

One morning, he came across an article about Batista, the island's deposed dictator. It described his comfortable exile in Portugal and showed a picture of the elegant building where he now lived in Estoril. It was common knowledge that Batista had not fled empty-handed. But then, the same thing had been said about President Machado. The family had always denied it. They had trunkfuls of old letters as proof of the tight financial circumstances that they had lived in during their first exile, yet Tia Babi sometimes doubted that Andres was totally convinced of this. And he was certainly not the only one who thought that if Machado had indeed left Cuba almost empty-handed, he was probably the only Cuban president ever to do so.

When he heard about Maria Regueros' claim to having seen the General on the fifth floor, Andres jokingly suggested that she should have asked if he had left any money hidden around somewhere. Maria, who felt loyal to the family, had not been amused by the comment. She ignored it and continued to erase her mistakes from the *Daily News* crossword puzzle, which she struggled through faithfully to improve her English.

One day Andres found a fifth-floor window cracked open slightly, and he accused Maria, who was the only one living up there, of the expensive waste of heat. When Maria assured him that she had not touched the window, Andres jested that perhaps then it had been the General.

"Now why on Earth would he want to do that?" Maria asked, dead seriously.

"Maybe he's coming from Purgatory and needs a cold draft."

Despite this being another one of his quips, the mystery of the open window continued to nag at him. He was, after all, from the Caribbean, where most people accept that there are inexplicable things in this world. Perhaps Maria Regueros did have some connection to the other side—and he had always been one to take advantage of connections.

"I'm not joking now. If the General happens to drop by again, please ask him if he knows where we might find a little extra cash."

Maria never mentioned whether she had any further encounters, but in his boredom, Andres soon developed a new pastime—searching for telltale signs of hidden loot. He poked behind picture frames, pried under loose floorboards, scraped at patches of plaster that looked bulgy or discolored. Then one morning he came across a somewhat suspicious spot on the second floor, right behind the Chinese screen that separated the butler's pantry from the dining room. One flight below, Tia Babi had just come home from the donation center with two full shopping bags. She was about to ask Maria Regueros to help her sort clothes when she heard the banging. Maria told her that it had been going on for quite a while. Tia Babi's bloodhound instinct quickly came to the fore. She tiptoed up the back kitchen stairs, which were seldom used and had become even creakier than the front ones. When she reached the top she found Andres kneeling by the baseboard, chiseling away at the wall with a hammer and screwdriver.

"*What* are you doing to my house, Andres Arellano?"

This jolted her son-in-law up to his feet. He told her that the paint had buckled, and he wanted to make sure that it wasn't another leak. But it was clear to Tia Babi what he was really up to, and it infuriated her that he should continue to question her father's integrity.

"Why on Earth would Papá not have told us if he had left behind any money?"

"I don't know. Maybe Maria Regueros should ask him that too."

After ordering him to stop tampering with her house, Tia Babi marched right back down and ordered Maria to put an end to all the nonsense about her father's nocturnal visits. It wasn't only absurd, but also disrespectful.

Although her mother and husband were on increasingly adverse terms, Mari decided to remain neutral, like Switzerland. After all, that's where Audrey Hepburn lived, so she felt a special connection.

• 15 •

We had started to receive other mail deliveries that also caused great excitement. These came from Cuba and were sent by Mimamá. They were large manila envelopes covered with colorful stamps and addressed in our grandmother's large flowery handwriting. Inside them, there was always a brief letter to the Cuban postal censors.

> *Estimados Señores,*
>
> Please let these photographs go through. They are memories of my daughter and grandchildren, with no political significance or interest to anyone else but them.

Mimamá had taken most of these out of old albums, which would never have made it through. We were already familiar with many of the photos, yet having had to leave almost everything behind, getting them felt like retrieving a small but important part of our previous lives.

During one phone conversation over a very bad connection, Mimamá had told Mami that Papín had been diagnosed with arterio-sclerosis, which appeared to be advancing rapidly. Mami begged her yet again to come to Miami. Nothing that she might still be trying to salvage was worth their continuing to stay down there. The only thing that mattered was being together. But for some unclear reason, Mimamá kept dragging her feet. Mami began to sense that she would never see her father again. She had started smoking more, and during her brief breaks from cooking or cleaning, she would sit at the breakfast nook, blowing smoke and staring into space.

But *some* things had begun to look up. Our dinnertime conversations were becoming more varied. We now talked about things like school projects, Halloween costumes, and even American football—which seemed incomprehensible to most Cubans. And since none of these topics led to heated arguments, dinner also became a lot shorter, which meant my siblings and I were then free to go watch TV.

On Fridays we all watched *The Twilight Zone*. On Sundays, it was *Candid Camera* and *Walt Disney's Wonderful World of Color*, in black and white. With only one TV in the house, our faithful Zenith, everyone had a night when he or she could choose whatever show they wanted. Mequi liked *Donna Reed*; Gerardo, *Father Knows Best*; Francisco and Carlos were fans of *Sea Hunt*. Even Mami had her own night and would usually choose *Sing Along with Mitch*. She had learned most of those old songs during her first exile and now relished the opportunity to sing them with us. We would all gather around the TV and follow the bouncing ball.

"H-A-double R-I . . . G-A-N spells Harrigan. Proud of all the Irish blood that's in me. 'Divil' a man can say a word agin' me . . ."

"That song was written by George M. Cohan, one of the most famous song writers and performer of the World War I era." She loved to add some extra bits of information.

"She's only a bird in a gilded cage, a beautiful sight to see . . ."

"And that one is about a young woman who let herself be imprisoned by money."

"*Por Dios*, Nenita! Now you are sounding communist!" Papi was not at all interested in singing with Mitch. He would sit nearby at his colorful Mexican desk paying bills and trying to block out the hearty chorus of Cuban refugees commencing our melting pot process.

"When you're smiling, when you're smiling, the whole world smiles with you . . ."

"How much longer does that man go on?"

"They called her frivolous Sal, a peculiar kind of a gal . . ."

One day Papi jokingly accused Mami of being a cultural traitor. She replied that her very patriotic grandfather had always said that people needed strong roots. "How long am I supposed to keep my children from continuing to spread theirs?"

The Cub Scout Indian headdresses and Pilgrim hats turned out so well that Sister Mary Robert, Francisco's teacher from St. Theresa, asked Mami if she would help make some decorations for the school's Thanksgiving party. Before she had a chance to say no, the sister handed her a stack of poster boards and a sack with paint supplies. At first Mami was upset for letting herself get cornered, but then she decided that it might be a fun project for all of us to do together. When she got home she spread everything out across the Florida room floor, and asked us to come up with suggestions.

We now owned two Mitch Miller albums, *Party Sing Along* and *Hayride Sing Along*, both of which Mami had bought on discount at Woolworth's. "This will be perfect painting music," she announced as she stacked them both on the new turquoise portable hi-fi that Papi had bought at his favorite store—Sears. And for those of us who still didn't know all the words, Mami's treasured LPs also came with lyric sheets.

"Way down upon the Swanee River, far, far away . . ."

My aunt Mari did have a knack for calling at the most inconvenient moments. This time it was me who answered. Mari was calling to report that she had just gone for drinks at her friend Nelly's apartment, a few blocks up Fifth Avenue.

"It's absolutely magnificent. How did that bitch get all her money out of Cuba?" Then she heard the bustling activity in our Florida room. "What the hell's going on now?"

"We're making Thanksgiving decorations . . . and singing along with Mitch."

"I swear, your mother's starting to lose it. Tell that budget-conscious father of yours to take her out to dinner once in a while, alone, before she loses it completely."

Mami was in no mood to talk, so I told Mari goodbye and rejoined the sing-along.

"East Side, West Side, all around the town. The tots sang 'ring a-round Rosie', 'London bridge is falling down' . . ."

Mami looked so happy that I did wonder whether she might indeed be losing it.

The revolution had taken everything away. Family members were freezing in New York, and some of them drinking heavily. Her father was ailing in Cuba, with no possibility of her going to see him. Yet here she was, drawing what looked like a scrawny turkey and singing with Mitch. Perhaps, as she told my father, it was because for the first time in her life she had a leading role. The house in Havana had run perfectly well without her having to lift a finger. In this new setting, she was indispensable, the cog without which the rest of the machinery would fall apart. And *that* meant a great deal to her.

"Mami, you're dripping paint!"

She rushed to get a rag from the kitchen, without missing one beat of the song.

"School days. School days. Dear old golden rule days. Readin' and 'ritin' and 'rithmetic. Taught to the tune of the hick'ry stick. . ."

It was into this group of merry sing-alongers that Ramón Antonio arrived one afternoon. Although Fidel had confiscated CMQ and taken the family-sponsored *telenovelas* off the air for being too bourgeois and class-conscious, Ramón Antonio had continued to produce and direct plays in a small *sala-teatro* that he had purchased a few years earlier. There he had staged the Cuban premieres of Broadway hits like *The Diary of Anne Frank*, and even the somewhat controversial *Tea and Sympathy*. This space became the center of his life, especially after the triumph of the revolution, even though the ranks of Cuban actors had also been split between those who applauded what was happening and those who didn't. Papi had hoped that Ramón Antonio would leave along with the rest of us, but my uncle was determined to put on just one more play, and challenge the communists with its powerful statement about individualism. So he announced the first Cuban production of Eugene Ionesco's latest work, *Rhinoceros*.

Unfortunately, most of the people who attended were families who had assumed it was the tale of some mischievous mammal. Audiences walked out in droves. One of the disgruntled patrons turned out to be a high *funcionario* of the new government. Claiming that the story about people turning into rhinoceri was meant as a criticism of *La Revolución*, the authorities closed the play and confiscated the theater—so Ramón Antonio finally packed.

He showed up at our door carrying a small suitcase in one hand and a sack full of classical LPs in the other. The first thing he did after unpacking was to ask that we drive him to an audio supply store. There he spent most of the money he had been able to sneak out buying a turntable and a set of speakers, which he then promptly installed in his new room. From that moment on, the strains of Mahler and Richard Strauss wafted through the kitchen to create a duet out in the Florida room with the Mitch Miller chorus or Fred Flintstone's "Yabba-dabba-doo!" while from the other end of the house, Abuela's radio, with its never-ending promises of Fidel's imminent doom, joined in to form a three-part harmony.

Ramón Antonio's arrival caused yet another reshuffling of sleeping arrangements, but by now we were experts at it.

Word of his being in Miami quickly spread through the exiled Cuban *farándula*—the theatrical crowd. Most of these former colleagues had already heard about the *Rhinoceros* incident and couldn't wait to get more details. Soon they were dropping by at all hours. They would drive up in decrepit cars that often failed to restart when it was time to leave. Mami kept inviting them to sit in the Florida room, which was bright and airy, but they seemed to prefer the tight coziness of my uncle's tiny *maid's* room, which began to look like a smoky den.

His artistic friends fascinated me. They were always laughing, unlike the men who came to talk about Cuba, who seemed to think that being in exile meant having to live in non-stop misery. When the visits of the two groups coincided, group members would cordially greet each other, then retreat to different ends of the house, like boxers going to their respective corners. I soon began to do my homework at the kitchen breakfast nook, which was right outside Ramón Antonio's room, and would pretend to concentrate on a textbook while pointing my ears like radars.

"Is it true that you-know-who has been fooling around with the guy Fidel put in charge of CMQ?"

"*Cariño*, she's doing a lot more than fooling."

"Well, you might have too, if that got you a starring role in a *telenovela*."

"You mean he gave a lead to that no-talent *puta*?"

"I could never trade sexual favors to get ahead."

"I'm sure that would depend on who you had to trade them with."

"Speak for yourself, Manolo."

From where my uncle sat holding court he could see my knee bouncing up and down, and probably guessed that my mind was not on algebra.

The conversation kept getting better. "How come it's always women who sleep their way to the top?"

"Because there's none of them at the top for us men to sleep our way up to."

"Men can sleep with men."

When things started getting too racy, Ramón Antonio closed the door. "Sorry, *cariño*. We don't want to distract you."

"Oh, I'm not being dis . . ." *Slam!*

Bach or Telemann would go up a notch and put an end to my spying.

On days when he had no guests, Ramón Antonio would let me

wander in and browse through his books and records. He would play excerpts from symphonies or opera highlights, then tell me something specific about each one and make them come alive. He played *The 1812 Overture* and spoke about Napoleon invading Russia. He played *O Terra Addio* and talked about tragic lovers locked inside a pyramid. My uncle could have happily turned these instructional sessions into a full-time endeavor, but he had to start earning his keep.

With a talent for sharing his knowledge of the arts, one line of work seemed like a natural—acting teacher. Unfortunately, there wasn't much demand for that within our newly exiled community. He was already looking into alternatives when one of his actor friends, now teaching Spanish in a high school, sent over a couple of his students. They had recently been in a school production of *The Crucible* and had been bitten by the stage bug. They showed up for an introductory class looking shy and self-conscious, then were so impressed that the next time they brought along a third classmate. The little group began to meet twice a week, although this time Mami did not offer them the Florida room. Having Ramón Antonio's pupils emoting through sensory exercises while Papi's friends hypothesized nearby about toppling Fidel would simply not do.

Spying through my uncle's closed door, I became intrigued by the mysterious acting process. One day I got up the courage to ask Papi if I could join my godfather's class. Papi told me that Fidel had already caused him enough headaches and that one new *artiste* in the family was plenty. He was referring to my mother, who had also gotten involved in her first theatrical endeavor.

The Little Flower School's Thanksgiving pageant was held on the Saturday before the holiday. Sister Mary Robert had told Mami that she had a natural artistic flair and reminded her that the Pilgrims were refugees just like us. Gradually, she manipulated my mother into volunteering yet more of her time. Mami spent the last afternoon helping to set up rows of folding chairs in the school cafeteria and trying to keep the Plymouth Rock from tipping over each time the Indians stomped by.

When she returned for a quick change before the performance, she found my younger siblings still in the pool and me at my new favorite post, right in front of the TV, watching giant spiders demolish Minneapolis. My father had been talking to a friend about the supposedly imminent Cuban invasion and had completely forgotten about the time. Mami was furious.

"Who do you think you are, Eisenhower planning D-Day?"

Ramón Antonio, who had just finished one of his classes, made some passing remark about Thanksgiving being a dishonest holiday. I asked what he meant.

"Those pilgrims accepted the Indians' charity, then went on to take their land and stick them all into reservations." But then, still being in teacher mode, he couldn't help giving my performing brothers a couple of acting tips.

"Remember that both the Indians and the Pilgrims used firewood to cook with. Try to *feel* what that smelled like." He turned to Carlos, who was playing an Indian. "You're bringing corn bread and pumpkin pie to these total strangers. Could it be because they got over-cooked and your family wouldn't eat them?" He turned to Francisco, who was a Pilgrim. "You don't really know these guys either. And they look pretty strange in all those feathers and face paint. Aren't you a little scared the food might be poisoned?"

By the time we all piled into our Chevy and pulled up at the school, Sister Mary Robert was in a frenzy. "I thought you'd bailed ship. It's almost curtain time and half the kids aren't even in costume yet."

"Tu ves?" My mother snapped at my father, *"Esto es lo que no quería."*

"English, please!" Sister objected with a grin. "You're in the U.S. now."

Her statement validated complaints that both Gerardo and Francisco had voiced about some of the nuns' total lack of sympathy for the fact that they were still struggling with their new language. One day, Francisco had turned to the kid sitting next to him to ask what their teacher was saying. "No talking in class!" the sister shouted, then made him go up to the blackboard and erase a whole row of little chalk zeros with his nose. Gerardo's incident happened when his homeroom teacher noticed that his eyes looked rather red and irritated.

"Have you been crying, child?"

"No, sister. Is the Clorox," he tried to explain with a still-thick accent.

"Clorox!" The nun became alarmed. "How on Earth did you get Clorox in your eyes?"

"In the pool, Sister. Swimming."

The nun's empathy quickly vanished. "You silly boy. That's chlo-*rine*. And there's quite a big difference. You scared the living daylights out of me." Other kids laughed.

But there was no time to dwell on that now. Everyone seemed to be having trouble with their pageant costumes, so Mami got to work, helping kids distinguish backs from fronts, ups from downs, and arm holes from head ones.

"*Ay*, Mrs. Santeiro," one panicky pilgrim begged, "please help me put my skirt."

Forgetting the race against time, Mary Robert stopped what she was doing. "My dear, you do not 'put a skirt,' you put a skirt 'on.' Here you are, about to portray one of our founding mothers, and you're butchering the language."

Mami had to control herself to avoid informing the good sister that the little "language butcherer" had merely translated literally from her native Spanish. But the audience was already stomping with impatience.

"Okay, everybody on stage!" the nun barked as she rushed off. She stood in front of the curtain that Mami had also helped decorate with cutout pumpkins and corn stalks, and held up her hand for silence. "I welcome you all to our annual Thanksgiving pageant. As most of you know, this is the most American of holidays—our special day to thank The Lord for His blessings. For some, it will be a first. I hope you will take time this coming Thursday to think about the many great things this country offers—such as its open-armed embrace of all you newcomers."

After the show was over, Papi, who had by now heard about Mary Robert correcting the little girl, walked up to her. "Excuse me, Mother . . ."

"I'm a sister."

"And also a linguist, I hear."

She detected sarcasm. "I believe in teaching my students to speak properly, if that's what you mean."

"Ay, yo estoy completamente de acuerdo."

"Beg your pardon?"

"Oh, I'm sorry. You don't speak Spanish?"

"No. I don't." She started to walk away. Then, determined to have the last word, she turned back. "Do you have a problem with that?"

"Not at all. But you see, that girl you corrected is fluent in it. So even with her imperfect English, she's still way ahead of you, Sister."

The performance was a big success, and the collapsing Plymouth Rock only made it all the more memorable. In view of this, Mami was surprised by the curt thank-you that she got from Mary Robert. After helping to tidy up backstage a bit, we all piled back into our Chevy Biscayne and headed home.

"Nuns are scary," Francisco said as we walked in.

"Yes," Mequi agreed. "I could never be one."

"Well, *that's* something to be thankful for," said Papi.

Even Mami had to admit that Mary Robert had been rather ungracious. "A little smile now and then would certainly help."

"Or, even better," suggested Ramón Antonio, who had overheard the conversation, "a big enema." And we all roared.

Papi had made it clear that he was in no mood for celebrating Thanksgiving. He said it was ridiculous to get all excited about a ritual that had nothing to do with us Cubans. Besides, he hadn't much to be thankful for. Not this year.

Mami strongly disagreed. "Our family's together. Everyone's healthy. We have a nice roof over our heads."

"But Fidel took away a much nicer one."

"During my family's first exile, even after all we had gone through, we always had a turkey. And I intend to have one in this exile too."

When word got out that we were celebrating whatever-it-was, friends started asking if they could contribute something and join in—even if it was just their humble refugee center rations. Some seemed intrigued by this *San Giving*, the unfamiliar saint in whose name the entire country closed shop. But whoever he was, the important thing was that it would give them yet another chance to get together and talk about Cuba.

Perhaps in retaliation for Mami's stubbornness, Papi started saying yes to everyone who asked if they could come. As the guest list grew longer, Mami began to get nervous.

"I have never cooked a turkey in my life, what if it doesn't turn out right?"

"Don't worry. Mercedita Lasa is bringing black beans, Ana is making *yuca* with *mojo* . . . and maybe I can find a pre-cooked leg of pork in La Calle Ocho."

I was horrified. "Who eats black beans and pork on Thanksgiving?"

"We do! Or else we won't have Thanksgiving at all."

Mami settled the issue, saying that guests could bring whatever they wished. She would order the traditional meal from Publix, which was offering a full holiday special at a very reasonable price.

The turkey just had to be heated, but Mami miscalculated how long that would take. By the time we sat down to eat, most of the adults were flying high thanks to the two bottles of rum that guests had contributed.

"I'm going to say grace now," Mami announced.

The only time I had ever seen this done was in Hollywood movies, and I kind of liked the novelty. It made our untraditional gathering feel somehow a little more authentic.

As Mami began, guests bowed their heads. "*Gracias, Señor*, for this food you have given us today . . . and please help those around the world who are less fortunate."

"But if that's too much to ask, just help the ones in Cuba," somebody added.

Marietta aimed her eyes toward Heaven, "And may we be back there by this time next year, so we can thank You for real."

"*Amén!*" Everyone chimed in.

"Long before next November, I hope!" said one guest.

"And with Fidel six feet under," said another.

"I'd appreciate it if you didn't say things like that at my table," my mother objected.

"Don't you want that son-of-a-you-know-what out of the picture?"

"I don't like him any more than you do, but that's for God to decide."

"Luisito, your wife is a saint."

"Or maybe a pinko."

Everyone laughed, except Mami, who ignored the comment and turned to us. "You may not realize it, but we have things in common with the Pilgrims."

I was eager to hear her explanation, but someone interrupted.

"*Ay*, please! Those people didn't drink dance or smoke. I hope we're a little more fun."

Glasses were clinked to that.

"What I mean is . . . that they came here for freedom, just like we did."

"What, a bearded lunatic chased them away too?"

Each round of laughter grew louder.

"Ah, but there's one major difference," said Pancho, who was now working as a night clerk at the Everglades Hotel. "Those Pilgrims were coming to stay. We're only here until that 'son of a blank-blank' is gone."

"Pancho is right!" Tiana agreed. "Fidel is our only problem."

"Isn't anyone going to have cranberry sauce?" Mami held up the bowl.

"I thought that was a dessert."

"No. It's for putting on the turkey, or on whatever you want."

"On the black beans?"

Carlos and Francisco giggled.

Then Ramón Antonio spoke up. "Fidel isn't our only problem. We all were—and still are."

"I agree," Rogelio Lasa said.

"I don't know what you mean," one of the guests took offense. "I never supported him."

"Did anyone watch the Thanksgiving parade this morning?" Mami tried once more to change the subject, but Pancho cut her off.

"I know exactly what Ramón Antonio means," said Pancho. "Just look at the brief history of our republic and you understand why we are where we are. We never gave democracy a chance. Everyone misused power."

I saw Mami wince.

"Pancho . . ." Papi gave him a warning look, which Pancho missed.

"We had coups, insurrections, people changing the constitution to stay in office . . ."

Mami pushed her chair away and left the table.

It suddenly dawned on our absent-minded guest who his hostess's grandfather had been. "*Virgen Santísima!*" His face turned bright red.

"Here!" Marietta passed him the cranberry sauce. "Camouflage!"

Papi excused himself and followed Mami to the kitchen. I started clearing plates to get away too.

"Nenita, he didn't mean anything personal. Just let it go. It's Thanksgiving," I heard him say as I came in. It was ironic for someone who had argued that this holiday had nothing to do with us to suddenly use it as an excuse to bring peace back to our celebration. "Maybe it's time we leave behind what happened so long ago," he continued.

"We're all here in the same boat now. If we pull apart we only hurt ourselves."

Mami slowly calmed down. Then, in the spirit of Thanksgiving, which she *did* believe in, she grabbed the apple pie, which had also come from Publix, and headed back to the table. The conversation there had become stilted, which was perhaps much more in keeping with that very first Thanksgiving.

"Mercedita, your black beans were delicious," Tiana said to lighten things up.

"*Ay, gracias*. The trick is to put in a little dash of guava jelly."

As Mami returned, Pancho got up and went to her. "Nenita, I'm so sorry. I really . . ."

She held up her hand to stop him and after setting down the pie, addressed herself to everyone. "I'm very happy that you're all here with us tonight. You know our doors have always been open, and will continue to be. I only ask one thing in. From now on, I would appreciate it if we could try to talk about something other than Cuba."

Papi looked startled but did not dare argue.

Us kids, sick of political talk, were ecstatic, and poked each other under the table.

"Excuse me," Rogelio pointed out, "isn't that curbing free speech . . . the same thing that Fidel has done?"

Guests mumbled in agreement.

"Not at all. I'm only exercising the all-American freedom to do what I wish in my own home. If you want to talk about Cuba, you're free to do so. Outside my front door."

Marietta, who had remained uncharacteristically silent, waved a dismissive hand. "*Ay!* We are starting to sound as serious and boring as those Pilgrims. We need some music."

Mami seconded the motion. "But I'm afraid we only have a couple of Mitch Miller albums."

"Get Abuela's radio!" said Mequi.

"Or better still . . .!" Ramón Antonio got up. "One of my friends left his guitar behind the other day."

"But who's going to play it?" I wondered, then saw various eyes turn to Marietta.

"No, no, no!" she protested. "*Que va!*"

Since entering our family, Marietta had swept her Zarzuela-star past under the rug. Being asked to perform again felt to her like a betrayal. When Ramón Antonio returned and held the guitar out to her, she recoiled. But everyone started chanting, "Marietta . . . Marietta . . .!"

Marietta folded her arms.

"*Now* who's acting like those stuffy old Pilgrims?" said Gerardo.

That did it. "All right, I'll play *one* song." Marietta cradled the instrument like an expert mother, and broke into a soft bolero. "*Cuando vuelva a tu lado, y esté a solas contigo. . .*" "When I am by your side again. . ."

Her singing surprised everyone, especially me, who until now had mainly seen her as just another Spanish-radio-news-obsessed adult.

After a couple of verses, others could not resist joining in. "*Une tu labio al mio. Estrechame en tus brazos. . .*" It was an old standard love song, but the chorus of nostalgic refugees had turned it into an expression of their longing for home. "*Y escucha los latidos de mi corazón.*" "Enfold me in your arms and listen to my heartbeat."

Marietta had now warmed up and was itching to play something livelier. The melancholy notes segued into rhythmic exuberance. "*Oyeme, Cachita. Tengo una rumbita. . .*" "Oh, my Cachita. Have I got a rhumba for you. . ." It was definitely not Mitch Miller.

When Marietta finally put down the guitar to rub her sore fingertips, another guest picked it up and started playing a lively Spanish *Sevillana*. Suddenly Marietta got up and started to dance. With one hand holding up her skirt, Flamenco style, she tapped her heels on the terrazzo floor. The other arm she held in midair, twisting the wrist around like a disoriented cobra. Everyone clapped in rhythm, egging her on to even more exotic movements. Then she broke into singing again. "*Cuando se muera mi suegra, que la entierren boca abajo. Por si se quiere salir, que se vaya. . .*"

"*P'al carajo!*" Others chimed in. "When my mother-in-law dies, bury her head-down the well. In case she tries to get out, she can go on . . . straight to hell."

Heels clacked and wrists wriggled, as the room turned into what looked like a convention of manic serpent-worshipers. Even Pancho, the earlier misunderstanding now forgotten, clapped his palms as he circled around Mami, while she spun in the opposite direction.

Our first Thanksgiving was in full swing when the telephone rang. I had been observing from the sideline and ran over to answer. It was my friend Robbie.

"So did you watch Macy's parade?"

"Uh-huh," I stretched the phone cord as far from the Florida room as it would go.

"We're getting ready to see the U of M game. Is your family into football?"

"Of course," I said, hoping that Robbie could not hear our Cuban-Puritan fiesta.

• 16 •

Among the latest batch of photos that Mimamá had sent was a large black-and-white one of a parade float emerging from a fancy building that Mami said was the presidential palace. It was a huge wicker basket on wheels with flower vines intertwined all throughout. Sitting on the top of the float were about a dozen little girls, each one dressed as a different bloom. And in the center of this live bouquet, under a trellised canopy, sat the chubbiest blossom of all, with a symphony of anthers and petals emerging from her headdress. Mami admitted to being the chipmunk-cheeked petunia.

"Was this for a parade?"

"No, *chico*. For *carnaval*."

On cue, with her usual bad timing, Mari's call interrupted us. When I told her what we were looking at, I heard a snort. "Yes, the little princess got her very own float for the first few years that Papá Gerardito was in office."

"And you didn't?"

"Darling, by the time I was old enough to have one, there were too may bombs falling."

"What do you mean?"

"Honestly, Luisma. Doesn't your mother tell you anything?"

"Sure, all the time. But nothing about bombs."

"Well, let me put it this way, she got parade floats. I got flying shrapnel."

I waited until their weekly catch-up conversation was over, then asked my mother, "Mari got hit by shrapnel?"

She shrugged it off. "As usual, *mijo*, she's exaggerating." Then making it sound as if it was an everyday occurrence, she added, "It was just shards of stained glass."

"Huh?"

"Luisma, I've told you about the palace bomb."

"No. *That* I would have remembered."

This was one memory that she didn't seem so eager to relive, but I insisted.

"The presidential palace nursery faced an inner courtyard, so to bring more light, the architect had put in a stained glass window. It was full of satyrs and vixens chasing each other. Well, I didn't know what they were called then, but you could tell they were up to no good. I loved to look at them whenever I went up to visit my baby cousin. And her crib—or what the family called a crib, though it was big enough for a baby elephant—had this tall canopy of white tulle cascading down like cake frosting. It was something out of a fairytale . . . perhaps one of those in which danger lurks for the innocent baby. See, after the 1929 stock market crash, what had been called "the dance of the millions" ended abruptly, and a lot of people who had worshiped your great-grandfather suddenly turned against him.

"One of them, someone who, as it turned out, we actually knew well but shall remain nameless, got hold of the original palace blueprints. Then with the help of a plumber, they traced the pipe that led down to Papá Gerardito's bathroom. They knew that every morning, punctually at seven, he would be in there shaving and doing his toilette. So one moonless night they sneaked up to the palace roof, found the pipe, and rolled down a time bomb.

"What they didn't realize was that after Mari was born, the pipe had been rerouted to add a little pantry closer to the nursery so that Amada, our *manejadora*, wouldn't have to go all the way down to the main kitchen in the middle of the night to heat up the baby's milk. So they tossed down the bomb, convinced that they would soon be celebrating Papá Gerardito's demise. But instead, it landed in an elbow joint, only inches away from Mari's crib. And that's where it exploded."

Well, the noise must have woken up half of Havana. Next thing I knew the whole family was rushing out of their bedrooms still throwing on their robes. Mamá Elvira told me to stay in bed, but I followed the grownups anyway. The first thing I noticed when I got up to the nursery was that all the satyrs and vixens were no longer in the window. There was just a big gaping hole letting in an early morning glare. Most of the colored glass was now on the crib, covering Mari, whose little face poked out from beneath it like something out of a Russian icon or a French Gothic cathedral.

Mamá and Tia Babi quickly began to pick away the glass, careful not to injure Mari any further. Then they saw that, miraculously, she didn't even have one scratch on her. As Tia Babi lifted the baby, Mamá Elvira crossed herself, and members of the palace staff who had run upstairs with us knelt down to praise Heaven. Then Papá Gerardito, who had remained completely calm throughout it all, said, "All right, the baby's fine. Nobody is hurt. Now everyone go back to bed."

I found the story fascinating, yet something about it also troubled me. "Why did so many people want to kill Papá Gerardito?"

"*Ay, mijo*. That was all so long ago. It's very complicated." My mother put all the photos back into the manila envelope, and that was the end of that story.

My brother Francisco's sixth birthday, on December tenth, was the first one celebrated in our exile. Lourdes and I had had ours during the two prior months, but those had been spent uneventfully within our respective boarding schools. Papi had found a piñata at a store in La Calle Ocho, where small Cuban businesses were already beginning to spring up.

It was a simple celebration, with an ice cream cake from Carvel, another wonderful new discovery, and the piñata as a final highlight. Papi had strung it from a branch of the big oak tree in our backyard. It was one of those with long tassels for kids to tug at. The little tassel-tuggers, besides the birthday boy, had been my brother Carlos and some children of other refugee friends.

Later, as I helped Mami do the dishes, she kept staring out the window at the remains of the piñata, which still hung from the tree branch like a deflated balloon.

"Did I ever tell you about the party Papá Gerardito gave me in the Hall of Mirrors?"

This particular story I had heard before, but it was one that I enjoyed. Besides, I sensed that she was going to tell it again no matter what.

"I think that it was for my sixth birthday also. All my guests were wearing those frilly white dresses that were so popular back then and hair bows that were sometimes twice as big as our heads. And of course, every girl had come with her own *manejadora* to watch over them: pink-cheeked *Gallegas*, ebony Jamaicans, curvy Cuban *mulatas*—all of them smelling of violet water and talcum powder and looking very dignified in their starched white uniforms. But the centerpiece of the party was an immense piñata, shaped like a giant white swan, with tassels, like the one that Francisco had. We were much too dainty in Cuba to swing at piñatas like they do in other places. But this had to be the largest one that I had ever seen, and also the one with the strangest contents.

"Something inside it was alive. Of course, we could never have guessed that, because there was a small band playing music, and the softest sound in that room made a huge echo. But finally the moment came for us to break the piñata. Each girl took hold of a swan tassel, then the band gave us a drum roll, a one-two-three count, and we pulled! Well, were we in for the surprise of our lives! A flock of white doves came tearing out of that thing, totally disoriented and desperate to escape. Unfortunately, a couple of them flew into the mirrors, like confused kamikazes.

"Whoever came up with this brilliant idea did not know me at all, because I have never liked anything with feathers. So I started screaming and ran to hide under my *manejadora* Amada's skirt. Then, seeing the party girl react that way, my guests all started to scream and dive under their *manejadoras*' skirts too. The noise was so deafening that a couple of palace guards burst in with their rifles, convinced that a coup d'état was under way.

"Finally all the doves either found an open window or smashed into a mirror, so everything was calm again. Then they sat us all down in a big semi-circle, and each girl was given a beautiful French doll with porcelain hands and face. To this day I still despise birds, although I must say that no one who was there that day has ever forgotten my sixth birthday. I've often wondered how many of those little girls ended up on a psychiatrist's couch because of my piñata."

"Now I'm furious at you, Nenita," said her friend Lillian who had brought in more dirty dishes and overheard the story. "Why wasn't I invited to that party?"

"*Mija*, half your family was in the opposition. Perhaps mine was afraid that one of them would strap a bomb to your bloomers."

After Lillian left, Mami confirmed that their families had indeed been political enemies, and yet the two of them were lifelong friends. I guess I looked surprised.

"*Ay*, Luisma," she said, "Cuba was too small to bear political grudges."

Then my father came in and corrected her. "Until Fidel."

• 17 •

Mari and Andres had gone to a cocktail party given by their friend Nelly at her Fifth Avenue apartment to kick off the Christmas season. Mari later called to give a full report. Nelly had hired a professional florist for the occasion. There were garlands of holly strung up all around and giant arrangements of white poinsettias. There had even been a black-tie pianist tinkling away old Cuban favorites to heighten the nostalgia. Most of the guests were dead broke, but at least for this one evening they had all looked as if they still owned the world.

Mari herself had worn her all-purpose black dress, the most elegant outfit that she had brought from Cuba. It was perfect for showing off her new pearl necklace, which she had bought on sale at Ohrbach's. It was plastic, but she was sure that no one suspected that. In fact, she had gotten many compliments on how wonderful she looked, and was convinced that Audrey Hepburn could not have pulled it off any better. She had loved being able to spend an evening amid such elegant surroundings—and away from crumbling walls. It was the kind of environment in which she felt she belonged.

Nelly had dazzled everyone in her shimmering gown, which was obviously the only model that wasn't a leftover from some bygone season. Everyone had oohed and aahed over her, then brought out the fangs the second that her back was turned.

Guests kept wondering how she had managed to get all her money out. Some said that it was because of her father's close ties to Batista. Others thought that it was Trujillo, the Dominican Republic's dictator, with whom her father had had dealings. Some even claimed that the money went all the way back to a connection with Mussolini, and that almost every penny made through that association had been reinvested abroad.

In an exemplary act of diplomacy that had made Mari proud, Andres reminded everyone that thanks to Nelly's father's foresight, and whoever he had had dealings with, they were all now able to enjoy a break from nouveau poverty.

With champagne flute in hand, Mari wandered over to a window. The alcohol had already kicked in, and so had the Christmas spirit. She was starting to feel loving toward the entire world, including Nelly. It was good to be surrounded by affluence, even if it wasn't hers. As she looked down toward Central Park, the strings of lampposts made her feel as if the stars were at her feet.

Their walk home, under a soft dusting of snow, had been magical. Before heading upstairs they went by the kitchen to turn off the lights, which Maria Regueros always left on for whoever came home last. They were still discussing how amazing Cubans were at putting their best foot forward, and were so wrapped up in their conversation that they failed to notice the sign that Tia Babi had left for them on the kitchen table.

IT'S GOING DOWN TO THE TEENS TONIGHT!!
LOAD UP THE FURNACE!!

By morning the house was an icebox. Windows were frosted over, and every breath condensed in the air like a cartoon thought-balloon. Mari said that it took her a moment to realize that she wasn't really at the North Pole.

She quickly jumped out of bed, slipped into a pair of leotards, and threw on her bulkiest sweater, which, according to her, made her look just like Audrey Hepburn in her *Funny Face* Bohemian period.

Maria Regueros was already in the kitchen, looking like a rotund Russian peasant under multiple clothing layers. She was standing by the open oven, which she had turned up all the way. Seeing her made Mari wonder if a gas suicide wouldn't be the easiest solution to all their problems. When she asked what the hell had happened, Maria just pointed to Tia Babi's note, which was exactly where she had left it the prior evening.

"Why didn't she go downstairs and shovel the damn coal herself?"

"Your mother is not fifteen anymore, Señora Mari. And this weather has her rheumatism acting up." But what infuriated Mari most was Maria reminding her that they had simply obeyed Andres' orders to wait for the eleven o'clock weather report. "It wasn't your mother's fault that you did not see her note."

Mari got back in the elevator and rushed upstairs to check on the others. Mamá Elvira seemed fine, sitting in a ray of sunshine by a window, all bundled up in the old fur coat. José Emilio was scrunched up next to an ancient electric space heater but seemed okay too. Then she saw the trembling bulge on the bed, which she said looked like the Sierra Madre during an earthquake. After peeling back four layers of blankets she finally unearthed Tia Babi. When asked if she was okay, Tia Babi's teeth just chattered. Mari pleaded with her to say something.

"I am going to kill your husband," a deep raspy voice replied. Mari told her that Andres was already down in the basement, stoking the furnace. The raspy voice spoke once again. "Too late."

Tia Babi's forehead was in a cold sweat. Mari looked around for something else to cover her with, but the only thing that wasn't already on her was the bedside area rug.

Now feeling really worried, she told Andres that she was going to take her mother to the hospital, but Andres reminded her that they had no insurance. Instead he suggested that they call one of their familiar Cuban doctors. There were many already exiled in New York, all without a license to practice. Surely one of them would not refuse coming over to take a look at an old friend—especially if the doctor happened to be a *Machadista*.

Within a half-hour Arturito was there, reassuring them that Tia Babi would be fine, as long as the house was kept a bit warmer. He apologized about not being able to fill out a real prescription, but made some illegible scribbles and told them of a reliable contact at a pharmacy up in Spanish Harlem.

While Andres went to get the medicine, Mari did her best to keep Tia Babi comfortable, but now she kept tossing off blanket after blanket. Andres had gone overboard with his coal shoveling, and in less than two hours the house had gone from arctic chill to tropical steaminess.

"Are we in Varadero?" Tia Babi mumbled, disoriented.

Mari pictured those clear turquoise waters and sighed. "Don't I wish!"

· 18 ·

Christmas was approaching, but my countdown to the start of our vacation was going far too slowly. Being able to spend two whole weeks with my family, away from the dreaded military academy, was all that I could think of. Back at our house, however, the bad news kept piling up.

Renecito Scull's parents had not been able to get the visas they needed to go to Venezuela, where they had relatives waiting, and they were still stuck inside the Brazilian embassy. Papín's illness was advancing rapidly, and Mimamá kept making excuses to avoid putting him on the phone so that Mami would not be confronted with his growing mental lapses. Then, news came that Mami's Santería-dabbling aunt, Tia Berta, who, unbeknownst to everyone, had gotten involved in the counterrevolution, had been arrested and was in jail awaiting a trial. This had put her daughter, Lugi, who could not understand why her mother wasn't coming home, in a frantic state. She was now staying with Mimamá, along with her caretaker, but between Lugi's outbursts and Papín's confusion, the situation sounded pretty grim. And there was yet another matter worrying my mother.

Members of the brigade organizing the Cuban invasion had already dropped by on two occasions. They were desperate to enlist volunteers and seemed to know where every last able-bodied Cuban-exile male lived. The first time they had come to talk to Renecito. My mother had been shocked that they could be thinking of recruiting a sixteen-year-old. Apparently the CIA was turning a blind eye.

"The fact is," one of the men explained, "most of us don't have birth certificates here."

"Yes, but you have passports, or visas, with birth dates."

"Señora, changing a little number or two on a passport is the easiest thing in the world."

Mami made it clear that she was not about to allow a boy who was under her care drop out of school and go risk his life—for any cause.

The next time, they came to talk to my cousin Rafa, who was studying at the University of Florida and had come to spend a few days with us. This time Papi intervened, and once again the brigade had to leave without a new recruit. Surprisingly, they never tried to enlist my father, perhaps considering him, at age forty-four, an old man. Still, seeing the deep commitment of these young brigade members, and their desperate need to increase their ranks, Papi began to feel guilty. Maybe it *was* his duty to go fight and help regain what he had done so little to prevent losing. One night he expressed these thoughts to my mother.

"That's all I need . . . to be left alone with seven kids and my mother-in-law." She pointed out that no one in their right mind could expect him to do that, or think him a coward for failing to. Still, my father, who had never let anyone shoot even a bird in La Finca, or allowed us have toy guns, now bought a Smith & Wesson .38 caliber revolver and started going twice a week, with his friend Rogelio, to a shooting range along the Tamiami Trail. This did not reassure my mother that he had fully put away thoughts of helping to liberate Cuba.

Two final strokes of bad news arrived right before *Noche Buena*—Christmas Eve. The first was that Tio Ramón, my great-uncle, had died of a sudden heart attack. Abuela laid the blame directly upon Fidel. It was from all the heartache that he had caused her brother, she said, by taking away the fruits of a lifetime's work.

There were three other people in our house deeply affected by Tio Ramón's death, each from a different chapter of his life—my uncle, Ramón Antonio, child of his first marriage; Marietta, his second wife; and Lourdes, child of his third marriage, the one for which he had left Marietta. Yet they all mourned in harmony.

The second bit of bad news came from Mario Mena, the former

administrator of La Finca. He called to report that the revolution had sent over two bulldozers, which were in the process of razing every single one of my father's beloved trees.

This affected Papi even more than his uncle's death. He kept asking, "What could possibly be anti-revolutionary about fruit trees? If nothing else, they can help to feed people." But with every passing day, the revolution kept doing more things that seemed to make no sense at all.

News of Tio Ramón's death quickly spread through the exile community, and by the following afternoon, our house was filled with friends who had come to pay their respects. It felt strange to be holding a wake, of sorts, so far away from the deceased. Abuela kept bemoaning that there was no family member left in Cuba to arrange for a funeral mass or even attend her brother's burial.

Our visitors fell into two categories: old lifetime friends of Abuela, and a younger crowd paying their respects to the others. The older group remained in the living room, while everyone else gathered in the room we now called *el Florida*. Mami kept making pots of *café* and asking me to pass around the tray with demitasses.

Once the standard formalities of the occasion were dispensed with, Abuela's friends began to exchange stories about their exile lives and discovered that they all shared a new thing in common. Having for the most part had chauffeurs back in Cuba, they were now experiencing the novelty of riding buses. Soon they were trading tips on where to make the best connections.

"But Lily, you're only a few blocks from the Salvatore Park bus. You can take that to the Coral Gables terminal, then get a free transfer for the downtown bus."

"No, no. I think she's closer to the Riviera line."

When I went by with the next batch of *café*, they were arguing about which place served the most inexpensive lunch. Some thought that it was the downtown Walgreens while others were adamant that it was the Woolworth's counter on Miracle Mile.

Meanwhile, the group in *el Florida* had also split in two. The husbands were to one side talking politics, as usual, while their wives' conversation veered to the things that they missed most about their former lives. One of them missed her cook's *arroz con pollo*, another missed the scent of the *galán de noche* that bloomed in her backyard. A third said she missed the Cuban breezes, which blew from sea to land during the daytime then switched direction in the evening. According to her, there was no breeze at all in Miami, only humidity. Then someone else, almost shyly, confessed, "The thing I miss more than anything else Fidel took away, is my bidet."

Her statement sparked a wave of enthusiastic agreement.

"*Ay, mija*. I'm learning to cope with poverty, being far from those I love, and having to speak English, but I cannot adjust to having no bidet."

"If I had been smart I would have brought mine from Cuba instead of my husband."

Soon every woman was waxing nostalgic over their lost bathroom fixture. The hubbub they created finally made the husbands curious. They stopped their conversation to listen, and then got drawn into the discussion.

"Why is it that in this country, which thinks of itself as the epitome of progress, you can't find a bidet anywhere?"

"Obviously they don't care about a certain aspect of their hygiene."

"Or maybe they do but are too puritanical to have such a blatant reminder of that necessity."

One of the men became especially intrigued. "You mean to tell me that there's no one in this whole city who sells bidets?"

"If there is we haven't found it," said one of my mother's friends. "I made my husband call all the major bathroom supply houses, and some were even offended by the question."

"You know why, don't you?" Marietta said with a devilish glint in her eye. The other women leaned forward curiously.

"Why?"

"They probably thought that you wanted it for . . . well, you know—naughty things."

Half-a-dozen mouths dropped open. "Then they have very dirty minds."

"And evidently bodies too," said one of the men, and everyone laughed.

By now the ladies seemed to have exhausted the subject, and began to exchange recipes. But a couple of the husbands remained very intrigued.

"I think I may just have found the perfect business opportunity."

"Do you want a partner?"

"Sure. If you can find us some cash to get started."

My mother had made it very clear that she was not going to let a death, fallen trees, or Fidel Castro ruin Christmas. It might not be as jolly as our former *Navidades*, but we were still going to celebrate. I was thrilled to hear this, but there was an even bigger reason for me to feel joyful: all those *pin-pan-puns* and sleeping bags were no longer cluttering our living room. It seemed as if our Christmas was going to be almost normal.

From the moment that my vacation began, we started to transform the house with artsy decorations, following instructions that Mami had cut out from the holiday issues of magazines like *Harper's Bazaar* and *Ladies' Home Journal*. She seemed utterly content directing her little troupe of assistant elves.

We glued empty glass jars of different shapes on top of one another, then trimmed them with colorful swirls of glitter. We made a gold-sprayed centerpiece out of fan-like palmetto leaves and little coconuts that we collected around the golf course. We also bought the least expensive nativity set available at Woolworths and dunked the figures into a pot of tea to make them look like precious antiques. It was amazing to see all the wonderful things one could make spending almost nothing. And playing in the background while we worked was Mami's favorite new album, Mitch Miller's *Christmas Sing Along*, which she had gotten with green stamps.

"Chestnuts roasting on an open fire, Jack Frost nipping at your nose . . ."

I could hear my father groaning while he juggled our finances at his Mexican desk. Then when Mami started teaching Carlos and Francisco the names of Santa's reindeer, he suggested that perhaps she should be teaching them the names of our native Cuban fauna instead: "*Sinsontes, Tomeguines, Jutías!*"

Although Mami shrugged off the suggestion, it did seem to send her down memory lane. She suddenly recalled a Cuban parrot, named Cachita, which they had had in the presidential palace.

"She had been born in the Isle of Pines, and was supposedly ancient. Apparently parrots can live for decades, and this one was a nasty old thing. But Mamá loved Cachita because she could say '*Viva el presidente!*' I think that's about all she said. Day in, day out, '*Viva el presidente!*'

"Well, we had to leave the country in such a rush that nobody gave a thought to Cachita. So when the mobs broke into the palace and heard a voice somewhere still daring to shout '*Viva el presidente!*' they headed straight toward it. Then they found Cachita on the terrace where her cage had always perched, and they wrung her neck.

"When Mamá heard about it she cried for days. But what I found truly sad is that Cachita had been taught to say those words during the days of Estrada Palma, the republic's first president. She wasn't even cheering Papá Gerardito. She was killed just for being patriotic."

Once her story was done, she dunked baby Jesus into the pot of tea, then continued teaching my brothers the names of the reindeer.

BY SIX O'CLOCK on *Noche Buena*, Mami was deep into the cooking of her first turkey, and looking rather frazzled. She was following a recipe that had come out in the *Miami Herald*, which also explained how to make stuffing. She had vetoed our traditional pork and black beans meal for something more American. We were all excited because we were also going to be breaking in our beautiful new set of dishes, which Mami had been collecting, one by one, with every ten-dollar purchase at Publix. We were in the midst of final preparations when one of Papi's Cuba-obsessed friends popped by, unannounced. I cannot remember his name, so I will call him Juanito.

The fact that it was Christmas Eve did not seem to have flashed onto his radar. He was rather surprised by the festive mood and the choir of voices caroling along with Mitch. Juanito's reaction made Papi feel self-conscious. He quickly turned down the hi-fi volume, then came into the kitchen to ask that we please tone down our merriment, reminding us that Juanito's brother was a political prisoner in Cuba.

"So is my Tia Berta," Mami reminded him back. "But how is our toning things down going to help either one of them?"

Not wishing to start an argument, Papi returned to the living room and took out a bottle of Chivas Regal that he had bought in a moment of recklessness. If Juanito was not in a celebratory mood, the big smile on his face when he was offered a drink certainly gave the opposite impression. Mami came out from the kitchen to greet the guest, wearing a red and green Christmas apron trimmed with candy canes. She made herself a drink too, then raised her glass.

"Well, here's to . . ." before she could say what Papi suspected might be *Feliz Navidad*, he completed the toast. "A free Cuba!"

"To a free Cuba!" Juanito echoed. Then Mami excused herself saying that she had a turkey to look after. Papi had barely settled back down when Marietta came by with a guitar, announcing that she had been practicing *villancicos*, Spanish carols that we could all sing together after dinner.

Again Papi felt a bit embarrassed, but Juanito seemed charmed. "Ah, you perform!"

"Only in private," Marietta gave him a coy smile, quickly making a new fan.

"Luis, you mind if I have another?" Juanito held up his glass. "I would love to hear this lovely lady sing."

"You would?" Instantly, Marietta sat down to honor his request. Then Juanito started drumming along on the arms of his chair.

"I used to play bongos with a trio back in Cienfuegos," he explained, and broke out in harmony to Marietta's Andalusian-style carol.

"Esta noche es Noche Buena. Vamos al monte hermanito, a cortar un arbolito, porque la noche es serena. . ." "It's the holiest of nights. Let us go into the forest and chop down a Christmas tree."

The singing brought Mami back from the kitchen. She seemed relieved to find that Juanito was human after all. Now more relaxed himself, Papi whispered to her. "Neni, I'm sure he has no one to go back home to, so I was thinking . . ."

"Yes, yes," she cut him short; "I'll squeeze in another chair."

The background dinner music was provided by Handel, courtesy of Ramón Antonio, who seemed to be in a joyful mood. Two of his acting pupils had gotten lead roles in their upcoming school production. As The Ambrosian Singers burst into the famous chorus, so did he. "Haaaa-lle-lu-jah!"

"That's not very Cuban, is it?" said Juanito, to which Ramón Antonio replied that good music had no nationality.

"You have a point. It's like the mambo or the conga. They come from our country but the whole world loves them."

"Something like that." Ramón Antonio did not sound impressed.

The conversation became a Ping-Pong game, with Mami doing her best to keep it away from the topic of Cuba.

"My turkey didn't turn out so badly, did it?"

"And the stuffing's delicious!" We all complimented her.

"No offense," said Juanito, "but there's still nothing like our Cuban *lechoncito* . . . with a nice crispy rind and some fried *yuquitas* on the side."

"We saw the Perry Como Christmas special last night. They showed different traditions from around the world."

"I bet they didn't show Cuba's," said Marietta, "now that Fidel made it illegal."

"He did?" Francisco was shocked. "So what do communists celebrate?"

"Nothing. Blank walls. Dead ends."

"Cubans not celebrate something?" said Juanito. "Impossible."

"But Santa Claus is still coming here tonight, right?" Carlos got worried.

"Of course, *mijo*."

"Well, we know one place where he won't be going," said someone else.

"Actually, Fidel should welcome him with open arms," Juanito seemed unstoppable. "He's a communist too, you know."

"Santa Claus?" Gerardo frowned.

"Why do you think he wears that red suit?" he laughed at his own bad joke.

Ramón Antonio was just getting up to go flip the *Messiah* recording, when I found myself blurting out, "I wish Cuba would sink and vanish." The words had barely come out of my mouth when I was already wishing that *I* could sink and vanish.

The conversation stopped cold, and Papi gave me a deadly stare.

"Don't worry. I'm going." I pushed my chair back and strutted off to my room.

After everyone had gone to bed, I got up to get a drink of water from our hallway bathroom. My parents' bedroom door had been left ajar, as it always was, and I could hear them talking.

"Fidel has already disrupted our lives enough, and now he almost ruined Christmas. We can't let him keep doing this to us."

"He took everything we had, Nenita . . . all that my father and grandfather worked for. And I just picked up and walked away."

"All that he took were material things, Luis . . . every one of them replaceable or unessential. What truly matters we still have. My family lost everything in thirty-three. Our lives continued."

"Do you really think for a moment that your grandfather's did?"

"Not the way he would have wanted, no. But he spent his days writing, trying to explain himself . . . and never gave up hoping that one day he might be understood. I know it's hard to believe. But yes, even his life went on. And ours will too . . . no matter what happens in Cuba."

My father remained silent for a moment, then finally said, "If losing my country and all that we had there is not truly important . . . then why should I care about rebuilding anything elsewhere?"

Santa Claus was not as generous as he had been on prior Christmases. Perhaps he had had financial setbacks too. But everyone got something that they wanted, and there were no complaints.

The flat rectangular shape of my package gave me no clue as to what might be inside. I quickly tore off the wrapping and found that it was an Ant Farm, the very thing I had dreamed of since my stay in Chimney Rock Camp. I carefully opened the small tube that came with it, then held it over the green plastic enclosure, the way the instructions said, and gently tapped at one end. The cramped-up ants began to slide down into their new home. For a moment it looked as if they might have all died during their postal journey, or perhaps waiting under our little tree. But then, as if the sleeping spell of an enchanted kingdom had been broken, one by one they started to twitch their legs and get their bearings. Seconds later they were all busy at work, digging tunnels with the efficiency of bulldozers through the soil that also came in the package. I was ecstatic to know that I now lived in a place where ants could be delivered.

In the afternoon Mami finally managed, after many tries, to get a call through to Cuba.

This time Mimamá did put Papín on. His mind seemed clear

enough to exchange a few words with my mother and tell her how much he missed us, but then he broke down and couldn't say one more thing. Afterwards, sounding cheerful, Mimamá told Mami about the Christmas pageant that Tia Berta, who was now serving a three-year jail sentence, and some of her prison mates had put on in their ward.

Keeping it a secret, they had spent months collecting the silver inner linings from cigarette packs that some of their guards smoked. They had also paid frequent visits to the infirmary, feigning ailments that called for methylene blue or gentian violet, then stashed away the small vials they were given. As *Noche Buena* approached, they cut out angel wings from discarded cardboard boxes and covered them with the silvery foil. The gentian and methylene they used for dyeing an old sheet, which they also covered with silver foil stars, to create a glittery nighttime sky. One of the prisoners, who had been a music teacher, taught the group *Noche de Paz*. Silent Night, in four-part harmony. They dyed some more discarded sheets to create robes for the choir. Finally, since they had no way to make a baby Jesus, they placed a lightbulb in a makeshift manger, for after all, Jesus was the light of the world.

On the morning of the twenty-fifth, without asking the guards for the permission that they knew would be denied, they filed in wearing their improvised robes and wings, stood in front of the starry night backdrop, which they had strung up with a clothesline, and broke into their harmonized carol. There had not been a single dry eye in the entire prison.

Their act of defiance, however, had earned them a stiff punishment that included reduced food rations, longer work hours, and a month without family visits. Yet, according to Mimamá, Tia Berta and her co-conspirators were all ecstatic with what they had managed to pull off.

Despite Mami's efforts to keep Fidel from ruining Christmas, that call did dampen her seasonal spirits. We did not sing along with Mitch for the remainder of the holiday.

• 19 •

Yet another calamity had struck the New York townhouse. Mari's story sounded grim.

"I had just gotten into bed to read *Advise and Consent*, a wonderful book that I highly recommend, when what sounded like a huge explosion shook the entire house.

"'Oh, my God! We've been bombed,' I cried out.

"'*Ay*, Mari! Who would want to bomb us here in New York?' Andres thought I was joking.

"'The corner drycleaner, the phone company, the electrician. We haven't paid any of them.'

"By the time I turned on my bedside lamp, Andres was already crawling around looking for his slippers. Even in a life or death emergency, walking barefoot over these splintered floors can be just as lethal.

"'*Que pasó?*' I heard Mamá's groggy voice calling from below, probably having a flashback to the palace bomb too. Then Andres had an equally horrible thought.

"'The furnace!'

"We both ran to the elevator, but Mamá shouted, 'No, no! You may get stuck.'

"At that very instant, through the round elevator porthole, I saw Maria Regueros' descending bowlegs, followed by her bulky body and white-as-a-sheet face.

"'Well,' I thought, 'we'll soon find out if that's true.'

"So we rushed down the stairs, hoping against hope that perhaps the explosion hadn't been in our house after all. Sounds can have a funny way of deceiving you. But my optimism was dashed the moment we reached the second floor landing. I could tell from the gust of frigid wind blowing through my nightgown that something was terribly amiss.

"Andres flipped on the lights, and Maria Regueros, who had just stepped safely out of the elevator, crossed herself and said, '*Dios mío santísimo!*'

"We all stood there, trying to make sense of what we were seeing. The stained-glass dome over the conservatory bay window was now a jumble of shattered glass and twisted metal. And there was an endlessly long thing jutting like a knife through the gaping hole. It took us another minute to realize that the intruding foreign object was the gutter from the eaves of the house. It had plunged all the way across the room, wrecking everything along its path, and then come to rest on the dining room table. The end flaps were sagging under its weight like humiliated warriors. Mamá and Papi had come down by now too. Then I see my mother stepping over the debris and heading toward the Greek slave girl statue, which was still sitting on her pedestal but also damaged.

"'Angela Elvira, *por favor!*' Andres tried to stop her. 'There's enough broken things already!'

"'Oh, let her break her neck.' I couldn't believe that in this moment of utter heartbreak, the only thing she could think of was to comfort a wounded statue. But that's what she did. She reached for her beloved fortuneteller's hand, or what was left of it. Her fate-casting fingers were all gone, and so was part of the foot that protruded from beneath her. They had both been sliced off like a guillotine by the goddamn gutter. Mamá just stood there caressing the amputations and wondering how this could have happened.

"'I can tell you how, Señora,' Maria Regueros said, 'Someone has cast a *brujería* spell on us.' Then she swung at the rubble with one of her canes.

"'Maria, please. This is not a golf course.'

"Finally, Andres noticed that what glittered and crunched beneath our feet wasn't only glass. Big chunks of ice were strewn all over the room. One end of the gutter itself was still enveloped in it, making it look like a lethal Popsicle. He realized that it had probably been the weight from all the ice that made the gutter collapse.

"'And the worst of it is,' Mamá said as she herself collapsed into the only intact chair left, 'we have no insurance.'"

Mari's account, Tia Babi confirmed, was no exaggeration.

To help the family pay for the urgently needed repairs, as well as some back taxes, Mami decided to sell a couple of pieces of jewelry. She sent them to New York to be appraised by the jewelers where my father had purchased them, one of the most reputable in the city. Looking her elegant best, Tia Babi took a bus down Fifth Avenue, carefully clutching her purse, in which she was carrying the jewels. The store manager greeted her graciously, and inspected each piece with his special lens, but something about Mami's emerald necklace seemed to be troubling him. He kept turning each stone over and over, which began to make Tia Babi uncomfortable. She reminded him of the store's policy of buying back anything that they had sold.

"Do you have the purchase receipt?" The manager asked.

"Of course not. That's the last thing one could think of when one is fleeing a country. Is that a problem?"

He said that it wouldn't normally be, but that in this case, unfortunately, the supposed emeralds were merely green glass.

Tia Babi was outraged. "That's impossible. My niece's husband bought that necklace right here."

He asked if the piece had ever been sent for repair down in Cuba, or perhaps loaned to someone. It was very possible for the stones to have been exchanged.

Tia Babi said that she did not know of any such instance, and if the stones were fake then they must have been so from the time that they were sold. The manager took this as a slight to the integrity of his establishment. He calmly put necklace back into its case, then stood up and said, "We're a reputable business, madam, with a very long track record." He then walked to his office door and dryly bid Tia Babi a good day. As she strutted out, sounding as if she had millions, she said to the man, "From now on I will buy all my jewelry at Cartier."

Part of the expenses to cover the damages caused by the collapsed gutter went to compensate the neighbors for a seemingly unimportant item that had stood in their yard and had been nicked by falling debris. What looked like a worn-out planter turned out to be some kind of Roman antiquity. At first Mari refused to pay one cent for what she insisted was a tacky ornament. Then the owner produced certified papers to prove the piece's authenticity and threatened legal action. For once, Mari began to wish that they had ordinary neighbors, who bought their garden accessories at Sears.

• 20 •

It was the middle of April, six weeks till the end of the semester and my being set free from the military academy forever. Papi was already looking into schools that we might go to in the fall, everyday ordinary ones, from which we could come back home each afternoon. I was very thankful that he could no longer afford any fancy boarding institutions, like the one I was suffering through.

Our platoon was falling into ranks one morning, getting ready for flag-raising formation, when Lieutenant Tinoco approached me with one of his sneering remarks.

"Well, looks like you *Cubanos* are up to your troublemaking again."

I had no idea what he meant, but did not dare ask.

"Anyone you know fighting down there? 'Cause it sounds like they're gonna get creamed. All right, platoon, tennnnn'shun!"

He left me hanging, but I assumed he had meant that the invasion my father and his friends had talked about for so long was finally happening. My first reaction was to feel relieved that no one close to me was taking part in it. Then I thought that surely there must be someone we knew fighting at that very moment, some perhaps only a few years older than me, and as Tinoco had said, getting creamed.

Nothing else about it was mentioned through any of my classes, or during soccer practice. But the minute I got back to the barracks to shower, I asked Little Trujillo if I could borrow his little radio for a moment. Perhaps softened by the worried look on my face, he said I could use it for a couple of minutes. It took me almost a whole one to find a station with the news. The invasion had indeed landed, in a place that I had never heard of, with the word "pigs" in its name. The reports that had come in so far were inconclusive, but from the sound of it, Fidel's forces had been waiting for the supposedly secret invasion, and the fighting was heavier than anticipated.

"Okay, your two minutes are up." Little Trujillo grabbed his radio back.

Except for the three of us Cubans in the barracks, nobody seemed at all interested in what was happening. During our brief shower period, the only time we were allowed some radio listening, every one of them was tuned to a top forties station.

"Who put the bomp in the bomp bah bomp bah bomp? Who put the ram in the rama lama ding dong?"

"I wah-wah-wah-wah wonder why. Why, why, why, why, why, she ran away!"

"I'll be crying, crying, crying, over you!"

"Are you lonesome tonight?"

"This land is mine. God gave this land to me."

Back home, I later learned, the scene had been quite different. My mother was in the midst of running a Cub Scout den meeting, helping kids make creative things out of Popsicle sticks, when my father rushed in announcing that the invasion had begun.

"The end is finally near, Nenita. We'll be going home soon!"

All that Francisco and Carlos cared about was getting their merit badges, which would now have to be put off till some future meeting, so there was some griping.

"Don't you understand what's happening?" Papi explained. "Our country is about to be liberated."

Mami suggested that they go watch TV, but to keep the volume down. Then Marietta wheeled in Abuela's short-wave radio and turned *that* up all the way, which made it impossible to hear what Lloyd Bridges was up to in *Sea Hunt*.

By now every Spanish-language station in Miami had stopped its regular programming to give non-stop updates and projections—all of them optimistic. Over-excited announcers kept filling up airtime with hopeful presumptions. One of them made it sound like this was the biggest landing fleet since D-Day; another said that the people in Cuba were already taking up arms against Fidel.

"What arms?" Ramón Antonio quipped. "Slingshots? Sounds to me like they don't know *un carajo*." Papi was not amused by the comment, so Ramón Antonio decided to go to his room and play Mozart. "Let me know when it's over."

Mami also walked away to go make dinner, but Abuela, Marietta, and Papi were not about to miss one minute of the long-awaited victory. Breaking his own strict rule, Papi even allowed the radio to keep playing right through dinner. They then stayed up half the night recharging their adrenaline with the rosy forecasts and cups of *café*. The evening became an emotional seesaw, as good news reports were later revised as having been premature. At one point, Fidel, the *máximo* leader himself, was said to have been captured. The more positive the reports, the bigger the disappointment as, one by one, they were all disproved.

Whenever the news on one station became too pessimistic, Abuela would switch the dial to another, hoping that the negative reports might be reversed, just like the good ones had been. Some announcers, still clinging to a thread of hope, claimed that the adverse reports they kept receiving were merely communist propaganda. One of them even brought up Tokyo Rose, and the damage she had done to American G.I. morale during World War II. But finally there was no denying it anymore. The invasion forces were losing. By morning their defeat was conclusive.

When my sister, Mequi, asked if we were going back, Papi remained silent.

WHEN I WENT home for the weekend, I found my father and his friends all trying to understand how the CIA, which had been so closely involved with the planning, could have made such blatant strategic mistakes. To them, the fact Fidel's militia was waiting at the beach could only mean that informers had infiltrated the ranks. But the one thing that had them all spewing fire was that the backup air support promised by the U.S. had been recalled at the very last minute. One pilot reported that he had become heartsick upon hearing the order to turn back, because he was already so close that he could see the men being massacred right below. This last-minute change of plans, which obviously came from the very top, did not endear President Kennedy to the Cuban exile community.

Yet perhaps the saddest incident of the invasion was what happened to a group of captured brigade members who were crammed into the back of a truck to be taken to prison in Havana. The truck was tightly sealed and had no ventilation. When the doors were opened after the sweltering, hours-long trip, most of the men inside were dead. Among these were the husbands, sons, and boyfriends of people that we knew. On the Sunday following the invasion, at the Spanish mass which was now being given in the Little Flower Church's auditorium, many of the women in attendance were dressed in black, mourning for loved ones.

Along with the invasion's failure came the realization that we were in the U.S. for a longer stay than most people had predicted. Now, even with Papi's tight budget, the money that he had left would surely be long gone before anything could possibly change in Cuba. It was time to start looking for a paying job.

Since everybody he knew was in a similar situation, he began by consulting the want ads in both of the Miami papers. When the few potential leads that he found there gave no results, he went to an employment agency. He soon discovered that having run his own company seemed to be a big drawback. At every interview that the agency sent him to, he received the same answer. "Your background is impressive, but I'm afraid you're overqualified for our position."

The concept of being too qualified to perform a job that you were otherwise perfectly suited for was a totally novel one. "I don't understand. Either I can do this or I can't."

"Mr. Santeiro, you ran a very successful business . . ."

"And that's still not good enough?"

"In my experience, people who've held positions such as yours have a tough time adjusting to taking orders."

"Then give me a trial period. My situation has changed. I have a big family to support. I need to work."

But nothing he said seemed to change his interviewers' minds. "I'm very sorry. With your superior resume, I'm sure you'll find something that you're better suited for." Rejections sounded like compliments.

Finally sympathizing with his frustration, one of the women at the employment agency said she had something that he might want to try. My father replied that he was ready to try anything. That very afternoon began his brief career as a door-to-door encyclopedia salesman.

The Crusellas Company had had a big marketing staff to promote its products. The last time my father had been called upon to sell anything was when he first joined the family business as a young man, traveling around the island contacting stores that were not carrying the family's products. But soap and toothpaste are necessities, and the Crusellas brand was already well known, so finding new business had not been a difficult proposition. This time, he was assigned to a specific district and given a quota of sales that he was expected to achieve each week.

Every afternoon around five, when people were starting to come home from work, Papi would put on a coat and tie, grab the sales briefcase provided by the encyclopedia company, then diligently set out on his route. He confessed to my mother how hard it was for him to knock on door after door of people who had neither requested his coming, nor had any interest in buying the product he was offering. On a couple of occasions, dogs had lunged at him when a door was opened. It had only been thanks to his dog-loving nature that they had not caused more serious damage.

During a brief training program, he had been taught two things: "Talk fast and do your utmost to get inside that door." But even when he did manage to get inside, if a client said that they were having financial problems or had no real use for an encyclopedia, Papi couldn't find it within his heart to give them the hard sell and convince them otherwise. He was much more likely to end up commiserating.

After one month without a single sale, he returned to his job-hunting and to yet more rejections for being over-qualified. Then, out of the blue, he received a call from a man he vaguely knew, named Luis Boeri. Boeri explained that he was about to launch a new venture and wanted to offer him a position.

The U.S. Information Agency had set aside funds to promote anti-communism in Latin America. Boeri had come up with a proposal to produce Spanish *radio-novelas* with a political message that fulfilled those needs. His idea had been accepted, and now he needed someone to oversee the financial end of the project.

America's Productions, Inc., created jobs for every exiled Cuban actor in Miami. The *novelas* produced always had words like "*Amor*" or "*Pasión*" in their title, but the stories dealt with class struggle, and the possibility for improving your lot in life without resorting to radical revolution. They often started with an innocent peasant girl falling in love with her rich employer and suffering his indifference in silence. There was usually a subplot about an exploited worker seduced by the leftist preachings of a false messiah. It was the noble ingénue who through kindness and perseverance finally made her *patrón* aware of the injustices suffered by his employees, prompting him to improve working conditions. Having seen the light, he would then reject, often right at the altar, the shallow society bitch who he had been engaged to and declare undying love for the peasant girl. In the end everyone was happy, while also saving capitalism.

The scripts often included a subtle message to the ruling classes for the need to make adjustments before the inequalities of their countries brought about a communist takeover that would undo them, as it had in Cuba. There was only one slight glitch to this second objective; it was mostly the lower classes rather than rich South Americans who listened to *radio-novelas*. But Boeri had managed to convince the U.S.I.A. that the wonderful dramas he would produce could change that too.

This job brought Papi right back to the Freedom Tower, where the new company's offices were located, just a few floors above those of the Cuban Refugee Center. And when the search for someone to direct the *novelas* came up, Papi immediately suggested Ramón Antonio. In one fell swoop, both men in our family had entered the American work force. Papi's spirits began to lift instantly. The over-qualified former company president was now thrilled to be bringing home a modest weekly paycheck.

My endless school year at the military academy finally came to a close, and to my surprise, it ended on a high note. Throughout the spring semester, Captain Brundage, our English Literature teacher, had given the class various creative writing contests. The first was a poetry competition, which even in my still-imperfect grammar I won—with a poem titled "A Perfect Day." The second was a brief essay competition, for which I wrote about our final days in Cuba; I won that one also. The third contest was for a short story. By now I had become fearless and decided to tackle a mini murder-mystery. My killer wore a black mask, walked with a limp, and stalked his victims through secret wall passages. Again, it was full of grammatical errors, but, perhaps impressed by my daring despite linguistic limitations, Captain Brundage gave me first prize for that one too.

I had no idea how to write dialogue, and the Captain took the time after class to teach me how, in English, dialogue is framed by quotation marks, as opposed to the dash that precedes it in Spanish. At my school in Cuba, both math and science had been much tougher than I found them to be in the U.S., but having a teacher encourage me for expressing my creativity was a new experience, and one that I treasured.

As my prize for winning all three contests, Captain Brundage took me to the Coconut Grove Playhouse. By coincidence, the play that we saw was a comedy murder-mystery, *The Gazebo*. I didn't fully understand some of the lines, but I still enjoyed it thoroughly. Afterward, as he drove me back to the academy, Captain Brundage said that perhaps one day I might see a play of my own performed on that same stage.

My much longed-for summer vacation soon evolved into a steady routine of TV watching. Each day after breakfast, I would sit across from our trusty little Zenith and begin another daylong marathon. It began with game shows: *The Price Is Right*, *Let's Make a Deal*, *To Tell the Truth*. Next came talk shows: *Merv Griffin*, *Mike Douglas*. At four o'clock there was a local kids' show featuring Willie the Moose and Charlie Baxter, for which I had to turn over the set to my younger brothers. Then finally came time for my favorite of all, *Creature Feature*, which showed the kind of films I was now addicted to, like *The Beast with the Million Eyes*, *I Was a Teenage Werewolf*, and *Creature from the Black Lagoon*.

My mother kept urging me to give the TV a break and go outside for some fresh air and exercise, but I was perfectly content to remain on the couch watching yet another monster attack. Besides, I didn't have any friends here to go play with and was too intimidated to try to make new ones. Even my precious Ant Farm pets, which I looked after diligently for weeks, had all died. I was impressed when the first one went belly up and the others carried it in solemn procession to the surface, then made a little dirt mound to bury it under, right beside the green plastic barn. But as more and more began to die, the mound rose to be as tall as the barn itself. I felt so sorry for the last remaining ant that I decided it to set it free in the backyard. Then Renecito informed me that ants are tribal, and mine would probably be massacred by some enemy tribe. This made me feel even worse.

With my Lieutenant Tinoco experience at the academy and the fiasco of the Ant Farm, my former American Dream had become somewhat tarnished. I was clinging to the images that I was seeing on television to help me forge a new one.

My father finally decided that the time had come to put an end to my self-imposed confinement. His cousin Antonio had recently enrolled his kids in the Coral Gables Swimming Association, which practiced at the landmark Venetian Pool. Papi saw this as the perfect solution for getting me out of the house. I was watching Betty White make funny expressions to help her *Password* partner guess a word when Papi told me to put on my swimsuit, grab a towel, and come with him. Despite my efforts to point out how much this particular show was expanding my vocabulary, he ordered me to get into the car, then drove me to the pool and signed me up with the team.

Venetian Pool was the fanciful brainchild of George Merrick, who developed Coral Gables in the 1920s. Created out of the coral rock pit from which the blocks for the original houses had been quarried, it had colorful gondola poles sticking out of the water, a rocky promontory with a waterfall, and, most intriguing of all, a cave. The latter was a favorite spot for young couples to make out in, and as I soon learned, also a great place to hide in and skip a few laps. There were usually enough swimmers for our coach not to miss you right away. If you were caught, however, you ended up having to swim far more than what you thought you had gotten away with. Another distinctive feature of the pool was its bright green water, kept that way by bucketsful of copper-chloride that the lifeguards sprinkled into it every morning. This would eventually make all the blond swimmers' hair turn to a similar color, which I thought was really cool. The pool was also refilled each day with icy cold well water, which to someone with Caribbean blood, like me, made diving into it for our eight A.M. practice a true torture.

At first I felt like a total outsider, with my baggy trunks standing out among everyone else's skimpy Speedos. I also discovered how out of shape I was and felt humiliated to keep falling behind everyone in my age group, finishing laps along with the nine- and ten-year-olds. But then I got myself a Speedo too, and my times improved, and I became just another regular team member.

Only a few weeks after my joining, we held a luau to raise money for our team travel to competitions. This entailed a big cookout and, as a highlight, the performance of an intricately choreographed water ballet, for which we wore flowery Hawaiian-style wraparounds while holding up tiki torches. My former Cuban self would not have been caught dead doing something like this, nor would any of my Havana friends, but here, nobody seemed to give it a second thought. My melting-pot process was now advancing by leaps and bounds. I was morphing from Luis Manuel into Louie.

To keep me busy during summer afternoons, Papi gave me a part-time job at his new office, running the ditto machine to make the *radio-novela* script copies for the actors. It was a creaky second-hand model, with an ink leak that always ended up making my hands purple—and sometimes my clothes as well. But after I had finished making copies, I would sit in the control room behind the technician and Ramón Antonio, listening to the tapings. I was fascinated by the total personality transformations that took place the moment the actors began speaking their lines. It was even more fun to hear the comments that they made between takes. It appeared that the actress playing the virginal ingénue was anything but, while the sexy young peasant competing with their *patrón* for her affections would have been more likely to go after the *patrón* himself. At times, Ramón Antonio would turn to me with a shrug, as if uncomfortable over some of the things I was hearing. But afterwards, when all the joking was over, I would also hear a different side of their stories—about the scrapes some of them had had with Fidel's authorities, the jobs they had lost for merely thinking differently, and always, the wistful reminiscing about the best roles that they had played, or ones they still longed to perform but were now highly unlikely to, in a country that did not speak their language.

• • •

In the eight months that we had been in the U.S., all my siblings had already gone from hardly knowing English to wanting to speak nothing but. Papi, who had always been an advocate for multi-lingualism, suddenly became fearful that his children would forget their native Spanish. He enrolled Mequi and Gerardo in a bi-weekly class that taught not only *Castellano*, but also Cuban history. The teacher was a former school principal who now worked evenings at the switchboard of a downtown hotel. Both Mequi and Gerardo resented having to give up two afternoons and take a bus all the way there for these lessons. They envied my greater proficiency in our mother tongue, which spared me that indignity. After class they would meet Papi at his office to drive back home with him. Along the way he would quiz them on what they had learned and dock them a nickel from their allowance for every English word that crept into their answers. He was not much more lenient with Francisco and Carlos, who were only six and four. They too were corrected for mixing languages, although Papi's battle was gradually beginning to feel like a lost cause.

With the realization that our stay in the U.S. was going to be longer than originally anticipated, many Cuban parents began to worry about more than just keeping us children from losing our Spanish. Afraid that we would also lose our traditions, they set out to recreate an environment in which these could be perpetuated. The Cuba that they knew was to be frozen in time, like Sleeping Beauty's kingdom, and to remain unchanged until Prince Charming arrived and banished that evil witch, Fidel.

To achieve this goal, some mothers began to organize little gatherings where their sons and daughters could meet offspring from *familias conocidas*—families that not only knew each other, but whose friendships often went back for several generations.

"Nenita!" one of these mothers telephoned mine. "Your older kids are already teenagers, aren't they?"

"Well, Lourdes is fourteen and Luis Manuel thirteen. Mequi's only eleven."

"Oh, that's old enough. I'll include her."

Lourdes was fourteen but going on twenty. She wouldn't dream of being dragged into one of these exile affairs. Mequi and I, however, had no choice.

A mainstay at all these gatherings was a row of gawking chaperones, lined up like birds of prey around the living room to make sure there would be no hanky-panky. They were content knowing that now the younger generation could keep up on our Latin dances with the help of scratchy Cuban LPs that played the music of Benny Moré, Perez Prado, and Los Chavales, music that they themselves had danced to during their youth. We could also socialize with the same crowd that we would have if we were still at the Havana Yacht Club, the Biltmore, or the Vedado Tennis. Anything foreign to that world could become a threat. One adventurous young guest showed up at the first party with the soundtrack to *Never on Sunday*, a movie condemned by the Legion of Decency. That very evening his name was scratched from future guest lists, and he was *never* invited back.

Whichever mother happened to be hosting made it her mission to introduce everyone, even if we already knew each other, and usually gave far more family background information than any of us cared to hear.

"Gloria, I want you to meet Maria Mercedes and Luisito Santeiro. Their father was a dear childhood friend of mine. And my father adored their great-grandfather, President Machado. . . This is Gloria, my daughter. We have a president in our family too, you know, Miguel Mariano Gomez. Oh, and do you know Delio and Cristina? They're great-grandchildren of President Menocal."

On occasions when the hostess wasn't sure who one of the young guests was, instead of asking his or her name, she would ask who their parents were. "*Ay*, Leslito! Of course! You're Chachi's son. *Ay*, when I was your age I had such a crush on your father. We almost got engaged, you know."

I began to wonder if everyone in Havana had either dated or been in love with everyone else at some point.

The fare at these gatherings seldom varied: potato chips and onion dip, the recipe for which came on the soup box that every Cuban exile mother seemed to have discovered. Sometimes there were *bocaditos* too, little square sandwiches made with crustless white bread, and filled with either refugee center spam or a mixture of cream cheese and strawberry jam. There was also a Kool-Aid punch, usually red, without any alcohol. As for the music, it was invariably played on a cheap portable hi-fi. Those of us already succumbing to *Americano* culture would sometimes slip in a recent 78 RPM hit single, but after graciously allowing us to dance to that for a while, an adult would retake control and put on yet another scratchy Cuban LP. If the dance floor started clearing out, parents would sometimes begin to dance themselves or, worse yet, ask one of us to dance with them.

For the most part, these efforts to maintain our cultural identity succeeded. As we got to know each other better, our culture-preservation gatherings began to actually be fun. Their success, however, created an unforeseen problem for the parents. We were all now meeting other exile kids at our new schools who had not been members of the *conocido* set back in Cuba, and we were eager to include them. These were fresh new faces that could bring added energy to our endlessly repetitive group. Many of us started taking the liberty of inviting them without warning our hosts. And sometimes these unofficial invitees, known as *colados*, or gatecrashers, also invited *their* own friends. Parties at which they expected maybe thirty guests ended up with three times as many. The parents hosting then began to stand guard at the door, questioning everyone like customs officials before letting anyone gain entry.

"De quien eres hijo?" "Who are your parents?" *"Que hacian en Cuba?"*

"What did they do in Cuba?" and most incriminating of all, "*Quien te invitó?*" "Who invited you?" If someone innocently divulged your identity, you too might find yourself scratched from the next *Cubanos conocidos* party list.

While these gatherings did give us a sense of belonging to something, we had also started to attend the mixers given at our schools. There, without any parental supervision, we could dance cheek-to-cheek and sometimes belly-to-belly with American girls, who were far less uptight. At these dances, instead of swaying our hips to Latin rhythms, we mostly just shuffled our feet to the slow sensual sounds of electric guitars. At times our arms and shoulders were also called into action, when the band broke into more upbeat numbers, but hips were strictly reserved for our Cuban side. We were fast developing two parallel identities, which forever onward we would have to straddle.

My mother's maternal grandparents Gerardo and Elvira Machado.

The Cuban presidential palace, my mother's childhood home.

My mother with her grandfather Papá Gerardito.

One of my mother's *carnaval* floats.

My maternal grandmother,
Nena Machado.

My maternal grandfather, Baldomero Grau.

La Calle Ene, where I was born.

My paternal grandmother,
Mercedes Crusellas.

My baptism, with godparents Mari and Ramón Antonio.

With my parents in La Calle Ene.

Ramón Antonio at a taping.

Marietta, left, with Abuela in Paris.

BELOW:
The Crusellas family mausoleum.

Mari and Andres' wedding.

BELOW:
My mother with, left to right, Mequi. me, and Gerardo.

Carnaval time! From left: Gerardo, Mequi, and Francisco.

Off to *Los Carnavales*.

More of Abuela's Spanish costumes.

Mami and Papi at a Belle Époque ball.

Mari and Andres at a
"Precious Jewels" ball.

Mami as Mary
Queen of Scots.

La Finca San Luis.

A children's party at La Finca.

My father's stables.

Papi, center, riding with friends.

Francisco's baptism with, left to right, me, Mami, Gerardo, Papi, and Mequi.

Papi with Carlos.

BELOW:
Our first Christmas in exile. Sitting, left to right, Jocko the monkey and me, Carlos, Gerardo, Lourdes, and Mequi, with Francisco and René Scull in back.

With my siblings, in Miami.

Tia Babi with my cousin Maria Teresa in front of the New York townhouse.

BELOW:
Mimamá's 100th birthday, Miami. Standing, left to right, Francisco, Lourdes, Mequi, Gerardo, and me, with Carlos sitting.

Tia Babi, left, with Mami.

BELOW:
Mami and Papi.

• 21 •

In New York, Mari had finally found a job, right around the corner, at the Burlington Bookshop on Madison Avenue. She saw an "assistant wanted" sign on the window, walked in, and charmed Jerry, the owner, with talk about her lifelong passion for reading. She might have been opposed to the concept of selling herself, but she still seemed to do a pretty good job of it. When she called Miami to share the good news, she made it sound as if she was giving literary cocktail parties rather than stacking shelves and ringing a cash register.

"Happy Rockefeller, who lives three doors down from us, has been in twice already. We've also had Jack Paar, Lillian Hellman, etc., etc. . . ." Then within a couple of weeks all last names had been dropped. "Lillian came in for an autographing session. She's a little crusty, but Jack is terribly amusing. And between you and me, I have a feeling that Happy is not quite so happy these days."

Apparently, everyone was turning to her for reading recommendations, and there was yet another interesting development brought about by her new job—a sudden expansion of her vocabulary.

"We keep all the extra stock down in the basement, so I'm *schlepping* books up and down all day long. But Jerry's such a *mensch*. After closing time we always stick around to *kibitz* about the customers. I bring him home for lunch sometimes. He has fallen in love with Mamá Elvira, and calls her *Mamele*."

There was even better news. Andres was now working too. The exact nature of what he did was not quite clear. The way he explained it, he had been hired to be the U.S. representative for a Venezuelan company exporting raw materials. It involved his going down to Philadelphia two days a week, but despite the lack of clarity about the job, he had sworn that it was perfectly legal, so Mari had stopped asking questions. As long as his paychecks kept coming in, she was happy. Tia Babi was thrilled also, because Andres' new work schedule left him with much less time for drinking.

Tia Babi herself was still going to the clothing dispensary a couple of afternoons a week, although it was no longer as rewarding. She had accepted that she was in no position to spend her life doing charity work, and she felt guilty about having to depend on Mari and Andres to help support her as well as José Emilio and Mamá Elvira. As she sat folding donated garments, she tried to think of ways in which she might earn a little money. Some of her friends had started to do alterations, but she had never been very good with a needle and thread. At seventy, she was also past the age where any fashionable store was likely to put her on display. Mari did her best to convince her that shoveling coal and snow, dragging out the garbage, and taking care of ninety-three-year-old Mamá Elvira was more than enough. But another thing that had made Tia Babi grow tired of the dispensary was her friends' endless lamentations.

"I lost my beautiful house in el Vedado."

"I lost one in El Biltmore and another in Varadero."

"We lost two sugar mills in Oriente."

"We lost our cattle ranch in Camaguey. Ten-thousand-acres. Poof! Gone."

Having had her fill, she finally stood up one day. "*I*, Señoras, lost my country." Then she walked out and never returned.

Back in Miami, the search for jobs among aging exiled women who had never held one had also become an urgent necessity. My once-spoiled orphaned Tia Ana had left Cuba without Tio Paco and was not expecting him to show up anytime soon. She had been receiving aid from the refugee center, but that was now about to end. She had already been to a few unsuccessful interviews when she heard about an opening at the DuPont Plaza Hotel. But from the moment that she walked into the personnel manager's office, she sensed from the look on the man's face that she was not what he had been expecting.

"Mrs. Crusellas, housekeeping work is physically demanding. Our maids have to push heavy carts, lift thick mattresses, kneel down to wash bathtubs."

Tiana realized that there had been a misunderstanding. "Oh, but I am not here for a maid's job. I came because you advertised for a supervisor."

The manager smirked. "Ma'am, I'm afraid the job you're referring to requires a good deal of experience. We have a highly demanding clientele, convention groups moving in and out, and crises happening every single day."

Tiana sat up ramrod straight and peered down at her interviewer, who now was lower than she was. "Sir, it is true that I have never had to work a day in my life. I was very fortunate. But the one thing that I've had plenty of experience with is dealing with a service staff."

The manager stood up to end the meeting. "I have no doubt, but . . ."

"I was also president of two charities, La Liga Contra el Cancer and a summer camp for poor children that our family founded. I organized many successful fund-raising events for both of them. You have crises? I have dealt with every kind, sometimes amidst hurricanes, bombings, and kidnapping threats . . . and not once under any of those circumstances did I allow my staff to cancel a function."

Right before his eyes, the manager watched the genteel older lady turn into a dragon empress. "Well," he started to reconsider, "our evening housekeeper *is* about to go on maternity leave. I would be willing to take you on for a trial period."

On the afternoon before her first night shift, Tiana was a nervous wreck. She told my father that she felt her life was going in reverse. At an age when most people were thinking of retiring, she was about to start her career. Deciding what to wear paralyzed her. Every outfit she pulled out seemed inappropriate. Finally she chose a plain but elegant gray dress that she had brought from Cuba, as close as high fashion could get to a uniform. She need not have worried. Within seconds of punching in her new time card, she was handed the hotel's regulation frock, a shapeless green thing with a stiff white collar. She was also given a clip-on tag that already had her name and title printed on it, "Mrs. Crusellas, housekeeping supervisor."

As she walked into the employees' locker area to change, her spirits sagged for a moment. But then, just as the personnel manager had predicted, a crisis broke out.

Some close associates of President Kennedy were coming to town for a fundraiser and had started to arrive earlier than expected. The entire floor set aside for them still had to be cleaned and garnished with VIP complimentaries. Having a dozen maids to oversee, Tiana quickly began to feel right at home.

She went from room to room making sure that every flower in every vase was perfect, and she double-checked that nothing was overly ripe in the fruit baskets. Noticing that some pillowcases had creases, she insisted that they be re-ironed. Then as time was running out, she rolled up her uniform sleeves and went to work right alongside her staff.

She was about to clock out, feeling rather proud after her very first workday, when a second emergency arose. Her assistant covered the room service phone's mouthpiece and whispered, "It's Mrs. Kennedy."

"Jacqueline?"

"Thank God, no! If *she* was here we'd really be hysterical. I think this one is a sister-in-law. She lost a button and wants to know if we have any red ones."

Tiana sensed that this was something she should attend to personally; after all, sewing and knitting were about the only things that she had been required to learn. A maid handed her a kit with compartments full of assorted buttons. When she got to Mrs. Kennedy's suite, however, the lost one had just been found. It was lined in red taffeta to match her evening gown, and designed to hold up a shoulder strap.

"This always happens to me right before an important function."

"Are you all right now, Mrs. Kennedy?" The guard who found the button asked from the doorway.

"Yes, thank you. Please tell Bobby I'll be right over."

Tiana was hoping that Mrs. Kennedy would slip out of the dress so that she could reattach the button more easily, but she merely stepped closer. "Please hurry, or my husband will kill me." Then she sighed, "I'm so glad Jack's the one who got elected."

Tiana got started, praying that she would not jab the needle into Mrs. Kennedy. "This will only take a minute," she lied. It had been a while since she had done this.

"You have the most charming accent. Where are you from?"

"Havana."

"Really? My family used to have a summer place in Varadero."

"Oh, so did mine." Tiana started to feel like she was bonding with a new friend, and became compelled to make her aware that she was not just any ordinary hotel housekeeper. "You know, Mrs. Kennedy, I am related to a president too."

"Are you? To whom?"

Tiana was about to explain her connection to Machado when the phone rang. Mrs. Kennedy, with the button now reattached, at least for the moment, excused herself. Tiana stood there, waiting to finish the story and establish her presidential connection, but the call became prolonged. When Mrs. Kennedy looked up again she seemed surprised to find Tiana still there. "Thank you so much, dear," she smiled and tugged at the button, then subtly waved toward the door.

Tiana left Mrs. Kennedy's suite, reminded that while she might have a connection to a former Cuban president, it was of absolutely no consequence in her new country.

• 22 •

It had now been two years since the beginning of our so-called exile, and any prospects of returning became even more unlikely after a brand new development—the Cuban Missile Crisis.

The network evening news, which my parents now watched faithfully, as well as the Spanish radio that Abuela continued listening to non-stop, kept giving pretty grim predictions. But there were other events that had made our impending doom feel even more of a reality.

At our schools, daily drills were being carried out so that we would know what *survival measures* to take when those missiles started flying. We were to duck under our desks and cover our head with both hands. I had watched enough horror movies about the aftermath of nuclear wars, the kind that resulted in mutations like giant ants or monsters like Godzilla, to know that our supposedly protective desks would be blown to smithereens along with every last one of us.

Following the advice of public emergency announcements, my mother had stored a few gallons of water and stacks of canned food inside our hallway closet. One day, before heading off to Publix for more supplies, she told Abuela, "If anything happens while I'm away, just go inside that closet." To which Abuela replied, "If anything happens while you're gone, I will be dead from a heart attack long before the missiles strike."

Returning from school one afternoon, I found a bulldozer digging a huge hole in our neighbor's yard, which was a continuation of ours. A group of neighborhood kids were watching the workmen, and I asked them what was going on.

"They're putting in an air-raid shelter for protection against you crazy *Cubanos*."

The next morning a truck arrived, carrying a huge metal cylinder that a crane then lowered into the big hole.

"They'll have guns in there, you know," one kid seemed eager to tell me, "and can legally shoot and kill anyone who tries to break in."

The bulldozer then covered the shelter with dirt. I watched from a window wondering how long our neighbors would have to remain down there after we were attacked, and how weird it would be to finally come back out and find the rest of us dead.

At age fourteen, the possibility that you might actually die doesn't totally sink in. Still, just in case, on the following Saturday I made a point of going to confession, and even told the priest about my long ago lies of having seen heavenly apparitions in our school chapel.

After days of great tension, we finally learned that President Kennedy had reached some kind of accord with Premier Khrushchev. I didn't find out the details but was very happy to know that we were off the hook, and that our neighbors would not have to shoot me, should I decide to break into their shelter and try to save my family.

I'm not sure that Kennedy's strong stance against Fidel's swaggering made the Cuban exile community like him much better, but the general consensus was that he had at least partly made up for his lack of resolve during the Bay of Pigs. A couple of months later he appeared with his wife, Jackie, at a big event in the Orange Bowl Stadium. She spoke in Spanish and charmed everyone with her words of praise for the brave men who had risked their lives to liberate their country. Afterwards, members of the invasion's brigade presented the president with their flag, which he promised to return to them personally in a free Cuba. Papi thought that it was at least a touching gesture.

Succeeding at placing a call to Havana was always a happy achievement. Receiving a call from there, however, always made my parents brace up for more bad news. Those fears came truer than ever on the day Mimamá called to say that Papín had died.

I could not have guessed from the tone of my mother's voice as she spoke to my grandmother the gravity of the news that she had just been given. I figured it was just another of their periodic calls. After hanging up, Mami walked past the Florida room, where we were watching TV, and with tearful eyes said, "Your grandfather died."

Papín had taken me so many times to Havana's Coney Island to ride *la montaña Rusa* and *los carros locos*, and to the dog races to place bets together. He had even fought with my mother to valiantly save my foreskin, and yet, it had now been almost three years since we had seen him. The news of his death seemed like being told about the departure of someone who had already stopped being a part of our reality. We were not unaware of what this meant to our mother, yet we didn't know what else to do beyond going over to give her a kiss. After doing so, we kept on watching TV.

My father went off with her to their room, where they remained for a long time. When he came out again, he headed straight to the TV and turned it off with a scowl.

"I think you're all old enough to show a little more respect for your mother's feelings."

His tone suddenly made me feel terribly guilty. I had tried to distance myself from Cuba, and in doing so, had stopped giving much thought to my *abuelos*, or to Tia Berta, who was still in jail, or to Lugi who seemed to be having such a hard time with it. I had practically blocked out Telma, Mercedes, Delia, and even José—all the people who had loved us, and been such an intricate part of the former me.

Lourdes and Mequi offered to take care of dinner, a worrisome prospect, but then Mami reemerged from her room saying that she needed to keep busy. Once again, as when my great-uncle Tio Ramón died, we were soon inundated with sympathy calls and visits. These, of course, led to more conversations vilifying Fidel for having split up our families. It must have been strange for my mother to have her father's wake and funeral taking place while all she could do was make more pots of *café* for the parade of sympathizers. Abuela seemed surprised that she did not put on black mourning clothes, or at least more muted-toned ones. Mami replied that the colors of one's clothes had no bearing on what one felt inside.

The day after Papín's burial, Mimamá called to say that he had had a beautiful funeral mass, and that probably no church in Havana had been as packed since the triumph of the revolution. Once again Mami begged her to please leave everything behind and come join us.

"*Sí, sí, mija.* I plan to do that . . . very soon."

The Marxist transition in Cuba was now complete. All private property had been taken over by the government, right down to the smallest bodega and snow cone cart. All able-bodied citizens were being sent off to cut sugar cane or to work in the fields. People who had cheered the revolution when it confiscated the property of the rich were now becoming disillusioned too and leaving the country in droves. Still, we were all surprised when we heard that Delia, our *manejadora* and former worshiper of Fidel, had landed in Miami. She had fled in a small leaky boat along with a dozen others. The motor had broken halfway through their crossing, and they had drifted for almost two days before being rescued by a passing ship.

"*Ay*, Señora Nenita. I was so fooled by that man." Coming to see us was the very first thing she did upon arriving. "All those months I spent picking tomatoes and getting sunburns, I kept thinking about my nice air-conditioned room in your house, and all those vacations in La Finca and Varadero."

After a lifetime of caring for privileged children and living comfortably, long days of hard work in the fields were not her idea of improvement. One day, when told that her work was not up to the revolution's standard, she exploded at her supervisor. This resulted in her being reassigned to a pig farm. The smell of the sty, which clung to her despite dousing herself with her last remaining bottle of Kolonia

1800 de Crusellas quickly cooled whatever revolutionary zeal she still had left.

When she had finished telling us her story, she dug into the little plastic bag that they had given her at the refugee center, then took something out and handed it to me. It was wrapped in a piece of *Granma*, the revolution's official newspaper.

"That's the only *recuerdito* I came with. I brought it for you."

I unfolded the crumpled paper and found a small gold medal with a tiny white square thing embedded in the middle.

"*Gracias*. Delia, but . . . what is it?"

"Your first baby tooth!" she smiled. "I saved it and had that made."

While finding it typically bizarre of her to choose, out of all her possessions, to save the tooth of a kid she had once cared for, I was also quite touched.

Not long after Delia's visit, my father had another unexpected encounter. He was walking out of his office, at the Freedom Tower, when he heard someone call out, "Santeiro!" He turned and saw a face that he recognized, though it took him a moment to realize from where. It was his former employee, the one who had blocked the door of the company the day after it was confiscated, the one who had said, "You can't come in. This is no longer yours."

"*Ay*. Santeiro. You don't know how glad I am to run into you, so that I can give you my sincere apology." The man held out his hand.

Out of a lifelong reflex, Papi started to extend his own hand, but then stopped himself. "I'm sorry," he replied, "but there are some things in this life that cannot be forgiven." Then he turned and walked away.

WE HAD BEEN in the U.S. just over three years when, in November of 1963, President Kennedy's assassination shocked the entire world. To Cubans, who had spent their whole lives experiencing political takeovers and violent revolutions, it was inconceivable that this would not lead to some major civil disruptions. The first thing my mother did upon hearing the news was to get into our Chevy and go pick up my siblings at The Little Flower school. It was with utter amazement that we then watched the very civilized swearing-in of President Johnson, with Jackie, still in her bloodied pink suit, standing stoically by.

We spent the next two days glued to our faithful Zenith, which was by now barely clinging to life, watching unbelievable episodes unfold right before our eyes: the capture of Lee Harvey Oswald in a movie theater, his assassination by Jack Ruby right inside a jailhouse while Oswald was surrounded by policemen. Then finally, there was the unforgettable sight of that horse-drawn carriage with the president's coffin, moving slowly through the streets of the capital, while his veiled widow walked right behind, surrounded by world dignitaries.

It took no time for conspiracy theories to arise, one of the more prevalent being that Fidel Castro was behind the whole thing in retaliation for the Bay of Pigs and for Kennedy's making Khrushchev withdraw the missiles from Cuba. Although this was just a rumor, it was enough for some kids in my school to lay the blame on us too.

"I swear! You *Cubanos* are nothing but trouble. Can't imagine what you're going to pull off next."

• 23 •

Our "temporary" exile was now going into its fourth year. Mimamá still kept promising to come join us, but for whatever reason, she always qualified the promise with "very soon." It had also been almost four years since Mami had seen the family in New York, and Mamá Elvira, now on the verge of ninety-five, was not likely to be around forever.

When Mami announced her plans to fly up to New York for a brief visit, I mentioned that by coincidence, the New York World's Fair had recently opened, and we would soon be on summer vacation. She had often told us stories about the 1939 fair. One of the photos that Mimamá had sent even showed Mami standing in front of the Trylon and Perisphere, the emblematic symbols of that event.

"We haven't been anywhere since we left Cuba. And I bet Mamá Elvira would love to see us too."

My siblings took up the hint, pestering Papi with a chorus of "Yes, yes! Let's all go see the World's Fair . . . *and* Mamá Elvira! Pleeeease!"

My father curdled the enthusiasm with a doubtful sounding, "We'll see." But then my mother started thinking that it might not be such a bad idea after all. She tried to convince him that if we all went by car, the cost would probably not be much more than her airfare—and we could all stay at her family's house for free. This made Papi budge from a "We'll see" to an "I'll think about it," which to us sounded a bit more promising.

Papi had become determined to find something more profitable—and fulfilling—than doing the accounting for the U.S.I.A. *radio-nove-*

las. At the moment, he was in the process of trying to get approval for a bank loan to build a two-unit townhouse. It had been designed by an architect friend, who would also be his business partner in the venture. Miami was growing rapidly, and Papi had decided that the construction business was the ideal field to go into.

Since he had never given us a definite "no" about the trip, Mami went ahead and set a tentative date for our departure. But now that date was fast approaching, and the loan approval had not come through. Papi made it clear that he could not leave town while this decision, which meant so much, was pending. Our bags had been packed for days, but by the eve of our scheduled takeoff, we had begun to lose hope.

As a last-ditch effort, Mami lit a candle to Mater Admirabilis, patroness of the Sacred Heart Schools, of which she was an alumna. Then just as we were about to sit down for dinner with sinking spirits, Papi arrived, beaming.

"The loan was approved. We're going to New York."

Early the following morning, seven of us, including Lourdes, crammed into our radioless, air-conditionless Chevy, and set off for Manhattan. Gerardo was the only one missing, because the lucky guy had been invited by my mother's cousin, Manon, a Bacardi heiress with plenty of money outside of Cuba, to be her son Billy's companion on a grand tour of Europe. They were already staying at the Waldorf Astoria and would sail for Le Havre in a week, on the ocean liner SS *France*. We were all very happy for his good fortune—as well as ours, since the Chevy could not have possibly squeezed in another person.

Before we left, Ramón Antonio gave me ten dollars so that I could go see some theater. "If you do standing room," he said, "you can probably see four Broadway shows."

The I-95 expressway, with which they planned to connect the entire Eastern Seaboard, was only finished in small sections, so we kept getting detoured back to A1A, which had lots of traffic lights and completely ruined Papi's projected schedule. He had hoped to drive straight through, but by the time we reached North Carolina, he was exhausted, and Mami refused to drive on roads that she did not know. So we stopped for hotdogs at a Howard Johnson's, then piled into two rooms at a plain roadside inn.

By the time we reached New York, on our second day, it was already evening. We crossed the Holland tunnel, which seemed endless, and entered through lower Manhattan, our car bumping its way through streets still covered with cobblestones. Francisco thought that the buildings looked dirty, almost as if they'd been burnt, but I felt this only made them look more mysterious. As Papi maneuvered through city traffic, we kept our noses pressed to the windows, searching for landmarks.

"Where's the Empire State Building? Where's the Chrysler?"

Then we reached Midtown and they both came into view. "I see them! I see them!"

Our mother had entered the city so many times, from every possible direction, but this time she was seeing it anew through her children's eyes, and she too got caught up in our excitement. She kept pointing things out as we went by—Rockefeller Center, Saint Patrick's, The Plaza Hotel, Central Park. My stomach was getting queasy.

The stories that she had told us through the years had turned the New York house into a place of wonder. But there was one thing she had never mentioned. The moment that Maria Regueros opened the door, we were enveloped in a scent of age-old mustiness, and I knew then that I would not be disappointed.

"Señora Nenita!" Maria threw her arms around my mother, forgetting that she relied on two canes to be held up.

Mari emerged from the elevator in time to see me trying to keep Mami from being dragged to the floor by their ancient housekeeper. "Maria, *por Dios!* Mamá Elvira may think that the messiah has come, but Nenita will *not* make you walk again." She looked very Audreyesque, in tight Capri pants and a long-sleeved blouse knotted at the waist. "Darlings! At last you've come!" She went around distributing hugs and squeezed me so tight that I heard my spine crackle.

She announced that she had distributed us all over the house and offered to take us up to our rooms. "But we'll have to go in shifts. The elevator can only take three at a time."

Mami suggested that we first go say hello to Mamá Elvira, whose room was on the third floor. As Mari opened the squeaky elevator door, I felt a little like Mr. Renfield being ushered into Castle Dracula. The climb was slow and creaky. "Don't worry, dear," Mari noticed the look on my face. "There's a buzzer you can ring when it goes dead between floors, and a repairman is usually here within two hours."

The mustiness of the house suddenly gave way to the scent of gardenia and Vicks VapoRub as we entered my great-grandmother's room. It was at least three times the size of any of ours in Miami and with two towering windows that faced 82nd Street. By contrast, Mamá Elvira looked tiny, sitting on a plain wooden rocker beside an unlit fireplace and surrounded by boxes of old photos and clippings.

When she saw us walk in she clasped her hands in wonderment. Mami, who adored her grandmother, had always said that she was not the kissing type. In fact, she was known for telling her, "*No me beses que la vejez se pega.*" "Don't kiss me. Old age rubs off." Still, one by one we lined up to do so, and she did not seem to object.

It felt strange to see her in these surroundings. I still pictured her back in La Finca Nenita, rocking herself across from the ruins, or slowly walking with us to go pick strawberries together.

"All right, my darlings!" Mari began to give out room assignments. This had been a major organizing feat, as the house was already quite full. Mari's younger sister, my Tia Fifi, along with her husband, Johnny Lopez Oña and their kids, Maria Teresa and Juani, were all now living there too.

"Nenita, you'll sleep here with Mamá Elvira, as you always did. Luis senior, Mequi, and the younger boys are all in the fourth floor.

Luisma and Lourdes, I've put you on the fifth, with Maria Regueros. But don't worry, not sharing her bed."

Before we all set off to unpack, she announced that although they now always ate down in the kitchen, tonight, in our honor, we would gather in the second floor library, and since it was already rather late, just *nosh* on Maria Regueros' sandwiches.

The second floor, with its big formal rooms, is where everyone who happened to be staying in the house had gathered for dinner during the first exile. Now some of the upholstery was a bit frayed, the ceiling paint was peeling here and there, and the stained glass cupola above the slave girl statue, through which the roof gutter had plunged, looked sloppily patched up. To save money, Andres had done it himself. Still, the rooms retained an unquestionable air of elegance.

This being our first night, we also put on the nicest clothes that we had brought. When Mari saw Mami come down, she quipped, "Oh, I must have forgotten to tell you. The Rockefellers had to beg off."

"That's all right," Mami replied. "*We're* here. That's all that matters."

Tia Babi, who had been at St. Ignatius for an evening service, and her husband José Emilio, now joined us also. Andres was already making drinks. After handing my parents their Scotches and pouring stiff vodkas for himself and Mari, he looked at Mami straight in the eye. "You don't know how happy I am that you're here. Now you can convince your aunt that it's high time to sell this damn place."

"I told you not to bring that up tonight, darling," Mari said, forcing a smile.

Andres ignored her. "We're counting pennies and lumps of coal, plus falling behind on taxes, while we sit on a property that's worth . . . I don't know, a few hundred thousand."

"Oh, please!" Mari laughed.

Tia Babi, who had remained silent, explained again how she wanted her mother to live her last days in peace.

"Her last days? The women in your family live longer than Methuselah!" Andres said. "We'll be in a debtor's jail long before she goes."

Hoping to ward off a confrontation, Mari started telling us how marvelous the World's Fair was and what a treat we were in for. "Sandwiches, anyone?"

Afterwards, I helped her take the dishes down to the kitchen, where Maria Regueros was spraying for roaches.

"If I don't do this every night, I find them doing conga lines in the morning." She picked up the huge purse with all her medicines and a wrinkled copy of the *New York Post*, then started waddling toward the elevator. "Come, *mijo!* We can ride up together." Between her bulky frame and her two canes jutting out to each side there was very little room left. "*Vamos!* Squeeze in," she insisted. "We can't keep sending this up and down. It uses too much electricity."

I stepped over one of her canes and flattened myself into a corner, and together we began our squeaky ascent.

As I walked back into the small room where I was staying, I discovered that there was a narrow staircase at one end of it, in what I had assumed was a closet.

"Where do those steps go to?" I asked Maria, when she crossed to her bathroom.

"To the billiard room. In the old days, the men gathered up there to smoke. And for the short time he lived here, your *bisabuelo* used it as a study. You can go up if you want."

I stared into the pitchblack tunnel and shook my head. "Maybe tomorrow."

Lourdes was already in bed, and her room was at the opposite end of the floor. Maria Regueros was a few doors down too. Once she flicked off the hall lights, I felt totally isolated, a feeling only made worse by that dark stairwell peering down at me. Even walking over to the bathroom now felt like an intimidating proposition. I decided to forgo my tooth brushing and prayed that I wouldn't have to pee till morning. After quickly stripping down to my underwear, I dove under the sheet and covered my head. As I slowly drifted off, I thought about

Delia, our *manejadora*, and wondered what bright or dark spirit auras she might have encountered here. At least I felt grateful that I did not possess those abilities.

When I woke up, with sunlight pouring in through the window, the stairwell that had seemed so forbidding in the nighttime now looked almost inviting. So I decided to go up and explore. The narrow steps opened abruptly into a rectangular room, paneled in dark wood and with a massive billiard table smack in the middle. Its green felt cover looked somewhat faded, and billiard balls were strewn all over it, as if someone had recently been playing and left in mid-game. Above each corner of the table was an ornate metal lamp, from which hanged flower-like Tiffany glass light fixtures. As I walked around, the floor under me kept creaking, and I could feel the dust gathering on the soles of my bare feet. I stopped to look at them and found that they were already blackened with soot. Then I noticed the bookshelves that framed a fireplace on the far wall, and started to inspect the volumes in them. There were old editions of the classics, all in beautiful but brittle leather bindings. There was a set that covered all of World War I, and a series of big heavy tomes of something called *The Graphic*. As I went to pull one out, a picture frame tipped over and fell to the floor. The sound of shattering glass startled me, and even though I assumed that I had been the cause of it, thoughts of otherworldly forces flashed through my mind, and goose bumps rippled up my arms. Suddenly feeling like an intruder, I quickly slid the volume back into place and ran downstairs as fast as I could, getting a big splinter stuck on one foot along the way.

While I fiddled with tweezers, Maria Regueros limped past my door.

"Did you run into anything interesting up there?" There was an insinuating tone about her question.

"Nope. Just splinters."

By the time I got downstairs for breakfast, my parents were already at the kitchen table with Francisco, Carlos, Tia Babi, and Mamá Elvira.

My younger siblings had not had a restful evening. They kept hearing rumblings through the fireplace in their room and were convinced that some creature would pop out any minute and drag them into it. Tia Babi had sat herself between their beds and the scary void, assuring them that there was nothing to be frightened of. Still, not convinced that their aging great-aunt could defend them against the forces of evil, they had posted their G.I. Joes with aimed bazookas right beside their pillows.

Mari soon came down to join us, bringing an old photo that she had dug up somewhere.

"Look, my darlings. A glimpse from the days when your family hosted world leaders instead of homeless refugees."

I recognized my *bisabuelo* in his signature round horn-rim eyeglasses, dressed in black tails and shaking hands with someone that I did not recognize.

"Who's the other guy?"

"*Niño*, that's President Coolidge, when he came to Havana!" Tia Babi said, as if I should have known. "Before he arrived, Papá threw everyone in *el Palacio* into a cleaning frenzy. We had to clear out all our rooms for his entourage. And every last inch of the place was scrubbed and polished to perfection."

"It was a very big deal," Mami explained. "He was the first American president to visit the island. Well, Teddy Roosevelt came with the Rough Riders, but that was before he had been elected."

"President Grant came too," Mamá Elvira seemed energized by our visit. "But that was *after* he had left office."

"There were over a hundred thousand people gathered at the dock to greet him," said Tia Babi. "And all along his ride to the palace everyone showered him with flowers. A man who was famous for not smiling suddenly could not stop doing so."

"And ever since that visit," Mami took over again, "whenever someone in the family starts doing some serious house cleaning, we say, 'Coolidge must be coming!'"

Mamá Elvira giggled, delighted by the recollection.

"You know, the United States had Prohibition at the time, so Papá had to be very careful that no one would offer Coolidge a drink," Tia Babi continued.

"But most of his entourage got sloshed anyway," offered Mari, who had stepped into the pantry, where I could see her pouring something into her orange juice. "Honestly, these Americans are so puritanical."

I could also see Maria Regueros rolling her eyes from across the room.

Then Mamá Elvira squeezed my mother's hand. "Neni, do you remember when your grandfather made them stop their car in front of La Finca Nenita, so that you could say hello to Mr. Coolidge?"

"Of course," Mami put her other hand over her grandmother's. "I'll never forget that."

I loved how the story trickled out of them, snippets of memory sparking off each other. After never having been too curious to delve much beyond my mother's reminiscences, suddenly I wanted to know more, and I suspected that many details still lay stored away, not just in their memories but within the house itself. All one had to do was open the right trunk or drawer, and bits and pieces of the past would come tumbling out.

The World's Fair did not disappoint. We went there three times, twice staying way into the evening to see the pavilions lit up. We also explored every inch of The Metropolitan Museum, which was just a few steps away from our house. And thanks to my godfather's gift, I got to see three Broadway shows: *Fade Out—Fade In*, with Carol Burnett, whom I'd become a fan of from *The Gary Moore Show* on television; *High Spirits*, starring Beatrice Lillie, which I saw with Lourdes; and *Oliver!* one of the biggest hits of the moment, which I saw with Mequi and our cousin Frank. And even though I only saw one in standing room, the ten dollars still covered all of them. One afternoon, we also took a taxi to the West Side docks and boarded the SS *France* to bid

Gerardo bon voyage. We did a lot of exciting things, yet the highlight for me was the experience of staying in my mother's old home.

We were only two days away from our departure when Mari made a grand announcement: "I've decided that we must have a great big bash to celebrate your visit!"

My mother assumed that she'd been drinking. "Really? And who will you get to come on such short notice?"

"Everyone, darling. They're all displaced persons. What else have they got to do?" Audrey Hepburn herself could not have sounded more confident.

"I agree with her," Andres chimed in. "And guarantee you not one Cuban exile in this town passes up the chance to poke their nose into the Machado townhouse . . . to see if our roof is still holding up."

By morning, the entire exile community knew about the impromptu gathering, and as Mari had predicted, every last one of them accepted the invitation.

"Of course, we can't possibly compete with Nelly's over-the-top exuberance," Mari said, "So we'll go for tasteful simplicity."

This meant putting Maria Regueros to work making *bocaditos*—the typical Cuban party sandwiches of crustless white bread spread with some kind of mystery paste. Mari also felt there was no shame in asking everyone to bring a bottle, "unless they're happy sticking to Coca Cola."

Both she and Mami dusted and vacuumed all morning, but as they went around wiping the dining room Chippendale chairs, they noticed that some of them were dangerously wobbly.

"Oh, dear. All we need is for someone to fall on their ass and sue us."

"So who needs chairs?" said Andres. "When Cubans start talking we forget whether we're sitting or standing. Luis Manuel!" He snapped his fingers at me. "Help me take these downstairs. It will give us lots more room for dancing."

Then Mari tilted her head back to rub her sore neck and saw the strips of ceiling paint hanging down like stalactites. "And what are we going to do about all *those*?"

"How about candlelight," Mami suggested. "It will conceal *and* be romantic."

"Yes, but with the crowd we're expecting it could also turn this into a Joan of Arc affair." Andres headed for the stairs. "I have a better idea."

A half-hour later he returned with a big box of balloons and a helium tank, which he borrowed from a nearby party shop. He snapped his fingers again. "I need an assistant!"

For the next two hours we inflated balloons, then let them float up to hide the unsightly paint patches and the amateurishly repaired glass dome over the slave girl statue.

"I think you missed your calling, darling," Mari said to Andres; "you should have been a decorator."

We were barely through with our concealing work when we heard the first guests already starting to arrive.

"*Oy, vey!*" said Mari. "They're like racehorses chomping at the bit. We better hurry and get dressed."

By the time I came back down, the second floor was packed. Someone was using the elevator, so I took the stairs. These provided a perfect bird's-eye view of the main rooms. It occurred to me that probably most of those present had left Cuba with nothing. There were doctors who had had to start over by mopping floors in hospitals and lawyers who had worked as messenger boys while revalidating their degrees. Yet it looked as if not a thing had changed. The men were as distinguished as ever in their dark suits, and the women, draped with every bit of jewelry they had managed to escape with, all looked like heiresses. The evening had barely begun, but between the many bottles the guests had contributed and a punch that Andres had liberally spiked with vodka, the crowd was already on verbal over-drive.

"What did I tell you, darling?" Mari said to my mother. "They're all here. My dear friend Nelly is going to eat her heart out." She looked beautiful in her little black dress and long strand of plastic pearls.

When my mother told her so, she stared back at her and replied, "I guess when one has class, one can look good in a shopping bag."

I'm not sure that my mother took this as a return compliment, but then a lady came lunging at her with her arms wide open. "Nenita, *cariño!* How wonderful to see you." I gathered from their conversation that someone in her family had been involved in Papá Gerardito's administration, and they too had had to flee in nineteen thirty-three.

"*Ay, hija.* Who would have told us we'd be back in exile again!" Her dramatics made others aware of my mother's presence, and soon she was swamped with melancholy embraces.

"If your grandfather had been alive, he would have never let this happen."

"But he predicted it," one man said with great authority. "I heard him myself: 'After me, the chaos.'"

"I believe that was Louis the Sixteenth," someone corrected him. "Or was it the Fourteenth?"

"Whoever it was, President Machado said something equally far-sighted."

"*Bueno, bueno!*" Andres clapped his hands. "We're not here tonight to talk politics!" He brought up an old Cuban saying, "*Que nos quiten lo bailado!*" "No one can take away the dancing we've already done."

Taking advantage of the fact that her *dear* friend had still not arrived, Mari announced, "Nelly may have had a pianist at her Christmas party, but we have an entire orchestra!" She reached for the portable hi-fi Andres had also borrowed and turned the volume all the way up. The Orquesta Aragon started playing their classic song, "El Bodeguero," and everyone began to dance, while singing the familiar lyrics: "*En la bodega se baila así entre frijoles, papas, y ají.*" "This is how we dance in the bodega, amidst beans, potatoes, and bell peppers."

I had been hanging around the bar and, when no one was looking, sneaking ladlefuls of the vodka punch, which were making me quite sociable. People I had never met kept hugging me.

"You look just like your Papi!"

"I have a confession to make," said a paunchy man with a big moustache. "I came 'this close' to being your father." Seeing my concerned look, he explained. "I always had a big crush on your mother. But like an idiot, I let Luisito get ahead of me."

"Well, as long as we're sharing old secrets . . ." a woman whispered into my ear, "I came very close to being your mother."

This time I chuckled.

"It's not funny. Your father was the love of my life. Then Nenita returned from New York and I was history."

"Can you blame him?" A man dancing by teased.

"Shut up, Jorge! You're drunk." My might-have-been mother leered and strutted away.

"Don't worry," the teaser reassured me, "she's my first cousin." Then he trailed off dancing and singing: *"Toma el chocolate! Paga lo que debes!"* "Drink your chocolate and pay your bill."

I pondered how close I had come to being someone else entirely. Everybody present seemed to be somehow related to everyone else. It made me think that, had we remained in Cuba, we might be on a fast track to developing serious genetic deficiencies.

"Can you pour me another one, darling?" Mari held out her empty glass, turning me into the unofficial bartender. "Pour, pour, pour!" I was pouring away when my mother approached, looking upset and subtly pointing at one of the guests. "Did you invite her?" she asked Mari.

"Of course. You don't think she'd have dared show up if I hadn't."

"Why? Who is she?" I got very curious.

"An old friend." Mari took a large sip from her refill and smiled at me. "*Mmmm*. Nice job."

"Well," my mother continued, "I hope Mamá Elvira doesn't see her if she decides to come down."

"*Ay*, Neni. Too much water has flowed not to let bygones be bygones. And now we're all united in the struggle against Fidel."

"I suppose you're right," Mami conceded.

I wanted more details. "So who's this woman, and how come you only tell me the nice stories?"

"*Mijo*, life is too short to waste any of it on bad memories." Then, spotting another long-lost face, she sailed toward it.

"How could I not invite the poor thing?" Mari shrugged. "We've known each other forever. Went to the same clubs . . . shared the same seamstress and gynecologist."

"Don't forget boyfriends," an eavesdropper threw in.

"You're right," Mari smirked. "And boy, do I regret not letting her keep Andres. Now, *that* would have been sweet revenge."

"But what did this lady do?" By now I was really intrigued.

"Nothing, darling . . . it was actually her father. And we can't let the sins of the father visit the children, can we?"

I wasn't up for a biblical lesson. "Aw, come on. What did he do?"

"Oh . . . he almost killed Papá Gerardito. And possibly a couple of us as collateral damage."

"What?"

"He's the one who planted the sorbet bomb."

"What sorbet bomb?"

"Honestly, your mother hasn't told you anything."

"Apparently not the good stuff."

The hi-fi needle had gotten stuck on another old standard. "Para Vigo Me Voy," had turned into "*Me voy, me voy, me voy, me voy . . .*" "I go, I go, I go."

"Mari!" dancers shouted. "Change that record, *chica!*"

She put her glass down to go do so, but I stopped her. "Let someone else do it. Please. I want to hear about the sorbet bomb."

Never one to resist the chance of elaborating on an already good story, Mari called out to the dance floor, "The records are all right there. Just take your pick." Then she led me toward the slave girl statue, where we could have a little more privacy.

"Every Saturday morning Papá Gerardito used to drive out to the Finca Nenita with his chauffeur, and sometimes he would take us with him. Along the way there was this little park that had a carrousel, and near it, on the sidewalk, there would always be this nice old man selling ice cream from one of those bicycle carts. He had all our favorite tropical flavors, *tamarindo*, *mamey*, *guanábana* . . . so Papá Gerardito would tell the chauffeur, whose name I can't remember but I'm sure your mother would, to pull up so he could buy each of us a cone. Mamá and your grandmother were always telling him he should not be doing that. It was too dangerous . . . plus unsanitary. But Papá Gerardito loved to spoil us. Besides, he was the president. He could do whatever he wanted.

"By now all of Havana knew that this was his weekly routine. And even when we weren't with him, Papá Gerardito would always make his chauffeur slow down so that he could smile and wave at our ice cream man, and the ice cream man would smile and wave back. Luckily, on this particular Saturday, something was going on at La Finca, probably yet another party for your mother, so we had driven out earlier in a different car. But then Papá Gerardito followed, down his usual route, at his usual time. Only this time when he passed by the park, he noticed that although the little cart was there, our ice cream man was nowhere in sight. He thought that was very strange and asked his chauffeur to stop. Luckily, the chauffeur sensed that this was not a smart thing to be doing, and told him, 'I'm sorry, Señor Presidente. I think we should drive on.'

"Well, my dear! They had barely gone half a block when this huge explosion sent the ice cream cart flying way up in the air. Cars parked nearby rocked like tin toys, and their windows were smashed to smithereens. It was by a sheer miracle that not only Papá Gerardito escaped, but that nobody else was hurt either. Although I understand that people did get pelted by sorbets. Green gobs of lemon ice cascaded down one man's forehead. A white woman was turned dark brown by chocolate ice, and a black one splotched in whiteness by a blend of vanilla and coconut. One little girl's fancy weekend dress became a rainbow of colors, streaming like mini waterfalls along the pleats of her skirt—

mango down one, *zapote* and *mamoncillo* down another. They say that one lady started to scream when she saw her husband's starched *guayabera* dripping with what looked like blood. Then she went to embrace him and smelled *mamey*, so she started licking. It was definitely *mamey*.

"Everyone around got splattered by those delicious island flavors that we all adored. Although to the disappointment of some, Papá Gerardito was still very much alive."

A conga line had started to snake by us. "You guys are no fun! Hop aboard!"

I was still somewhere back in that sorbet-splotched park. "All that really happened?"

"As God is my witness," Mari crossed her heart. For a moment, Audrey Hepburn seemed to be playing Scarlett O'Hara.

"But how were they able to trace the bomb to that lady's father?"

"Darling, have you ever known a Cuban who could keep their mouth shut for more than two minutes?"

The conga line snaked by us again. Mari was about to join it, but then the number ended. The exhausted dancers were all mopping their brows, so to give them a breather Andres put on a *danzón*, a slow formal dance that went back further than my *abuelos*. Couples, still unwilling to give up, struck formal stances and began to glide gracefully to the strains of Cheo Belen's Orchestra. Even Mari went off in search of Andres.

"*Lleva en su alma la Bayamesa, lindos recuerdos de tradiciones.*" "The lady from Bayamo carries within her soul the lovely memories of old traditions."

Now my mother saw me standing alone. "May I have the pleasure?"

"Are your toes covered? You know I can't dance this stuff."

"Sure, you can." She took my hand. "Just imagine a little square tile that we're tracing with our feet. Right, back, left, then front again." I remembered her telling me that Papá Gerardito had once used those exact words to teach her.

"Right, back, left, front . . ." I tried to stop repeating the mantra and put a little more *sabor* into my movements . . . a little more shift of the hip and graceful glide, the way others around me were doing. "Right, back, left, front . . ." I began to fear that my Cuban dancing gene was gone forever. Then as I tried to turn Mami around, just to break the monotony, I saw something that made me lose the beat entirely. Mamá Elvira had decided make an appearance after all.

Everyone stopped whatever they were doing and turned to stare, as if a rather unassuming goddess had descend from Mount Olympus. Tia Babi was with her, looking incredibly chic. No one could have suspected that the *grande dame* escorting her mother into the party now spent part of her days shoveling coal in yellow rubber gloves.

From the moment Mamá Elvira arrived, she became the center of attention. Sitting on an ornate velvet-upholstered chair, beside an exotic Indian lamp, she was a maharani accepting homage from her subjects. At least for this one night, the whole world seemed to be *Machadista*.

"*Ay*, Doña Elvira! If we could only bring Gerardito back."

"Our country deserves what it got, for having treated him like we did."

Mamá Elvira just made non-committal nods, as if thinking, "Rather late for this, isn't it?"

Then someone else, who for all I knew had once been a political enemy too, held up his glass and toasted, "To President Machado. A true Cuban patriot!"

All around glasses clinked. "To President Machado!"

Another popular *danzón*, called "Almendra," had started to play. Upon hearing its first familiar notes, "*pa-ra-rám, pa-rám, pa-pám!*" everyone who could walk usually headed straight toward the dance floor. But contrary to form, everybody was now leaving it and heading toward the conservatory. I followed the crowd, wondering if a political argument had finally erupted. Then I noticed that everyone was looking up, and smiling.

A big, fat, full Moon was shining down through what remained of the glass dome that Andres had haphazardly repaired. And for some reason, which I could not quite figure out, this too had brought on a wave of nostalgia.

"Ay, Cubita bella! . . ." "The most beautiful land human eyes ever beheld . . ." "How I miss you . . ."

For a brief moment, a roomful of compulsive talkers remained in perfect silence, gazing up at the sky in wonderment.

The last thing we did, before leaving the following morning, was to go say goodbye to Mamá Elvira. She was already dressed and perfectly groomed, sitting at her usual post by the unlit fireplace, and with another box of clippings on her lap. After we all kissed her again, despite her theory that old age rubs off, she held up what looked like a postcard. It had a photo of Papá Gerardito, walking cane in hand along a tree-lined boulevard.

"This was taken during his exile in Paris," she said as she handed it to me. "Turn it over and read what it says to the others."

It was a list of items: "The Capitol building. The Central Highway. The Prado Boulevard. The expansion of the University. The extension of El Malecón . . ." I was only halfway down the list when Mamá Elvira interrupted.

"Those are just a few of the things that your great-grandfather did for Cuba. I want you to keep this, so that you will always be proud of him."

Reading of those wonderful achievements only made me wonder about the series of events that had taken my *bisabuelo* from such heights to all the strange bombings, assassination attempts, and the family's eventual midnight flight from the country.

• 24 •

The modest two-unit townhouse that my father and his partner built had sold in no time and made them both a nice profit. This gave Papi enough confidence to quit his job with the *radio-novela* group and become a full-time developer. Their next project was much more ambitious, five single-family homes, modest ones too but creatively designed. This time they had no trouble securing the bank loan.

The houses were in the South Miami district, and when they were finished, Papi announced that we would be moving into one of them. Although it was a fine neighborhood, it was nowhere near as nice as the one where we had been living, and my mother was not at all thrilled. Papi then admitted that perhaps he had been a bit overly ambitious in jumping from one small duplex to doing five whole houses. He was confident that the project would eventually pay off, but for the moment finances were tight again, and the move, which would cut down on our expenses, was not a matter of choice.

The five houses were quite attractive, if basically slight variations on the same theme. Three of them had straight driveways leading to a garage, the other two a semi-circular one. Two had exposed brick trimming around the front door; the others had vertical wooden slats. Some had white roof tiles, others red ones. But the master bathroom in each of them had that one item indispensable to so many Cubans—a bidet. It was a clever design now being manufactured by one of Papi's old friends, attachable to the rim of a regular toilet and with a lever that could be swung in and out.

There was another thing that all five houses had in common—a total lack of vegetation. The chain-link fences that separated each of them could not prevent one family's lack of taste from infringing upon their neighbor's sensibilities.

As Papi surveyed the newly placed squares of sod, I passed by him with an armload of things that we had started to bring over.

"Just like La Finca, eh?" he said with irony.

I pictured those long rows of royal palms and mango trees, the giant banyans with their labyrinthine roots, and the vines of bougainvillea and *lluvia de oro* that enveloped *el chalet*. Suddenly, our modest new home looked all the worst by comparison.

"Don't worry," Papi read my thoughts. "It's going to look very nice by the time we're through."

Hiring a professional landscaper was out of the question, but Papi began to put aside some extra cash each week and turned into an obsessive gardener. His enthusiasm was contagious, and soon I too had caught the greening fever. We became weekend regulars at the Gumbo-Limbo Nursery. The larger plants that could have provided an instant canopy and obliterated our new neighbors' rusty boat were way beyond our budget. We had to settle for foot-tall scheffleras, crotons, and ixoras. Together we planted these all along the bare chain-link fence, then watered them faithfully, praying to San Isidro, the farmer saint, to help them grow quickly.

The announcement of our move brought about other big changes in our household. The time had come for Marietta and Ramón Antonio to find their own accommodations. Marietta moved to a tiny cottage on the grounds of a big old house. It was in the area now known as Little Havana, where many Cubans had moved and opened businesses. Unlike our vegetationless new home, hers was surrounded by thick foliage and sat under a huge mango tree. She confessed to us that she had never spent a single night on her own, and on her very first one, the sound of strange objects pelting her roof kept her awake all evening. Scared to death of stepping outside to investigate, she called my father and asked him to come over. What he discovered was a rooftopful of ripe mangos. Marietta proceeded to buy earplugs, which helped her to make it through the rest of mango season.

Now that Miami was no longer a stopgap, Ramón Antonio had come to the conclusion that his future was not in this city. Government funding for the *radio-novelas* was looking more uncertain, and as for teaching acting, he had long ago realized that it was not a thriving profession within a community of struggling refugees.

"I'm moving to New York," he announced one night as we were about to sit down to dinner.

"Oh, take me with you, Tío. Pleeeease!"

My father looked at me as if I was insane.

"Don't worry, *cariño*," Ramón Antonio patted my shoulder. "One day I will rescue you from suburbia."

Then one morning, while listening to the Spanish radio's ever-hopeful news about the fall of Fidel, and still dreaming of a return, Abuela suffered a stroke. Her speech became garbled and her right side paralyzed. The doctors gave Papi little hope of those things improving. Her vital signs, however, remained strong, which meant she might still live on a few more years.

Papi, whose father's last words had been "take care of your mother," would not consider putting her in a nursing home. But now she would need round-the-clock nursing care, and there was hardly room to accommodate that within our new home. He felt at a total loss over what to do, until Tiana came to the rescue. Her apartment was a small one also, but she offered to move into the living room, so that Abuela, who had been like a true mother to her, could take over the bedroom, along with her nurses.

The stroke had the most curious effect on my grandmother. Her deep longing to return to Cuba faded away. Now, ninety percent of the time, she simply thought she was still living there. She would tell Tiana to go down to the kitchen and ask Pedro, her former chef, to make whatever dish she happened to have a craving for. Yet when Tiana served her the far more ordinary meal she had prepared, Abuela was absolutely fine with it, having already forgotten her special request. When an old friend dropped by one day, she regaled her visitor with the plans for her upcoming European trip.

"I am taking the *Queen Elizabeth* to Southampton, then hiring my regular chauffeur in Paris and driving down to Spain to see my relatives."

But even more ironically, her friend, already experiencing mental lapses of her own, later remarked to Tiana how lucky Mercedita was to still be able to travel in such grand style.

Like a dutiful son, Papi went by to see Abuela almost every single afternoon. My mother began to complain that he hardly had time for us anymore, because now every night, right after dinner, he also had another mission to accomplish.

Fidel, who had been paid over fifty-three million dollars by the U.S. to free the prisoners from the Bay of Pigs invasion, had taken that as a very profitable precedent. He now set a price on a number of other political prisoners. My father, who had various good friends among them, would get on the phone and start calling a list of Cubans, asking for donations to help free these men. It was difficult to expect people who were barely remaking their own lives to give money. Yet someone who had been a total failure as an encyclopedia salesman took on this task with a complete sense of urgency and conviction.

One bit of good news was that Tia Berta had finally been released from prison. Mimamá sounded thrilled when she called to let Mami know. But even more wonderful than her sister's release seemed to be the fact that Lugi, who had grown increasingly difficult, could finally be taken off her hands. Tia Berta had already applied for permits to leave the country with her daughter, and Cuban authorities would surely be glad to get rid of two women who were nothing but a burden to the revolution. But there was one little glitch. The last time they had left the U.S., Lugi had apparently made a scene at customs and had been placed under a category that denied her reentry.

"And what about you, Mamá?" I heard my mother ask. "Have *you* applied for your exit permit?"

"Yes, yes. Don't worry. I'm getting all my business in order so that I can do that."

"What business? Just go ahead and come, for God's sake!" The voice that began these conversations sounding loving and gentle usually ended them shouting with frustration.

But while my family's ties to Cuba remained a source of anxiety, my American life kept taking me further away from it all.

My father's push to make me join a swimming team had successfully snapped me out my self-imposed isolation. During the school year, I now practiced two hours a day with my high-school team, and then went on to practice two more with the team at Venetian Pool. Breaststroke had become my forte, although being fairly good at all four strokes I also began to compete in the individual medley. By now I was placing first in most of our school's dual meets, and as my times went down, my popularity increased. The swimming world opened a whole new social life, an American one. Latin music was never played at my new friends' parties. There were also no eagle-eyed chaperones sitting around the living room to make couples separate when they started dancing too close.

I had succumbed to that common teenage affliction of wanting to be like all my peers. One result of this was a growing resentment of my father's refusal to answer the phone with a "Hello." He continued to do so with the Cuban "*Oigo!*" And when I asked him why, he replied, "Because it's usually Cubans calling." It also bothered me that we were still having dinner at eight or eight-thirty, while my American friends had all had theirs by six. If they happened to call while we were at the table and asked for Louie, someone was likely to say, "Sorry, Luis Manuel can't come to the phone right now. He's having dinner." Somehow my two names blended together to their Anglo-centric ear and all they heard was my middle one. This would invariably lead to their taunting me with, "Manuelll? I didn't know your name was Manuelll. And what the hell time do you guys eat, anyway?"

I still continued to have Cuban friends, some of whom I had known since long before our exile. This presented a different problem. At school I was now fully accepted by both the Latin and *Americano* groups, but I was constantly being forced to choose between one and the other. It made for an especially tricky balancing act during our lunch breaks. The number of Latins in our school was still not very large, and they always sat together at one specific table. On days when I decided to join them, my swimming teammates would pass by without acknowledging me. But when I chose to give the *Americanos* equal time, then some of the Latins would call me *"Cubano arrepentido,"* which sort of translates as "Renegade Cuban."

In the middle of my junior year I underwent what was probably the most important rite of passage for a suburban American teenager. I got my full, non-restricted driver's license. Only a small percentage of students at my school owned cars. Most of these were either old VWs or undefinable jalopies that they had purchased with earnings from newspaper routes or other part-time jobs. But whatever the condition of the vehicles, driving to school was definitely a big status symbol.

My mother was too dependent on our Chevy to let me have it for an entire day, just so that I could feel like a hot honcho as I pulled into the school parking lot. But on this particular occasion, I had a once-in-a-lifetime reason for borrowing the car, and I begged and pleaded until she gave in. The Beatles were coming to town.

For weeks prior to their arrival, WQAM, one of the main top-forties radio stations, had been promoting the visit and urging listeners to join their DJs in greeting the Beatles at the Miami airport. Even before my mother agreed to lending me the car, I had already told my swimming team buddies that I would definitely be bringing it on D-

Day, and I had offered rides to any of them who wanted to come help me welcome the Fab Four.

Going all the way to the airport would be the farthest that I had ever driven, and I was a bit nervous about it. But the moment that the last bell rang we all raced toward the car. As it turned out, a couple of my friends had invited other friends, and there were now nine of us. This led to some moaning and groaning, but since it was the only chance any of them had of getting to the airport, they all did their best to squeeze in. Along the way, we passed a couple of police cars, and half my passengers had to slither down and hide their heads, afraid that the cops would stop us and we'd never reach our destination.

When we got to the airport, we found that practically every teenager in Miami had decided to be there too. The main concourse, along which big orange posters announced, "WQAM welcomes the Beatles to Miami," was already a mob scene. Perhaps afraid that the crowd would break through and make it down to the runway, airport officials closed the glass doors that led to the gates. As more and more fans arrived, the forward thrust kept increasing. I could hear the frightened complaints of those at the very front who were being crushed against the glass partition. Then the mounting pressure finally made the doors shatter, and the crowd lunged ahead with a roaring cheer. I could feel myself being dragged downward by the people behind me, as if I had gotten caught under a rotating wheel. Luckily, there was a tall guy in front of me, so I reached up and clung to his shoulders, probably creating a downward pressure for him too.

As I was swept along past the spot where the glass doors had stood, I saw a couple of girls who had fallen and were bleeding, and I did my best to avoid trampling them. Some brave guy was standing above them, yelling at the onrushing crowd to be careful and frantically waving his arms trying to push people aside. Then just a few feet away from me, I saw the face of Ofita, one of my sister's closest friends. The startled look she gave me was that of someone getting caught where she shouldn't be. Then I saw another of my sister's friends right behind her. It gave me the sinking premonition that Mequi must be there too. The only way that these eighth-graders could have made it here was by skipping school and taking two different buses. Suddenly, added to my fear of getting trampled was the horrible thought that my sister might be one of the girls that I had just barely avoided stepping on.

At one point, my feet were lifted completely off the ground. It felt as if I was bodysurfing in a powerful wave. I tried to remain ramrod straight and prayed for a safe landing. Finally, I came to rest with my nose squashed into the screen of a louvered window. But as luck would have it, this looked straight down at the runway where the Beatles' plane had just landed. There were four beauty queens in bathing suits waiting on the tarmac, each carrying a big bouquet to present to the Fab Quartet when they descended from the aircraft. Unfortunately, airport security had gone into emergency mode. As the steps were wheeled toward airplane door, the beauties were pushed aside. Then a big black limousine pulled up, blocking the way between them and the descending idols. The moment their feet touched the ground they were whisked into the limo, which then peeled rubber, leaving the girls with stunned, deflated looks.

As the crowd dispersed, I was relieved to see my sister, still in one piece. She seemed totally unconcerned by my having caught her. In fact, she was glad, thinking that I could now give her and her friends a ride back.

"Sorry, but I have nine in the car already. You'll have to go back the way you came."

In gratitude for my having brought them, two of my passengers ripped off one of the WQAM Beatles welcoming posters. Since it didn't fit in either the trunk or inside the car, we had to carry it on the roof, with hands sticking out of every window to keep it from flying away.

Disturbing as the experience had been, once it was over I had a feeling of utter satisfaction. This had now made me a full-fledged, *bona fide*, all-American teenager.

• 25 •

The rent-controlled fourth-floor walk-up that Ramón Antonio moved into was on Thompson Street, in the Village, just one block away from Washington Square. It was in a tenement building, with laundry lines draped across a sunless air-well and hallways that echoed with Italian, Yiddish, and Ukrainian, and smelled of garlic, oregano, and cat piss. The Eastern European women who had raised families and lived there for decades had now been infiltrated by a group of Cuban refugees, all of whom were somehow involved in the performing arts.

It was Henry Boyer, an Argentine dancer who became a headliner at Tropicana, who told Ramón Antonio that one of the *viejas* had died and there was a vacancy in the building. Henry had created somewhat of a stir back in Havana, when the husband of one of the city's richest women left her to move in with him. Since arriving in New York, he had already been in the chorus of two Broadway shows that called for exotic-looking dancers. And he had recently been cast in a new musical about Manhattan fortune-telling Gypsies, called "Bajour."

As the building's super opened the Houdiniesque lock-filled door of the recently vacated apartment, he asked Ramón Antonio how many people would be living there. His reply was, "Six million." The man did not seem amused by what he took as an attempt at a joke.

"I'm dead serious. That's the population of Cuba. And if any of my countrymen needs a place to stay, my door will be open to them."

Despite suspecting that he had a crackpot on his hands, the super offered him a lease for seventy dollars a month. This still did not seem cheap to a person with no income or a prospect of that changing anytime soon. Ramón Antonio needed to find someone to split the rent with—quick. Then in came Jorge Diaz, a friend of a friend. Jorge, another recent arrival from Cuba, had been in advertising but was for the time being working as a cashier at Tad's Steak House, on 14th Street, where one could eat a full T-bone steak dinner for a dollar twenty-nine. He always managed to sneak off with some food at the end of his shift, which also helped enormously in reducing grocery bills.

These tenement buildings originally had communal bathrooms in the hallways, but those had long since been done away with. Ramón Antonio's apartment now had a rusty metal shower stall right in the middle of the kitchen, and also a tiny water closet with a doll-sized sink and a toilet that you could barely sit on without your knees hitting the opposite wall. Still, he was thrilled to have found a place in New York, and one in which he was surrounded by kindred spirits.

Another artistic resident of the building, just one floor below, was Carlitos Rafart. He had been an actor in Cuba, performing in theater as well as *telenovelas*. Like everyone else leaving the country, he had only been allowed one suitcase. Unlike most people's, his had been filled with theatrical memorabilia. He owned two dinner plates and three glasses, but the walls of his little apartment were covered with photos of himself in roles that ranged from *Yerma* to *Sweet Bird of Youth*.

Carlitos was washing dishes at a restaurant during the day so that he could be free at night to rehearse with a group that was trying to start a Spanish-language theater company. Ramón Antonio thought this was a total pipe dream, and was determined to find himself a realistic job, one that had nothing whatsoever to do with the arts.

He had just come home from a long day of futile interviews and was struggling with his multiple door locks, when a hulking man with long-lashed, inquisitive eyes crept up and startled him.

"Are you my new neighbor?" His voice was squeaky but resounding.

"I guess I will be, if I ever learn to open this *hija de puta* door."

The man's laughter echoed through the stairwell as he held out his hand. "Well, I'm right across from you. My name is Min."

Ramón Antonio shook his hand and returned to the unyielding locks. "Are you part Chinese?"

Min roared again. "*No, mijo*. It's short for Benjamin. Benjamin Ariza, from Sagua La Grande. One-hundred percent *Cubano*. Though I did play an Asian in *Madama Butterfly*."

"Oh," Ramón Antonio stopped his key jiggling. "You sing opera?"

"In the shower. But I was an extra. You know, scenic decoration. I'm actually a dresser."

"At the Met?"

"Uh-huh. Corelli and Bergonzi refuse to have anyone else. And they're the top tenors."

"I know that well. I've been an opera fan since I was six. And the first thing I plan to do when I can afford it is treat myself to hearing Maria Callas."

"*Ay, mijo!*" Min's wrist did a pirouette. "Next time La Callas sings I'll ask Carlo or Franco to get you a comp."

"You could do that?"

"I can do lots of things." He gave an impish smile and grabbed Ramón Antonio's keys. Within two seconds the door creaked open. Then he struck a macho pose. "Everyone thinks basses and baritones are more masculine, but they should hang out backstage at the Met sometime."

Ramón Antonio developed an instant rapport with Min. They were soon spending hours listening to opera together. After long days of fruitless job searches, Min's stories lifted my uncle's spirits.

"If one more singer defects from behind that iron curtain, I'm quitting."

"You don't like Russian singers?"

"Oh, I love their singing. Who else could do a decent Boris Godunov? What I can't stand is undressing them."

"How come?"

"*Mijo*, because I have to spend half my salary on air fresheners. Mind you, I'm not blaming the poor Russian singers. I blame the communist system that didn't show them any deodorant ads. Now this sensitive Cuban nose has to pay for the failings of Marx and Lenin."

Min offered to use his connections to try and get Ramón Antonio a job as a wardrobe assistant. But Ramón Antonio pointed out that he could barely dress himself.

It was Augusto de la Soiré, another neighbor, and a former aspiring actor now taking night courses in sociology at Baruch College, who suggested, "Have you thought about becoming a social worker?"

Ramón Antonio laughed.

"I'm serious," Augusto insisted. "The system keeps running into trouble dealing with our people."

Ramón Antonio wondered what he meant by "our people."

"Spanish speakers, *chico!* The city's desperate to hire bilinguals. Real ones. Not the kind who say they're fluent, then can't get through one sentence without a 'you know' or 'I mean.'"

"But I don't know the first thing about social work."

"Neither did I, and now I'm up for a supervising position. I'm telling you," he winked, "if I could fake it, so can you."

• 26 •

Tia Babi was still determined to hold onto the house until her mother was gone, but Mamá Elvira was heading into her late nineties and still going strong. Meanwhile, they kept falling further behind on their property taxes.

"We have three choices," Andres told his mother-in-law, "freeze to death, starve, or go to jail."

But Tia Babi had come up with a different solution, one that she thought was brilliant.

"I have decided to start renting rooms."

"To whom?"

"I'm sure we'd find lots of winos, if we were closer to the Bowery," Mari joked.

"Please keep quiet and listen." Tia Babi explained that they had four perfectly nice empty rooms up on the fifth floor.

"Empty? They're stacked with junk all the way up to the ceiling," Mari reminded her. "Most of it not even ours."

"Right. And it's about time we stop feeling responsible for things that people left here decades ago."

The promises to retrieve these items, unfulfilled during the first exile, remained unfulfilled. There were suitcases and hatboxes, winter coats now long out of fashion, and wrapped-up packages of who-knows-what still stacked away in those unused rooms.

"I was thinking that Maria can help me clear all that out."

"Me?" Maria Regueros held up her canes as a reminder of her limitations.

"You better earn your keep," Andres teased her, "or she might rent your room out too."

"Laugh," Tia Babi continued, "but four rooms, at a hundred a month each, will be an enormous help."

"A hundred?" Mari chuckled. "You're hallucinating, Mamá."

"To live in a townhouse, practically on Fifth Avenue? Of course we can get that. Probably more." Tia Babi suggested that they start spreading the word around Miami.

"Why there?"

"People we know must have daughters coming here to study . . . at Marymount or Sacred Heart. It would be less expensive than a dormitory. And probably safer these days."

Her last statement intrigued Andres. "Oh, you mean, start a kind of . . . bed and breakfast for young ladies."

"Forget it!" Mari jumped in. "I will not have my husband surrounded by a bunch of hormonal teenagers." Then she grinned. "But perhaps we could rent to nice young men."

"Why not both?" said Andres.

"And turn my house into a bordello? No, no, no!"

"I know it's none of my business," said Maria Regueros, "but girls *are* messier than boys . . . and clog up bathroom drains with their hair."

"They're a bigger responsibility too," Mari agreed. "God forbid one of them should get pregnant."

"We would not be renting to *that* kind of girl, *hija*."

"Potentially they're *all* 'that kind of girl,' Mamá."

Andres pointed out that young men were also more likely to sneak *that* kind of girl into their room and cause real trouble. He was all for sticking to girls.

"That's it then." Tia Babi cast the deciding vote. "We will rent to nice young ladies from well-known families. That should keep us going until this Fidel nightmare is over."

NICE YOUNG LADIES from respectable Cuban families, in need of a moderately priced room in New York, turned out to be a scarce commodity. So when the prospect of renting to Margarita and Isabelita, great-granddaughters of another ex-president, came up, Tia Babi was delighted—even though their ancestor had once also been a political rival of Papá Gerardito.

Their parents now lived in Palm Beach, having deemed exile in Miami to be too plebeian. Unlike other Cubans who had settled in that fashionable town, however, they were almost as broke as anyone lining up at the refugee center. What they did seem to have was an enormous talent for keeping up appearances.

Through the influence of a relative, scholarships had been procured for Margarita and Isabelita at the nearby Duchesne Academy finishing school. Their family had already spread the word that they would be staying as guests of the Machados in their elegant East Side townhouse.

The two young women appeared at the door one afternoon, looking like escapees from *Mademoiselle*, and carrying their mother's monogrammed pre-Castro luggage. They had brought a vast wardrobe, collected at Worth Avenue thrift shops, plus an equally large set of expectations—which were dashed the moment they saw their rooms.

After the cleanup that Tia Babi and Maria Regueros had done, and also Andres' spackling and paint jobs, the rooms looked quite charming. Tia Babi was especially proud of the bedspreads, which looked like expensive brocade but had been bought for a song at Lamston's.

Margarita frowned at the big antique desk that Tia Babi had made Andres move there. "It doesn't leave room for much else, does it?"

"Well, I thought it would be useful for your studying."

"But where will my friends sit when they visit?"

"Oh, you're welcome to entertain them in one of the parlors."

Mari took the girls down to the second floor, which had been collecting dust again. And to comply with Andres' imposed frugality, every lamp and chandelier had minimal wattage.

This time, it was Isabelita who frowned. "Is that all the light there is here?"

"If you want bright lights, dear, entertain your friends at Chock Full O'Nuts."

Margarita and Isabelita soon developed very active social lives, but they made sure none of their friends ever set one foot inside the Machados' townhouse. They were always running off someplace and staying out till all hours. Tia Babi, who felt a responsibility for them, would stay awake until she heard the elevator going up and her boarders' footsteps on the fifth-floor landing. After a few weeks she began to wonder whether losing sleep was worth their monthly two hundred dollars. One night she had her fill.

"*Muchachitas*, do you realize it's after two A.M.?"

"*Ay*, really?" They feigned surprise. "The friends we were with wouldn't let us leave the party."

"Party? I thought you had gone to someone's house to study."

"We did. But then she invited us to the Waldorf . . . for a prince's birthday."

"Oh, a prince," Tia Babi decided that on top of being snooty, they were fanciful liars.

"No, really! A Saudi prince. He's a nephew of the present king, and is studying at Georgetown with a good friend of ours," said Margarita.

"Can you believe he asked for my number?" said Isabelita. "I suppose one would have to convert to marry someone like that . . . but hey, then I'd be a princess!"

Tia Babi wondered what the good sisters at Duchesne would think about one of their scholarship pupils considering a conversion to Islam. "*Mija*, men like this prince keep their wives under veils. I can assure you that they would never seriously consider any woman who would go up to their hotel room."

"Oh, it wasn't a room. It was an entire floor of the towers. Overlooking all Manhattan."

"Whatever it was. All you two were to him was a potential conquest."

The girls did not appreciate reality checks. "We're both over eighteen. In New York that makes us adults."

"I don't care whether you're eighteen or eighty. While you're in this house you are *my* responsibility. So next time your parents call and I have no idea where you are, I will not lie to them."

"Well, if you mention that we're with a prince, they'll love it."

Tia Babi decided that being broke was no reason to put up with insolence. The next day she told Mari and Andres that she had had a change of mind. "If Saudi princes is what they're after, I'll tell their parents to find them another place."

But by now the others had gotten used to the extra income.

"After all the trouble we went through to find someone you approved of, Mamá, now you're going to get rid of them?"

"I need to sleep again, in peace."

"Then I'll get you some strong sleeping pills," said Mari.

"And what will I tell their parents when one of them gets into trouble? Because believe me, if they keep this up, one of them will."

Maria Regueros, who usually tried to keep her opinions to herself, waddled over. "If you mean *unwed*-trouble, Señora, I would not worry. These girls today are too smart." Then she qualified her statement. "Unless, of course, one of them decided to trap somebody, like a Saudi prince. But even in the worst case, you think that her family, who cares so much about appearances, would let anyone else find out?"

"There!" Andres felt vindicated. "Our in-house philosopher has spoken. Now you can sleep with total peace of mind, and we can keep on getting their two hundred dollars."

• 27 •

My hands became sweaty tropical jungles as I waited at the Coral Gables terminal for Gina Galifante's bus to pull in. The junior prom was coming up, and I had made up my mind to invite her. It would be my first formal date ever. I had already meant to ask her the last two times I ran into her but then had lost my nerve. I was determined that today was it.

The bus terminal was a wonderful crossroads through which students from various local high schools had to pass to get their connecting lines. It also had a great bookshop, at which one could hang out to browse and socialize. I would faithfully buy *Mad* magazine there, and sometimes, if I had money leftover, also *Classic Monsters*.

The first time I went through the terminal in my freshman year, I was startled to see the sign on a bathroom door, which said "Whites Only." There had been a similar sign above one of the water fountains. The Civil Rights movement was now doing away with things like that, but even though they were no longer enforced, these vestiges still remained.

When I saw Gina step out of the Biltmore Way line, my temples began to drip also.

"Louie!" She seemed glad to see me.

My lips had gone bone-dry, so I licked them, hoping Gina wouldn't think I was sticking my tongue out at her. "Uh . . . I was wondering, if, uh . . . you'd like to, uh, come with me to the prom a week from Friday."

"Oh, Louie. I wish you'd asked me sooner. I already have a date.

But I look forward to seeing you there!" She ran off to catch her connection, and I felt like an utter fool.

I had been so consumed by the experience that I never noticed a couple of my sister's friends standing nearby. By dinnertime, my whole family knew I had been turned down.

"Maybe she doesn't like Cubans," Gerardo, whose friends now called him Jerry, said encouragingly. "Some girls in my class just don't."

"Of course she likes him," Mequi disagreed. "My friend Ofita said she was drooling."

"She was not!" I was mortified.

"Well, it's not the end of the world, *mijo*." My mother suggested that I go ahead and ask someone else.

"Yes, maybe someone Cuban," my father added.

I just wanted the conversation dropped. "I'll think about it, okay?"

The next day I ran into Susie Benson on the Salvatore Park bus. I gathered up my courage again and stammered through a second invitation.

"Oh, Louie, thanks so much. But my dad won't let me date till I turn sixteen."

Despite my father's fear that we would lose our roots, he continued to plant lots of his own, right into American soil. His passion for greenery had now expanded beyond our modest-size lot and into the entire neighborhood. Lady Bird Johnson, the president's wife, whose best-known catchphrase was "Everyone should plant a tree, a shrub, or a buuuuuush," should have given him a medal. I would often find him talking to our neighbors, advising them on the kind of things they should plant and whether they needed bright light or semi-shade. He would also recommend their using the special Miracle-Gro formula that was sold at Sears so that their new plantings would mature quicker. He even splurged on five four-foot-tall flamboyants, or royal poincianas, and planted them all along our street. These tropical trees reminded him of Cuba, and he could already envision the lovely canopy of orange-red blossoms that they would create each spring, once they matured.

One small drawback to planting in our new neighborhood was that once you dug beyond a couple of inches you encountered cement-hard coral rock. I was sweating and wielding a pickaxe to help Papi dig the holes for his flamboyants when he once again brought up the subject of my junior prom.

"I hope you're not turning into an oyster again. You *have* to go to that dance."

"But I've already asked two girls."

"You haven't asked any Cuban ones. And you know plenty."

His prodding finally made me get on the phone and call Gloria, whose parents knew mine quite well. I had always enjoyed talking to her at our Cuban exile parties, and she seemed to share my skeptical view of them.

Like a nice proper girl, Gloria said that she would have to ask her mother, but then she came right back and told me that she'd be delighted. Then two days before the prom, my friend Claudio called to ask if he and his date could ride with us. I also knew Silvia, the girl he'd invited, who was Cuban too, and very nice. So I thought it would be fun for the four of us to go together. Claudio had said that he would be at Silvia's, so after picking up Gloria, who looked beautiful in a light summery dress, we headed over there. Silvia looked lovely too, but as Claudio stepped out of her house I noticed a disgruntled expression. Seconds later I realized why. Silvia's mother emerged, looking even more dolled up than her daughter.

"Luisito! So nice of you to take us to the prom." One whiff of her pungent perfume almost gagged me.

Claudio had not been warned that Silvia's loveliness came with strings attached. The second we pulled into the school parking lot, I grabbed Gloria's hand and rushed toward the cafeteria, hoping no one would associate us with the 1950s-vintage lady. Then Claudio did the same with Silvia.

"*Muchachos, esperen!* Wait!" I heard her calling from behind us.

"Is the older one yours too?" the guy collecting tickets asked me as Silvia's mother came panting in.

"No, no. She's *his*." I pointed at Claudio, who did not appreciate my gesture.

The lights in the cafeteria were romantically low, and couples were already gravitating to the darker corners, where they could make out and maybe cop a feel or two. The music was much too loud for conversation, so after finding a table to leave the girls' purses, we both escorted our dates onto the dance floor.

Fortunately, Silvia's mother had gone off to sit with a couple of other chaperones, but each time I spun around I could see her eagle eyes, fixed not just upon her daughter and Claudio, but also on Gloria and me. Still, I noticed Claudio inching closer and closer to Silvia. Then as the band broke into a sultry rendition of "It's the End of the World," Gloria whispered, "Oh, I love that song!" which encouraged me to pull her closer too. A second later, from all the way across the dance floor and loud enough to top the electric guitars, I heard, "*Sepárense! Vamos!*" "You're too close!" Our self-appointed guardian was waving her arms like spastic fishtails.

Mortified by her mother, Silvia headed for the ladies room, and Gloria excused herself to go keep her company. Claudio shrugged helplessly and lit up a cigarette. I decided to escape to the only place where Mrs. Eagle Eye couldn't follow.

A few of my classmates were huddled by one of the toilet stalls; passing around a bottle of Seagram's that one of them had sneaked in.

"Hey, harem man! One chick alone not good enough for you?"

"Where'd you find your big mama?"

"She's not mine."

"Well, whosever she is, there's plenty of her to go around."

"Yeah, and keep you busy for days just tryin' to find what you're lookin' for."

The men's room echoed with laughter.

When I got home, the light on my mother's side of the bed was still on, as it always was, no matter what time we arrived. "How did it go, Luisma?" I heard her sleepy voice call out as I tiptoed to my room.

"All right." I wasn't about to go into it at this late hour.

"See?" My father stirred also. "I knew you'd have fun with a Cuban."

· 28 ·

Me cago en Fidel!" Ramón Antonio cursed each time that his new winter boots sank into a slush puddle, or slipped as he tried to maneuver the mounds of compacted snow that had accumulated at every street corner. There were at least a dozen of these between his apartment and his new office, on Great Jones Street, in the East Village. "*Coño!* I shit on Fidel again!"

By eight A.M. the social services reception room was already packed. Before entering the building, Ramón Antonio stopped to finish a cigarette, then took one deep breath. It was too early in the day to confront the smell of stale liquor and unwashed bodies.

The rules for dealing with people in your caseload were cut-and-dried, but he had already decided that most of these were ineffective, and he was refining them with his personal touch. Some of his clients seemed totally unreachable, but he found himself becoming very motivated by those who he felt had a real chance of being helped. The young man waiting for him on this particular morning appeared to be one of those. After ushering him into his cubbyhole, Ramón Antonio opened the case file: Rudy Wiekowski. White male. Nineteen. Five foster homes and multiple arrests—mostly for petty theft and possession of marijuana.

"Hello, Rudy. I'm Mr. Crusellas, your new supervisor." He shook his hand with a smile, which Rudy did not return. "So what's going on?"

"Same old shit. My mom kicked me out."

"How come?"

Rudy shrugged. "Who knows?"

Ramón Antonio gave him a sarcastic look.

"Okay. Maybe 'cause I called her new boyfriend a fucking scumbag."

"Oh. I would have kicked you out too. Why did you call him that?"

"'Cause that's what he is." Rudy avoided looking at Ramón Antonio and stared instead at the basket of kittens on the Humane Society calendar that a previous supervisor had left on the wall. "The son of a bitch tried to get into my pants. And this time I ain't going back there, or to no foster home either. They all suck. So you got other ideas?"

Ramón Antonio had none.

"That kid's been a pain in the ass since he was first sent here," said the office supervisor. "Tell him he's got to go back or you're putting him in jail."

Ramón Antonio decided that there had to be a better alternative. After consulting with colleagues, he learned that a teen shelter had just opened on Bleecker Street, only a block from his own apartment. It still wasn't an ideal solution, but at least Rudy would have a bed and a roof over his head. He even offered to go check the place out with him, and on the way, he made a detour via Tad's Steak House.

"Are you hungry?" He saw the boy hesitate. "Don't worry. It's on me."

When his roommate, Jorge, was at the register, he would let him get by with only a minimal charge, so Ramón Antonio could afford to be magnanimous. Rudy attacked his T-bone with the subtlety of a piranha. When the plate had been licked clean, he shoved the tray aside.

"I don't know what it is, man. My whole life it's been the same shit."

"What do you mean?"

"Getting in trouble for things that ain't my fault."

Ramón Antonio looked him in the eye, already getting drawn into Rudy's private life. "Look, I really do want to help . . . But you'll have to learn to trust me."

• • •

While the decorative objects that Min Ariza surrounded himself with were gaudy to an extreme, Ramón Antonio had found his neighbor to be truly genuine. Even more important, Min could make him laugh. He was a respite from Jorge, who would come home in a grumpy mood and smelling of fried onion rings, or Henry, who now kept moaning about having to play a Gypsy, lost in the chorus, after having been a headliner at Tropicana.

"You want to hear how I got out of Cuba? It will make you believe in miracles. I had applied for my exit permit, but years kept going by and I wasn't hearing anything. I couldn't understand why. Then one day, Rodolfito, this nasty *miliciano* from my town, who hated me since the day we started first grade together, drove by in his patrol car and saw me at a corner, wearing my best Sunday outfit. So he slowed down and yelled, 'Benjamin, *maricón!* As long as I have a breath in my body you're not getting out of this country.' But as he yelled he kept on driving and didn't see the truck crossing the intersection. *CATAPLÚN!* Rodolfito was killed instantly, and one month later I was here in New York City."

The lighthearted Met dresser had also become his confidant.

"*Ay*, Min. I'm not sure I did the right thing by leaving this boy in that shelter."

"*Cariño*, be careful!" He pointed a warning finger. "Remember how much the Marschallin in *Rosenkavalier* suffered for getting involved with young Octavian. Have a pistachio!" He placed a faux-silver bowl in front of Ramón Antonio, then went to his turntable and gently set an album on it. "*Voila!* La Nilsson's *Turandot*! I'm feeling Chinesey tonight. Let's order some dumplings later." Then Min opened a drawer and took out an exotic tiara, which he held up like a Holy Grail. "This sat on Renata Scotto's head when she sang the role of Liú."

"But Liú's a slave girl."

"*Mijo*, it's opera! You can't have the lead slave dressed in rags. You should have seen the tiara that Birgit wore. I would have loved to bring that one home, but this apartment isn't big enough."

Like Napoleon crowning himself, Min lowered Renata's headdress onto his balding pate, then moved the needle ahead to Liú's big aria.

"*Signore, ascolta!*" He recited the tragic words along with Scotto. "*Non regge pi*ù . . ." "I can bear it no longer."

Loud banging suddenly made the Cuban Princess Liú jump a foot up in the air. When Min landed again, the needle scratched through the entire aria. He cracked the door open and found Desi, the least gregarious of the building's Cuban residents.

"You know, *some* people sleep normal hours, and your loud *puta música* is keeping me awake. So turn it down!" Desi strutted back to his apartment and slammed the door shut.

"*Dios mio!* What an unexpected cameo!" Min grinned. "There we were with Princess Turandot, and who pops in? Mephistopheles!" He put the needle back to the beginning of the aria then raised the volume all the way.

When Ramón Antonio got to his office the following morning, Rudy was already waiting. "Some fuckin' asshole tried to steal my things while I was sleeping. Then *I* got blamed when his face got smashed in."

Rudy looked like a mess and was obviously starving. He suggested that they go to Tad's Steakhouse again, but it was Jorge's day off, and Ramón Antonio wasn't willing to pay full price.

"So what do we do with you now?"

"You tell me. You're my supervisor."

Ramón Antonio decided that it was useless to consult his own supervisor again. Rudy was determined not to return to his mother's, and taking him to another shelter would probably end with similar results. This seemed to leave only one alternative.

"You're bringing a criminal into our apartment?" Jorge Diaz was furious. "What are you, insane? He'll steal everything. Maybe even kill us."

Ramón Antonio assured him that Rudy was harmless. "I have an inner radar about these things. He's just had a lot of bad luck and is starved for affection."

"Then let him go get it somewhere else."

Ramón Antonio tried to keep their voices down, since Rudy was sitting in the kitchen, having a coffee. "Jorge, we're refugees. We know what it's like to be thrown out of our homes . . . and this is just for a few days. I promise to keep an eye on him every minute."

Jorge finally gave in, reluctantly. "Okay, two days! And I'm not sharing the living room with him."

Rudy had already been scouting around and had seen that besides the living room sofa, there was only a narrow bed in the tiny room. "So where the hell will I sleep?"

"I give you three guesses." Ramón Antonio began to spread a blanket out on the floor, which Rudy was not thrilled about.

"Hey, neither of us is very big. If we lie in different directions we can both fit on the bed."

Ramón Antonio knew that he was already stretching the rules far enough. "You're sleeping on the floor."

In the middle of the night, he was awakened by Rudy's snores. The boy's feet were poking out from under the blanket, and the light filtering through the window made his toes look like a row of pink cactus bunnies. Ramón Antonio lay there, staring for a moment, then tugged at the blanket to cover them and turned away to try to get some sleep.

He had every intention of taking the boy with him in the morning to start looking for other accommodations. But when he came out from a long steaming shower, he found that Rudy had gotten into the bed and was cozily curled up. Now he felt reluctant to disrupt his peaceful sleep. Jorge had already left for Tad's, and his inner radar told him that it would be safe to leave Rudy alone for a couple of hours. After all, there was nothing of much value in the whole apartment. So he took a pen and scribbled, "Please come to my office as soon as you get up."

• 29 •

When I got home from school I found my mother ironing. We now had a little old lady, Isolina, who had been a nurse in Cuba and combed her hair like Queen Victoria, coming one afternoon a week to iron our uniforms and my father's dress shirts. But Isolina had been sick, and clothes were piling up. Mami was absentmindedly staring toward our pool, which was much smaller than our previous one. For some reason, the image made me think of a picture that had hung in one of my classrooms back in Cuba. In it, the Virgin Mary was kneeling by a well, washing what looked like baby Jesus' diapers. I visualized a swap—Mami scrubbing rings-around-the-collar at some muddy water hole in Nazareth, while the Virgin dipped diapers into our turquoise pool.

"What are you staring at?"

"Nothing." I sat down nearby to do my homework and dug a big heavy volume out of my school bag, one that I had checked out for a report. But something had been nagging at me, so I decided I might as well ask. "Why do so many books say awful things about Papá Gerardito?"

"We've gone over this before, Luisma. When someone's in power it's impossible to please everyone. Conflicts arise . . . and often get ugly. Why? What are you reading?"

"Just something I got from the library."

"May I see it?" When I hesitated, she plunked down her iron. "Come on, let me see it."

"Okay, but you're not gonna like it."

I handed her the book, which was titled, *The Pageant of Cuba*, by

Hudson Strode. Mami pushed aside the shirt she was working on and began to leaf through it. It didn't take long for her to come across a chapter that was totally devoted to her grandfather, boldly titled, "The Reign of Terror." Her forefinger raced down the pages until she reached another chapter, this one called "The Flight of the Beast." I had used a pencil to underline a few phrases, like "fascistic hubris" and "unmatched megalomania." She slammed the book shut and shook it like a dishrag.

"This garbage was in your school library?"

"Uh-huh. And I've found others that say pretty much the same things . . . like his having had a good first term but then extending it and becoming a dictator."

She stared back out toward the pool for a moment. "Look, I'm no historian, but I can tell you that he was a good man and loved his country. I know that he made some mistakes, extending his term being the biggest one . . . but there was no opposition when he did that, in fact, mostly just fawning applause. It was only after the stock market crashed in 'twenty-nine and sugar became worthless that all the troubles began. I loved my grandfather, so I realize it's hard for me to be impartial, but I do think that a lot of unfair things have been said about him. You're free to make up your own mind, of course, but I do hope that you will at least try to be a fair judge when you write your report." With that, she returned to her ironing.

It was my sister Mequi's turn to do the dishes. The rest of us were watching *The Dick Van Dyke Show*, when the phone rang. It was Tiana, to say that the doctor had just been to see Abuela. He did not expect her to make it through the night.

Right away we all got into the car and headed over. Abuela was slightly propped up on her bed; her eyes were closed, and she was breathing softly. Her cheeks were so pink it seemed hard to believe that she could be close to the end. Tiana and the nurse, Lucrecia, had dressed her in a pale blue nightgown and placed a small matching bow on one side of her snow-white hair.

As we gathered at the bedside, hearing her breathing grow fainter, I looked around at the modest surroundings and thought about the incredibly privileged life that she had previously led. I felt guilty for having ever complained about those endless Cuban news broadcasts that she had listened to. It had been the only thing keeping alive her hopes of returning. Now she was about to become the first one in our family for whom that dream would never come true.

Standing at the foot of her bed, I suddenly felt like making one final contact, then reached under the sheet and began to caress her feet gently. While I did so, the gaps between her breaths became longer, until one last tiny spasm conveyed that it was over.

My father, whom I had been standing next to, turned to embrace me, his shoulders quivering with controlled sobs, and he held on to me for a long time.

Abuela's *velorio* was at the Caballero Funeral Home, on 8th Street, which friends of the family, long in that profession back in Cuba, had opened with much success. Despite their being sad occasions, these early-exile funerals became gathering points for people who had known each other forever but, now consumed with the rebuilding of their lives, rarely had time to see each other. Abuela would have been pleased by the huge turnout that her death elicited. And if some of the overly effusive greetings and loud conversations seemed more in keeping with a cocktail party, I thought that it also helped turn her final farewell into a celebration of a long, exceptional life.

• 30 •

Tia Babi was heading over to St. Ignatius for the weekday mass that she often attended, when she noticed the envelope that someone had left on the house's service entrance. It was from the coal company, to say that they would not be delivering another lump until they received the full overdue amount. Andres, who was supposed to be handling those payments, had apparently not done so for more than two months. This time, instead of the usual one-dollar candle that she lit at the altar of St. Francis Xavier, Tia Babi decided to light two.

St. Ignatius had always had its share of celebrity parishioners, but now that Jackie Kennedy had moved to the neighborhood, Tia Babi would often see her there. It made her feel a bit guilty that a sighting of the ex-first lady would always distract her from her prayers, but then upon returning home she would give the others a detailed report of every single item that Jackie was wearing, right down to the style of her current sunshades. Jackie had also become an occasional customer at Mari's bookshop. Mari had called us to relay every word that they exchanged on the day she sold Jackie a copy of Truman Capote's *In Cold Blood*.

"But she hasn't set one foot back in the store since Jerry put on our window that new book about Joseph Kennedy—the one where they talk about his bootlegging and Nazi sympathies."

Jackie had moved into the same building that Mari's friend Nelly lived in, on Fifth and 85th Street. It annoyed her that Nelly now spoke of Jackie as if they were intimates.

"Trust me, darling. I've crossed Jackie's path while walking down the street with Nelly. She acknowledges her the same as she would a cute Pekinese."

But beyond the coal company's refusal to make another delivery, which Andres assured Tia Babi they could live with because *The Farmer's Almanac* had predicted an unseasonably warm March, her candles to St. Francis appeared to be working.

There were now *two* more boarders in the house, and these happened to be male. One of them was José Emilio's nephew, Tony. The other, Fernando Mendoza, came from yet another family that ours had known forever. Both were working day jobs while taking night courses at Fordham. When they arrived, the question arose again about the propriety of putting two handsome young men on the same floor as two party girls. But the prospect of the extra income overrode the propriety. Tia Babi opted for putting the guys as far as she could from Margarita and Isabelita and trusting their upstanding upbringing, as well as Maria Regueros' chaperoning.

Although Maria liked the new additions far more than she had the previous two, their arrival also meant more towels and sheets for her to wash. She had barely been keeping up with the requirements of Margarita and Isabelita, who insisted on having their "bed linens" changed punctually every Monday.

The washer in the basement was of World War II vintage, and the rinse cycle did not work too well anymore. Soap powder often got caked along the creases, and Maria would have to cart things over to the sink and rinse them by hand. There was also no dryer, nor the prospect of having one. The simple process of hanging up a sheet became an ordeal for the half-crippled housekeeper. She would fling it over the clothesline with one hand while balancing herself with a single cane. Then, holding both canes again, she would limp from one side to the other tugging at the sheet, like an artist stretching her canvas. On sunny days, or days that promised to be, she hung things out in the small back patio. On rainy ones, and all winter long, the laundry hung like soggy ghosts from wires that had been strung up near the furnace sometime in prehistory. The family was used to the end results by now, but Margarita and Isabelita kept complaining about the smoky smell of their "bed linens," and the soot particles that often got stuck within the felt of their towels and smeared over their freshly washed faces.

"You should make laundry optional, Señora," Maria Regueros suggested one day, clearly exhausted by the lengthy ritual. "For what they're paying now, they can take their towels and sheets to the corner Chinese laundry. If they still want us to do them, then they can pay extra."

Tia Baby thought it was a sensible idea but then was too embarrassed to broach the subject of money again with her boarders, and things remained as they were.

Andres was still going to Philadelphia every week for his vague prime materials import job, but whatever it was that he did, he seemed to be able to do more of it now via telephone and stay at home. This time around, he had found something besides liquor to keep up his spirits.

While carting down to the basement all the boxes and trunks that they had cleared from the fifth floor rooms, he had become curious about their contents. He was still very aware of Batista's rich exile in Portugal and of General Perón's in Madrid. He also knew that Trujillo had accumulated a fortune in banks across the world. In view of this, he had never let go of the hope that his wife's grandfather might have left something somewhere that they had overlooked, even if just a small fraction of those millions that he had been accused of taking. So he spent hours poring through decades-old business records, bank receipts, and faded letters, like a detective convinced that he was closing in on his mark. He never did this while Maria Regueros was doing the laundry, but she had caught him sneaking down the pantry stairs on various occasions and had become suspicious.

"You are spending lots of time down there, Caballero Andres. Is there a problem with the furnace?"

"No, no. Just rearranging those boxes, to avoid a fire hazard."

Under one naked lightbulb, he read page after page of squiggles, often straining to decipher the penmanship. But the clues he kept hoping to find were not materializing. The ledgers were full of commonplace entries: Sacred Heart tuition payments, grocery deliveries from La Marqueta, a new refrigerator. Defeated, he would go back upstairs to pour himself a stiff vodka. But his drinking now kept being interrupted by emergencies on the fifth floor.

The first time Maria Regueros asked him to go upstairs, he was resentful. Margarita had overloaded one of the ancient sockets. Now her hair blower wasn't working, and she was already late for a party. It took no electrical wizardry to replace the blown fuse, but Margarita was so grateful that she planted a big kiss on Andres' cheek. The second time, Isabelita wanted to take a bath, but one of the ceramic water faucets kept falling off, which made it impossible for her to control the water temperature. She was impressed by how quickly Andres reattached it firmly. Soon his handyman services were called upon almost daily.

"Andres, my clothing rack collapsed." "Andres, my window's stuck and I can't open it." "Andres, my door is warped and I can't close it."

Sometimes he was called upon to fix more than just inanimate objects.

"*Ay*, Andres. I forgot to put on slippers and got a huge splinter on my foot."

He was more than happy to put down his drink and rush to the rescue. After getting a pin and sterilizing it, he told Isabelita to lie back on the bed, plopped her foot on his lap, then began the delicate surgical procedure.

This was the scene that Mari came upon when she tiptoed upstairs, following a disturbing hunch. "What the hell's going on?"

Andres jumped, jabbing the needle right into Isabelita's foot.

"*Coño!*" A most unladylike curse escaped her virginal lips.

"She has a splinter," Andres flashed an innocent grin. "You know these terrible floors."

"Yes, and so should she. I've warned her."

"I know, but the phone rang," Isabelita replied, in an appeal for sympathy, "and I'd been waiting for an important call."

"Then try not to be so desperate the next time." Mari snatched the needle from Andres. "Here, I'll do that."

"Thanks!" Isabelita quickly retrieved her foot. "I'll do it myself."

31

When it came time to apply for college, I knew exactly where I wanted to go—any place within the island of Manhattan.

"Forget it!" my father said. He felt there were too many distractions there, as well as idiosyncratic relatives. My next move was to find schools that were within a reasonable distance of the city. With brazen optimism, I sent for an application to Princeton.

"Forget it!" my father said again. "Ivy League schools these days are nothing but leftist incubators."

I then asked him what kind of college he had in mind.

"How about a medium-size, non-urban, Catholic one?"

Villanova University had opened a branch in Havana back in the fifties, which Fidel later confiscated along with everything else. That alone made Papi partial to the institution. But besides that, my cousin Frank was already studying there, and my Tia Fifi now lived only three blocks from the campus. Villanova also had a very good swimming team that my high-school coach had often spoken to us about. And best of all, I found out that it was only a two-hour train ride from Philadelphia to New York's Penn Station.

The truth was that a place like Princeton would have never accepted me. But despite my less-than-stellar grades, somehow Villanova did.

On the day of my departure, Papi loaded my luggage into the trunk of our Chevy, which was still hanging on after six years of constant use. Then everyone piled into it to see me off at the airport. I had so been looking forward to going away, yet now, with my goodbyes having turned into an epic, full-cast production, there was a big knot in my stomach. I had a flashback to another farewell, the day Gerardo and I were left at the military academy and our parents returned to Cuba. Throughout the multiple hugs, I did my best not to show any emotion. It was only later, as we flew somewhere over the Carolinas and I found the two pop-tarts and banana that Mami had packed in my shoulder bag, that I kind of lost it. Less than two hours gone, and I was already feeling homesick. At least it helped to know that my transition would be a gradual one. Before heading down to school for registration, I would be stopping for a few days in New York, where Mami had enlisted Mari to take me shopping for a not-too-expensive winter wardrobe.

WHEN THE TOWNHOUSE door creaked open, I was enveloped by the same mildewy smell that had so intrigued me on my prior visit.

"Darling! Welcome back to Manderley!" Mari received me with a sweeping gesture.

I had no clue of what she meant, but I liked the exotic ring of it.

"*Corazón! Bienvenido!*" Tia Babi was at the kitchen table, knitting, seated beside Mamá Elvira, who at ninety-seven still was upright and alert. Tia Babi peered at me over the top of her bifocals. "You're looking very well. But we'll have to do something about that acne.

"*Ay*, Mamá, *por Dios!*" Mari reprimanded her. "How would you like it if he'd come in and said we need to do something about your double chin?"

"*Bueno, muchacho!*" Maria Regueros made her presence at the far end of the room be known. "No kiss for this old lady?"

As I headed over I noticed that her legs looked more bowed than ever. The gap between her knobby knees and thick ankles now formed an elongated heart.

"*Dios mio*, I *am* getting old," she sniffled. "To think that I started with this family when your *mami* was much younger than you are now."

"Maria, please," Mari winced. "Spare us the melodramatics."

Then Andres made his entrance, looking dapper in a three-piece suit and carrying a fancy briefcase. "Ah! The college boy arrived!"

"You must tell him about your new venture," Mari prodded him.

"*Ay, por favor*, not now. He just got here." Tia Babi gave me an apologetic look.

Ignoring her, Andres fiddled with the briefcase combination lock as if he were opening Fort Knox. Then he lifted the lid to reveal a glittery array of misshapen gewgaws.

"You're selling jewelry?"

"Not jewelry, darling. Art," said Mari.

Andres held up a glitzy brochure. "I'm an authorized representative for a new Dalí line. A limited edition of wearable masterpieces, signed by the maestro himself."

Mari noticed my blank look. "That's *Salvador* Dalí, dear."

There were melted watches and melted hearts, melted eyes with melting teardrops—and for the religious-minded, Andres pointed out what looked like a melted crucifix.

Tia Babi did not seem to be a fan of *the maestro*. "Come, *corazón*," she took my hand. "Enough of melted things. Let me take you up to your room. This time I put you on the fourth floor, next to José Emilio and me, in Mari and Fifi's old nursery."

AS I TUGGED at the ornate handles of a dresser drawer, one of them came off, and the whole drawer almost slid to the ground. Naphthalene balls rattled around like wayward billiards. Tia Babi had cleared the two top ones for me. The trellised rice paper that lined the drawer bottoms was brittle and curling up at the edges. As I began to put away my socks and underwear, I realized that I hadn't done this since military school. All these years Mami had been replenishing my drawers without my even giving it a second thought. Then I remembered the banana that she had packed for me in a loving farewell gesture, and I decided that the least I could do was eat it.

"You're eating a banana!" Mari's deep voice jolted me, sounding as if she'd caught me masturbating. "Relax, darling. It's just that I'm not very fond of them . . . since the banana truck incident."

"What banana truck?"

"Honestly, Luisma. I can't believe the ignorance that your mother has kept you in . . . Too much Americana. Too little family lore. But don't worry. Your *madrina* is here now to fill in the gaps." Sounding as if she'd already had a nip or two, she sat on the concave mattress, ready to tell me the story whether I wanted or not.

"When Papá Gerardito was elected, Cuba was importing everything, even eggs. Talk about being beholden to the Americans. He wanted to set the country free from that. It's one of the reasons why Washington turned against him. And if there's one thing that that island is, my dear, is fertile. Toss two garbanzos out of any window and next thing you know you have a more luxurious vine than Jack's overrated beanstalk. So your great-grandfather became determined that everyone should start consuming more national products.

"'Our own goods for our own good,' became his motto. And he declared Monday as National Products Day, hoping that everyone would eat only what we produced. So every single Monday night, families from Cabo de San Antonio to La Punta de Maisí sat down to casseroles of *ajiaco*, made with Cuban *boniatos*, *yuca*, *malanga*, *ñame*, *maíz*, *plátanos verdes*, and for those who could afford it, also a little bit of Cuban beef or *lechón*. Mamá Elvira, who was a faithful follower of this popular health food guru named Gaylord Hauser, insisted that everything we ate at Palacio be absolutely fresh. So every morning, produce trucks would line up at the palace gate to make deliveries.

"Now you would think that once all the unrest began they'd have inspected these trucks thoroughly before letting them pass through. But this was Cuba, land of trusting pats on the back and friendly handshakes. Besides, these deliveries were coming from Pepe the butcher, Paquito the egg man, Mariano the green grocer. It would have insulted them not to be trusted.

"Well, one particular Monday, apparently someone from the opposition got hold of the banana delivery truck, one that came by more than any other. I mean, can you imagine Cuban cuisine without *plátanos maduros*, *chatinos*, *fufú*. It had just pulled up to the kitchen door, when suddenly there was a huge explosion!"

"Mari, what nonsense are you telling this *muchacho*?" Tia Babi had come in without our noticing and heard part of Mari's tale. "Absolutely none of that is true."

"Are you denying that Papá Gerardito got the whole country to consume national products on Mondays?"

"No. It's the rest of it I'm referring to."

"Well, excuse me, but my whole life I've heard about that damn truck blowing up."

"It was just a faulty motor that backfired, Mari. And because of everything going on, it got a few palace guards a little overexcited. That's all," Tia Babi rolled her eyes as she turned to me. "And whatever else she tells you, please come double-check the facts with me."

I was rather sorry that she had refuted Mari's fanciful story. Same as with the sorbet bomb one, I was already picturing hundreds of flambé *plátano* missiles soaring through the air and smashing into the palace exterior, like gobs of dripping icing on a tropical wedding cake.

"Well, whatever did happen," Mari said to wrap things up, "ever since my palace childhood I have not been partial to bananas."

EARLY THE FOLLOWING morning I took a subway down to the Village and waited outside a paint-encrusted green door, listening to locks unbolt inside—and barking.

"Shut up, Plon-Plon!" My *padrino* finally managed to open the door and stood there draped in a stained terrycloth robe. "*Mi Chino!*" He embraced me. "Plon-Plon! Pipe down!" he shouted at a little black dachshund. "It's your cousin from Miami."

Ramón Antonio explained that he had named him after one of

Napoleon's nephews, and like a true Bonaparte, he seemed to have taken over the entire place. The vinyl-tile floor was littered with sections of the *New York Times*, on each of which Plon-Plon had left a yellow blotch or a couple of brown pellets.

"He was an abused dog. Can you imagine anyone hurting a sweet thing like that with cigarettes? Obviously someone high on who knows what. A friend of Henry's rescued him but couldn't keep him. So, Plon Plon found me!"

I looked around and recognized my uncle's unmistakable decorative imprint: ceiling-high shelves loaded with books and record albums. After he poured two mugfuls of coffee we sat at the tiny kitchen table, on which there was an ashtray overflowing with cigarette butts.

"I'm sorry, *cariño* . . . but I just received some bad news." He slid a letter toward me, which I quickly skimmed over. Along with it was the photo of a smiling soldier, with a dedication, "To my true father. Love always, Rudy."

"Who's Rudy?"

"Someone I think you would like . . . and will hopefully meet one day, if he makes it back. Can you imagine *me* suggesting to anyone that they join the army? I truly thought it might help break his bad patterns. Nothing else was working. But the risk of his being sent to Vietnam never even crossed my mind. I'm such an idiot." His eyes became teary.

I had never before been in a situation of needing to comfort an adult. All I could think of was to tap his hand gently and say, "I'm sure he'll make it back." Then the doorbell rang.

"Could you open, *mi chino?* I need to change Plon Plon's papers."

The vision I encountered paralyzed me for a moment. Min Ariza glided into the kitchen wearing a red kimono with gold curlicues, which, he soon explained, was one of his souvenirs from *Turandot*.

"Ah! You must be the beloved nephew." He swept me into a bear hug, then turned toward Ramón Antonio with solemnity. "I just heard, *chico*." Min enveloped him with his butterfly kimono wings, under which my uncle's shoulders trembled for a moment. "Yes, yes. Let it all out." Then, as if the chrysalis stage had quickly come to term, Min spread his wings again and stepped away. "All right, enough! Rudy's a survivor. And he would definitely hate to hear that his going to Vietnam is spoiling the visit you've so looked forward to. *Voila!*" he held out an envelope. "A present for both of you."

Curiosity got the best of my depressed uncle and he looked inside. "Theater tickets?"

"For today's matinee of *Man of La Mancha*. And I hope you realize how impossible those are to get. I had to go through Richard Kiley himself." He grinned at me, "The star of the show. I was his dresser's assistant when he did *No Strings*—a very underrated musical." Then the kimono swirled again, and Min was gone.

The show, which had just recently opened to great reviews, was playing at the Anta Theater, only two blocks from Ramón Antonio's building. It was performed in the round, and I was completely absorbed throughout. At the climactic moment, when Don Quixote climbs a long set of stairs singing "The Impossible Dream," you could feel the entire audience being swept away with sentimental idealism.

As we walked out into a pink late afternoon, Ramón Antonio said. "I hope I can bring Rudy to see this some day." Then he took my arm "Come. I'll treat you to a steak dinner."

We ambled over to Tad's Steakhouse, discussing the show and stopping occasionally for my uncle to point out some curious landmark. Luckily, his roommate Jorge was behind the cash register.

"Dios mio, Ramón!" He stared me up and down. "You didn't tell me your nephew was so handsome."

Ramón Antonio seemed annoyed by the comment but kept on scanning the posted menu. "Don't you still have the one-twenty-nine special?"

"Yes, only now it's two-thirty-eight." Then he winked. "Don't worry. I'll get you your usual discount."

When his shift ended, Jorge came to our table. "I heard *Man of La*

Mancha is very good, but I wish you could have seen our friend Henry in *Bajour*. Now *that* was something else!" It did not sound like a compliment. "So where else are you taking him, Ramón?"

"Nowhere. After this he's heading back up to his great-grandmother's."

"You know, there's a Latin American film festival at the Twelfth Street Cinema. And they're showing a Cuban one tonight." He flashed me a big smile. "I know an usher who can get us in for free."

Ramón Antonio made a point of sitting between Jorge and me, which did not make his roommate too happy. The film being shown was an adult animation, titled *Vampires in the Caribbean*. To my astonishment, it was partly a satire of my great-grandfather.

"Maybe we should go," Ramón Antonio suggested when he realized this.

"Yes, yes." Jorge seemed embarrassed. "I had no idea . . ."

But I wouldn't budge.

It was a tale about Count Maracas, a dance-crazed bloodsucker who hated the bleak Transylvanian weather and developed a secret formula that allowed him to move to the tropics. This formula called for his victims' blood to be at a specific temperature, which could only be reached by making them dance the *rumba*. Every day, he needed to find new dancers to satisfy his needs, and finding them grew increasingly difficult. Desperate, when there was no one left who could dance to his rhythm, he entered politics and passed a law forcing everyone to take *rumba* lessons. Count Maracas became President Maracas, then proclaimed himself *King* Maracas. And as if to erase any doubt of who was being satirized, his cartoon character had round horn-rimmed glasses—exactly like Papá Gerardito's.

Jorge leaned over and touched my knee. "I know the actor who did his voice. He's such a big ham. It's a miracle nobody has eaten him for *Noche Buena*."

"*Shhh!*" someone complained.

"Shoo yourself!" Jorge shouted back, then whispered to me, "The only reason he turned communist is because all the good actors left, and at last he stood a chance."

King Maracas sang a big production number in a nightclub with beds called Tropi-cama, where he ended up sucking dry an entire chorus line of *rumba*-crazed, wide-hipped Cuban beauties. Then, just as I was becoming immune to the mockery, Maracas married a pretentious Cuban *condesa*, who wore Paris couture and called herself Ooh-lala. With her big balloon breasts, she couldn't have resembled my great-grandmother less. The minute Ooh-lala was behind closed doors she ripped off her Chanel suit and turned into a blood-sucking nymphomaniac.

Ramón Antonio finally said, "I've had enough."

As I groped my way up the dark aisle, I turned to sneak one last glimpse of the musical number now building to a climax.

Skeletal peddlers marched like zombies through the streets of Havana singing a dirge-like *rumba*—"The Plasma Vendor." More and more blood-drained citizens kept joining in, all heading toward the palace to take revenge on their tormentor. But King Maracas was too busy humping the insatiable Ooh-lala to take any notice of his impending doom.

When I reached the swing-doors at the rear, I surprised myself by shouting, "It's a bunch of sick fucking crap!"

"WHERE THE HELL have you been?" Mari yelled the second I walked in.

"*Muchacho!* It's after eleven and you have been gone since this morning." Tia Babi was waiting up too.

"My rosary was already out." Maria Regueros held it up as proof.

Seeing the three of them at the kitchen table reminded me of the proverbial monkey trio, only this trio seemed to imply: I see evil. I hear evil. I speak evil.

Mari started sniffing me.

"What are you doing?"

"Checking for marijuana."

I could smell the alcohol on her breath.

"*Mijo*," Tia Babi said lovingly, "it has become a very dangerous city. You could have at least called."

"I'm sorry. I thought I'd be back long ago . . . then ended up seeing this movie." I handed her the festival brochure. "It was sort of about Papá Gerardito."

She put on her glasses to read the synopsis and was outraged. Then Mari read it too.

"Relax, Mamá. That description fits at least a dozen Cuban presidents. Besides, portraying Mamá Elvira as a nymphomaniac? Oh, please!"

I laughed, but Tia Babi's eyes flashed me like rays of Kryptonite.

"If I had any money, I would get a lawyer and sue."

"Sue who, Mamá? We have no relations with Cuba."

"Well, someone had relations with someone to get this film here."

"And what on Earth would you sue them for?"

"Defamation of character." She kept staring at the brochure and shaking her head. "After all these years, why won't they leave Papá in peace?"

Seeing her pained expression made me wish that I had kept my big mouth shut.

• 32 •

I enrolled in the school of Liberal Arts, although my father seemed determined to keep thinking that I was studying business. He could not conceive how any of the courses that I was taking would ever help me to make a living.

By the time I got around to requesting a room on campus, all the dorms were full. So I moved in with my cousin Frank, who was renting the attic floor in the home of an Irish family in nearby Bryn Mawr. It turned out that Frank was dating the family's older daughter, Cathy, who was always either working late or babysitting her younger siblings. Like a supportive boyfriend, Frank would stick around to keep her company, so he was not much help in my developing a social life. For that, I began to rely on friends from the swimming team, which I had tried out for and been accepted into.

We were jumping into the water on our first day of practice when I saw a familiar face from Venetian Pool.

"Hey, John! Remember me?"

He was quite a bit older, but while studying at the University of Miami, he had trained for the Pentathlon and would often come to work out with us.

"Sure! Louie, right? You studying here now?"

Other team members seemed impressed by our being on a first-name basis.

"You know who that is, don't you?" one of them said to me after practice. Beyond his name and interest in sports I had no idea.

"He's John DuPont, one of the fucking richest guys in the country.

He's got this amazing estate nearby, Foxcatcher, and sometimes invites our team over."

Years later, John would die in jail, after having shot and killed a wrestling coach that he had brought over to train the U.S. Olympic team on his famous estate.

Many of my fellow freshmen had attended Catholic schools, like me, and since we were required to wear coats and ties to classes, all looked fairly homogenous. Soon I found myself gravitating toward the more eccentric kids, like Ed Scheible, who sat next to me in Philosophy 101. Scheible was a bushy-haired Buddha from Strawberry, New Jersey. Within seconds of our meeting, he was expounding his views on life.

"I detest societal expectations and think one should rebel against anything that seems prescribed or predetermined. That's the only reason I'm at a conservative Catholic school. It's the last place anyone expected me to go."

I deduced from the chaos inside his book satchel, his wrinkled shirt, and his messy hair, that neatness was another of the expectations that he believed in flouting.

"Oh, by the way," Scheible whispered as our teacher walked in, "Hope I haven't offended your religious sensibilities."

"What do you mean?"

He pointed to a spot above the blackboard with a remnant silhouette of something that appeared to have hanged there.

"I took down the crucifix."

"Why?"

"*Time* magazine said God is dead. And I hate looking at dead things."

One of my first assignments was a paper on Cubism for my Art History class. I was searching through the card catalogue under c-u-b, when I came across "Cuba." And that's as close as I got to Pablo Picasso that day. I filled out a request for a book called *Cuba, Island of*

Paradox, by Ruby Hart Phillips, a former correspondent for the *New York Times*, then took the volume to an isolated cubicle.

There were two chapters that spanned my great-grandfather's presidency. The first one was impressive: the author spoke of President Machado as "a committed nationalist, who had launched an ambitious program of unprecedented public works." She said that after his first three years, "he was riding a tidal wave of popularity," and even noted that he was "reputedly one of the best dancers in an island famous for its native rhythms." Then I got to the second chapter. My finger zigzagged down the text, past phrases like "unfettered slavish praise" and "delusions of indispensability," and finally, the most disturbing passage of all.

> Machado was the cleverest politician ever produced by the island, greedy, revengeful and unscrupulous. . . . To suit his egotistic ambition, he extended his term of office. With one stroke of the pen he ushered in tropical fascism, and became the Mussolini of the Caribbean.

These were more than enough revelations for one evening. I returned the book and went to the cafeteria to buy a hoagie before hitchhiking back home. There I found Scheible, sitting by himself, with legs folded under him and staring into space. He was not appreciative of my approaching.

"You've interrupted my blooping."

Blooping, he explained, occurred when you reach a state of perfect communion with the essence of the universe—a kind of nirvana, but more intense.

"Why would you even attempt to do that here, with all this traffic and noise?"

"There's no merit to blooping yourself alone in your room. I want to succeed at blocking out everyone else."

I started eating my hoagie, doing my best to ignore him, but then he stared at me with a puzzled look. "So what the fuck's wrong with you today?"

Perhaps he was more sensitive than I'd given him credit for. "I just found out that my great-grandfather was the Mussolini of the Caribbean." As I said the words I could picture my mother's reproachful look. "Well, not initially. But then he changed the constitution and things got . . . kinda messy."

Scheible stared in silence for a moment, and I prepared myself to be told that he refused to be friends with the offspring of a fascist pig. But instead, he broke into a childlike grin.

"That is so cool!"

"No, it's not. He turned his back on democracy. Promised one thing, then ended up doing another."

"That's even better!" His hands shook with excitement. "It's so . . . anti-expectational!"

"Not in Latin America." Scheible pondered this for a moment and then returned to his blooping.

THE VERY FIRST chance I got, I took a train back to Manhattan. Much had changed in the weeks I'd been away. Mari was now working at the Metropolitan Museum.

"One of her customers from the bookshop helped her get the job," Tia Babi brought me up to date. "It's in their research library, mostly cataloguing old books, but you'd think she was now the head curator."

Andres, on the other hand, hadn't had such good luck. The corporation selling the Dalí jewelry was being sued by the artist's estate.

"*Ay, hijo.* That man keeps jumping into hare-brained schemes without investigating them. Apparently," she whispered, as if the crumbling walls had ears, "the pieces were all forgeries."

"Not according to el Señor Andres," Maria Regueros piped in. "He insists that Dalí was being criticized for getting too commercial and decided to kill his own idea."

"*Ay*, Maria. It had to be forgeries. No respectable artist could have such bad taste. Even a surrealist."

"Darling, you're here!" Mari's ever-deepening voice echoed in the hallway.

Tia Babi leaned toward me and whispered again, "Please do not bring Dalí up in front of your godmother."

She strutted in, looking like the ultimate career woman. "I was dying to be here to greet you, but the museum was utter chaos. We just restored two Goyas that are absolutely magnificent. I must take you on a private tour." She poured herself some orange juice, then disappeared into the pantry.

Maria Regueros caught my eye and jiggled her eyebrows, implying "Observe!"

Seconds later Mari re-emerged with a much fuller glass, then sat down to sort the mail. "Oh, look! A letter from your mother." She opened the envelope, then held up a snapshot of my parents and siblings. "How sweet!"

They were at a restaurant, wearing paper crowns. I could tell exactly where it was by the logo on their giant milkshakes. Papi was in the picture too, though unlike the rest of the family he wore neither a crown nor a smile.

"What the hell *are* they doing?" Mari looked closer at the photo.

"Eating whoppers at Burger King," I pointed to the giveaway clue.

Tia Babi was already halfway down the letter that had come with the picture. "She says they went there to celebrate. After their citizenship ceremony."

"Oh, right!" I remembered that their applications had recently been approved. "Guess that makes me the only alien in the family now."

"I seriously doubt that Papá Gerardito would have approved of that picture. I mean, celebrating, after what this country did to him?"

"*Ay*, Mari." Tia Babi shrugged off the comment.

"It's true. Nenita may pretend to be Betsy Ross, but she's really Benedict Arnold." She headed again into the pantry.

"What did this country do to Papá Gerardito?" I asked.

"For starters"—Mari U-turned—"F.D.R. sent Ambassador Sumner Welles to conspire with the opposition and overthrow him."

"Please don't mention that man." Tia Babi winced.

"Then, as if giving him twenty-four hours to get out wasn't insult enough . . . the minute the new Cuban government requested his extradition back to the island, the Americans were ready to comply . . . even though it was totally against international law."

Tia Babi closed her eyes. "*Dios mio.* I will never forget the day they came to arrest him."

Maria Regueros, who had lived through it all, hobbled over. "The General was right here in the kitchen, when the U.S. Marshalls started pounding at the front door."

"And what did Papá Gerardito do?"

"He borrowed the cook's uniform," said Mari.

"You mean he got dressed as a woman?"

"God, no! Can you imagine a sturdy six-foot person running down Fifth Avenue in a dress? We had a male chef back then, dear."

"No, no, Mari. That's only what some newspaper claimed. He just ran out in his white twill suit. I can still see him struggling over that backyard wall." Maria Regueros squeezed her canes. "By then, the U.S. Marshalls were already inside."

"They went through every inch of the house searching for Papá . . . and insisted there must be a secret panel where we had hidden him."

"The manhunt made every front page in the city," Mari said, now sounding rather proud. "The *New York Post* named him 'number one fugitive'."

"But the worst thing . . . is that for days we had no idea where or how he was."

"And where was he?"

Tia Babi went silent.

"Let's leave that for another time," said Maria Regueros.

"Yes." Mari had now emptied her glass. "But the point is, this country treated Papá Gerardito like shit. And now his pet granddaughter is waving the flag and singing 'Yankee Doodle'."

"Mari, enough," Tia Babi pleaded, then stared fondly again at the picture with the new American citizens, enjoying themselves at Burger King.

In the morning, I threw on a funky tweed overcoat that I'd discovered in the entrance hall closet. Mari had said that it was nobody's. Then I took a bus down to the 42nd Street library.

"How do I go about finding old newspaper articles, like from the thirties?" I asked a wrinkly librarian.

She took me to the card catalogue and pointed out how I could tell whether an item was available on microfilm or microfiche. There was quite a long list under "Machado, Gerardo," so I jotted down a few of the more promising entries, then was led to a booth with a machine on which I could view my requests.

Preserved on brittle coils of celluloid were records of long-ago events in my family's history. One article, from the *Evening Journal*, reported their arrival in Miami, shortly after their flight from Havana.

> The ex-president's family walked through the police barricade that separated them from the derisive crowd, with the disdain of French aristocrats marching to the guillotine. Not an eye flickered. Not by any movement did Señora Machado or any member of her party acknowledge the presence of their antagonists.

When I checked my watch it was already one o'clock, and I had agreed to meet Ramón Antonio in Times Square to see a matinee. I was quickly winding through one last coil when a headline caught my bleary eyes: "Mysterious Meeting for General Machado." I scrolled on down.

> Afraid that the authorities would find him if he contacted a friend, the fugitive found his way to the apartment of a beautiful Cuban dancer.

I read faster.

> The young lady, a former headliner at Havana's naughtiest nightclub, "La Verbena," had never met the General, and said she was in New York with a chaperone to do a screen test. She had also come on another mission—to kill the deposed dictator—and had sworn a secret pact to shoot him on sight. Taking advantage of his appreciation for dancing and the weaker sex, a collaborator had seen to it that the starlet's address and phone number would reach the ex-president. Machado had looked forward to using this information, but not under these circumstances.

The reporter then went on to express admiration for the number one fugitive.

> He was undoubtedly courageous for taking a chance and walking, unarmed, into what he must have suspected could be a trap. It was this very courage and trust that seduced the would be seducer, and turned an assigned killer into the instrument of his escape.

Now needing to run off myself, I rewound the film, hoping that however long my *bisabuelo* stayed with the beautiful dancer, they had found enough time to do a couple of rumbas.

RAMÓN ANTONIO HAD bought two seats on the next-to-last-row of the balcony. But I found this an improvement over the previous time, when he had made me see *The Persecution and Assassination of Jean-Paul Marat as Performed by the Inmates of the Asylum at Charenton Under the Direction of the Marquis de Sade*, in standing room.

The play we saw now, *The Royal Hunt of the Sun*, was about Pizarro's conquest of the Incas and Atahualpa's fall from proud god to mere mortal.

Being a descendant of Spaniards and a product of Catholic schools, I had always been taught that the Conquest was a good thing. It had brought the true faith to pagan cultures and had saved millions of souls that otherwise would have burned in Hell. But now suddenly I was leaving the theater filled with an intense dislike for the *conquistadores*.

"Does power always corrupt?" I asked my uncle.

"Let me put it this way, *mi chino*. It's pretty hard to get up there without stepping on quite a few toes." Ramón Antonio kept weaving through the crowds that were now emerging from other matinees. "I suppose one could portray a figure like Pizarro as both good *and* evil, same as you could so many other powerful leaders. In which direction the scales ultimately tilt probably has more to do with who ends up writing your memoirs."

I thought about my great-grandfather again, and decided that he definitely had not had much luck in this respect.

"Listen, if you're not up to anything, want to come down to the Village for a bite?"

When Ramón Antonio turned on his apartment lights, a young man who had been sleeping on the sofa jumped up. "What the fuck?"

"Relax. It's me, Herving." He introduced us. Herving was wearing a yellowed pair of boxer shorts, and his thick black hair was matted down in places and poking up in others. When I shook his hand I saw that there were letters tattooed on his knuckles and blue lines running up his forearm.

"Plon-Plon, stop it!" Ramón Antonio shouted at his dachshund, which was spraying everyone as he wagged his tail and peed from the excitement. Then as he spread out more New York Times sections to soak up the mess, my uncle felt a need to explain the status of his visitor. "Herving's just here until we can find him a job and another place to stay."

"And believe me, either one ain't easy when they hear you just got out of prison," Herving himself volunteered.

"Oh." I didn't dare ask what he'd been in for, but Ramón Antonio sensed my curiosity and gestured toward Herving's forearm. "*That's* what they got him for."

All I could see were the strange blue lines. "Tattoos?"

Herving burst out laughing. "God, Ray! Where's your nephew been living, the Moon?"

Ramón Antonio approached with three coffee mugs. "You think everyone needs to know about pathetic things like your track marks?" He turned to me. "He's a heroin addict."

"I *was*!"

"Whatever. The point is there are far better worlds than the one you've been stuck in. And I see no reason why you can't one day live in one of them."

Herving took a slurp from his mug. "Your uncle is the first good thing that's ever happened to me. Nobody else in this fuckin' city could give a fucking shit . . . just him." His eyes got teary. "He's like . . . a second Jesus."

The second Jesus grinned like a Cheshire cat. "Herving, bubby. Would you mind going down to the corner Chinese and getting us the fried rice special and some dumplings?" He handed him a ten. "And I better get change."

When Herving left, Ramón Antonio put on a Vivaldi concerto and sat beside me. "You asked me about power. I have quite a bit over this kid right now. Not that I particularly wanted it. And it still doesn't make me a Pizarro, or . . . a President Machado. It's just one life that I have a chance to influence. But I would be a complete shit if I were to misuse that power." He lit a cigarette. "Actually, he has power over me too. If my supervisor found out that he's here I'd be in really deep trouble." Then as he took a deep drag another thought came to his mind. "And don't you dare tell anyone in your mother's family that I've had you socializing with junkies."

• 33 •

After seven years of exile, the hope for a return to Cuba had still not abated in Miami.

On a regular basis, Spanish radio stations broke into news flashes about the revolution breathing its last sigh, making spirits soar all over again. But one thing *had* changed. Whatever the length of our stay here, most Cuban exiles had stopped putting their lives on hold. Everyone was reinventing themselves, and financial success had become the best way of getting back at Fidel.

Another curious thing happened as the community became more affluent. It decided that if they could not return to Cuba, then they would bring Cuba over to them. As the island became sovietized and Cuban effervescence was curbed under the controls of Fidel's Marxist regime, Miami became a thriving museum, designed to perpetuate the Cuba that was, prior to 1959.

Restaurants with our *criollo* cuisine had sprung up all over. One could feast on *ropa vieja* or a *bistec empanizado* smothered in *papitas a la Juliana*, while staring at murals of our scenic Valle de Viñales, or ox carts loaded with sugarcane inching their way across royal palm-studded fields. New record companies were reissuing all the music that Cubans had danced and made love to during previous decades: Benny Moré, Celia Cruz, La Orquesta Aragón, Fernando Albuerne. All of it was available again at most bodegas, along with plantain chips, *Wajay* salt crackers, and guava paste– each of these items also being produced right in Miami by newly created Cuban exile businesses.

This insatiable longing for the homeland had also given rise to an industry of printmakers producing evocative images of our lost Eden: the crystal clear beaches of Varadero, Morro Castle rising majestically from Havana Harbor, countryside landscapes with quaint thatched-roof *bohios*. There were picaresque scenes with our beloved Cuban prototypes: *loteria* street vendors, straw-hatted *guajiros*, sassy tight-skirted *mulatas*, and our most emblematic street character of all, *El Caballero de Paris*, with his long hair and flowing robe, offering a rose to a lady fair along the Malecón. There was practically no Cuban exile family that didn't have at least one small picture with an image of La Habana Vieja or a brightly blooming flamboyant tree hanging somewhere in their home.

My father was proud to be a part of this new and thriving Latin Miami. The five houses that he and his partner built had finally turned a nice profit. They now had set their eyes on another South Miami property, this one being big enough to subdivide into ten lots. It bordered an old Jewish cemetery, which would assure buyers the quietest of neighbors. The property was also dotted with beautiful Florida pines, which meant that this time Papi would have a good head start with the landscaping. By the time the houses were finished, he had fallen in love with one of them and decided to put our present one up for sale.

"You mean you're going to abandon all these beautiful trees that you planted?"

Even though the new house would be much nicer, my mother had become attached to the miniature green *finca* that my father had created. Those scrawny twigs that I had helped him plant had taken root and grown tall, giving the once-bare neighborhood a sense of stability. I could drive around the whole block and feel intimately acquainted with its flora. I remembered exactly when each tree had been put in, the ones that had shot up like weeds, and those that we had struggled with to help survive. Perhaps my favorite of all was the slightly crooked avocado tree that Mami had trampled one day by not swerving sharply enough into our garage. Papi had reattached its splintered trunk and propped it up with a wooden slat, not giving it much hope. The tree had not only survived but gone on to give yearly bumper crops, which many family friends got to enjoy along with us.

"It will be fun to start over again," he gradually began to convince her. "And with all those pine trees around, I think I'll do something entirely different this time."

Unfortunately, Florida pines were falling prey to a plague of beetles that burrowed into their bark. The least disturbance of their roots tended to weaken them and make them even more susceptible to these parasites. Soon after moving into our new home, one by one the beautiful pines began to die.

"Oh, well." Papi remained positive. "Now I'll have room for more tropical fruit trees."

Sometimes in the late afternoon my parents would go for a stroll around the neighborhood. Since there were no sidewalks, and far too many annoying dogs, they often wandered into the Jewish cemetery to walk along the grassy lanes between the graves. There was a giant Hong Kong orchid tree right in the middle of it all. They enjoyed sitting under it, to watch the daily kaleidoscope of sunset clouds. It had been a long, convoluted road that had brought them from La Calle Ene to the Star of David Memorial, yet what amazed them most, as they sat there holding hands, was that they were still happy.

• 34 •

Over the summer of 1968, the entire world seemed to change. Friends that I had last seen sporting short Ivy League cuts now had hair that reached down to their shoulders. Gray flannels and chinos had given way to funky bell-bottoms, and sedate button-down Oxfords to wild flower-power prints. Most of my once-clean-cut classmates now looked like escapees from acid rock album covers, making my formerly eccentric buddy, Scheible, just one of the bunch. Still unsuccessful at blooping himself, he had deigned to return for another term. I had now moved into a dorm, hoping to enhance my collegiate experience, and discovered that his room was just two doors down.

"I'm going to an S.D.S. meeting tonight. Wanna come?"

"What's S.D.S.?"

"Students for a Democratic Society."

"You're a Democrat?"

"God, no! *They're* almost as far right as the G.O.P."

I thought about my parents who, like many new Cuban-Americans, had become staunch Republicans, and I realized that left or right all depended on who you stood next to.

"Come!" Scheible grabbed my coat sleeve. "This'll expand your mind."

I WAS HOPING to sit at the rear, where I could easily escape if things got boring, which I expected they would. But Scheible insisted on heading right to the front row. He had even brought a pad for taking notes.

The topic for the evening turned out to be student activism. The speaker, unlike most lecturers at Villanova, wasn't wearing a jacket and tie. His bulky sweater had fuzz balls that curled up from thin threads like hundreds of tiny question marks. His unruly hair, which had seen neither comb nor brush in ages, stuck straight out, making the spotlight above him create the effect of a saintly halo.

"We cannot continue to stand by, like placid sheep being led to the slaughter," he said, stressing every word. "This government has mired us in an unjustified, indecent war without our consent. It is a war that no civic-minded citizen should be supporting. In fact, it is our duty to do all we can to bring it to an end." He kept pounding his fist, each time jolting Scheible into making erratic squiggles. "And just in case you think I'm making a subversive statement, then let me read a brief passage." He held up a thick textbook. "It is the duty of the people to destroy a system that denies them their freedom." His eyes slowly scanned the room. "Those, my friends, are the words of our very own Thomas Jefferson, enshrined in our beloved American Constitution."

Scheible turned to me with a wide-eyed non-verbal "Wow!"

"We, as students," the speaker continued, "have the power to achieve those changes."

"He's a student?" I whispered. "Looks kind of long in the tooth to me."

"And that power lies in unity. Want to bring our boys back from Vietnam? Boycott the record industry. I guarantee you, within a week, Columbia, RCA, Apple, they'll all be in Washington supporting us."

I turned to Scheible again. "Who'd have thought? LPs as a tool for subversion."

The man's esses kept sending showers of spittle upon us, especially each time he derided "the system." Scheible used the tip of his scarf to subtly wipe the droplets off his notepad, but they kept coming. "The system doesn't give a shit about sacrificing innocent lives with napalm and God knows what else. Ah, but just let 'the people' try to expose those atrocities, and they go berserk. Why? Because they know too damn well that we have the power to stop them!"

The speech ended to wild applause. Then he opened the floor to questions.

Scheible's hand was the first one up. "I take it that you're just advocating pacifist means—like Ghandi's."

"Ghandi?" The speaker sneered. "I'd like you to ask any Native American stuck in a reservation today where a century of pacifism got them."

"Then you *are* talking about active revolt."

"I'm talking about whatever the specific situation calls for to bring about the necessary changes." The man had almost won me over. Then he said, "Take Cuba, for instance. Change there was brought about by only a handful of men."

Suddenly I wished I'd sat at the rear.

"And why did that work?" He looked around again, savoring what he was about to say. "Because the fight was a just one. Once someone began it, the people flocked to it."

I could feel my stomach clenching. "It's not that simple," I wanted to tell him. "Yes, we had a dictatorship. Yes, many people flocked to the revolution—at first. But what about all those lies Fidel told to make so many follow him? And why did people like my father, who had worked hard and honestly, deserve to lose everything?" But I didn't have the courage to speak up. It was only afterwards, as we were heading toward the cafeteria, that I expressed my thoughts to Scheible.

His reply was no help. "Are you so sure that your father was on the right side?"

Despite mediocre midterm grades and promises to study harder, I was now heading up to New York almost every Friday, often with some scholastic excuse: "There's a research book at the Forty-second Street library that I can't find on campus," or "There's a major exhibit on Wassily Kandinsky at the Modern."

"Who's Wassily Kandinsky and what does he have to do with business administration?" My father always questioned the need for these visits, but he never fully opposed them.

When I got to the house this time, Tia Babi was in a tizzy.

"Imagine! My sister Berta left Cuba and is now in Mexico City . . . with Lugi and the lady who takes care of her."

That sounded like good news to me. She had been trying to get out forever. But Tia Babi explained that this had only complicated matters. They still had no visas to enter the U.S., and now there would be the added expense of having to support them for however long it took to resolve their situation. Tia Berta had already been calling everyone to ask that they wire her money, as soon as possible.

"My sister has never done anything like a normal human being. Since she was a little girl, whatever she did became a major ordeal." Tia Babi was also feeling guilty for having lied to her. "She asked to speak to Mamá but I told her she was sleeping. She hasn't been well lately, and Berta has always had a knack for distressing her."

"Bueno, Mamá," said Mari. "Now *you're* the one letting your dear sister distress you. She seems to have plenty of contacts in the other world. Let's hope one of them pulls through and gives her a hand."

We heard the bump of the elevator landing. It was Tia Babi's husband, José Emilio, looking his usual distinguished self in a dressing gown and silk polka dot ascot. He normally made himself a simple supper in the fourth-floor pantry, but tonight Maria Regueros had announced that in honor of my visit she was making an *arroz con pollo*, so he had decided to join us. Maria opened the oven door to show me the oval casserole with her creation: a mound of yellow rice and *petit pois* elegantly garnished with strips of pimentos.

"*Ay*," Tia Babi sighed, "So what are we going to do about Berta?"

"Mamá, enough!"

Hoping to lighten things up, I sat down to tell her about that Cuban girl that I had a date with this weekend. It was someone I knew from Miami, who was now studying at Marymount. Tia Babi became intrigued, but when I mentioned the girl's last name her enthusiasm instantly vanished.

"Please don't tell me that her grandfather tried to kill Papá Gerardito too."

"No," she paused. "It was actually her own father. He tried to kill the entire cabinet."

"Not to mention us," Mari jumped in. "We might have all been blown sky-high."

"Well, to be fair . . ." said José Emilio, who was always more measured, "it was really the ABC." He turned to me, "That's the opposition group he had joined, which was mostly made up of university students."

"But what made it worse is that he had grown up amongst us." Tia Babi, already on edge, became even more so. "His father was the majordomo at the presidential palace. And he turned out to be such a bright child that Papá paid for his studies. Then he goes and joins the ABC, which advocated terrorism."

This was yet another story that my mother hadn't told me.

"So how did he, or they, try to kill everyone?"

Tia Babi turned to her husband. "Why don't you tell him?"

José Emilio put his fork down, wiped his lips, and began.

"It all started with the assassination of Vicente Vazquez Bello, who was president of the senate. He was young, handsome, intelligent, and beloved by everyone. He was beyond partisanism, and had always stood behind whatever side of an issue he felt was right. If there was someone who seemed far from any danger, it was Vicente. Even after other cabinet members began to use police escorts, he continued to drive alone in his convertible. And that's how his assassins found him.

"He was heading home after playing a set of tennis at the Yacht Club, still wearing his white outfit, and with his racket beside him. He was about to cross the little bridge over the Quibú River, when a car blocked off the far end. If he had never felt fear before, I imagine he did then. He quickly put on the brakes and shifted into reverse, but by then his rear was blocked off too."

"I will never forget Papá's face when they came to tell him that they had killed Vicente," Tia Babi interrupted. "I only saw him cry three times in his life. The day his mother died, the afternoon that we met him again, after leaving Cuba, and the night they killed Vicente."

José Emilio continued.

"It didn't take long for the police to trace the murder to the ABC. But nobody could figure out the motive. Why Vicente? He was the epitome of our country's hope. Then a few days later, when everyone had given up on making any sense of it, a maintenance man at the Colón cemetery literally stumbled upon a clue.

"He was working along the perimeter wall when a walkway tile collapsed under him. As he went to get up, his foot got tangled in what looked like electric wiring. But it didn't lead to any lamppost or power line. It also looked brand-new, which made the man suspicious. He reported this to the cemetery guards, but there were enough problems in Havana for anyone to worry about some piece of electric wiring. Fortunately, the man was stubborn. With the help of another maintenance worker they began to dig, and they found that the wire kept winding its way around one marble tomb after another—until it reached the mausoleum of the Vazquez Bello family. And that was just the tip of the iceberg. The entire area surrounding it had also been mined with explosives . . . enough to blow up everyone within a fifty-meter range."

"But why? Vazquez Bello was already dead, and so was everyone in the cemetery."

"Ah, that was their macabre brilliance. Vicente's popularity was the guarantee that everyone in the government would attend his funeral."

"Our entire family would have disintegrated, darling," Mari smirked. "None of us would be here tonight to enjoy this *arroz con pollo*."

"I still don't get it. If this was discovered days later, hadn't Vicente already been buried? How come they didn't blow things up?"

"An ironic twist of fate." José Emilio smiled. "Vicente's family was originally from the town of Santa Clara. And to the plotters' immense disappointment, his widow decided to have him buried there. That one arbitrary decision foiled the entire plot."

"Wow!" I was impressed. "That would make a great movie."

"It did, darling," said Mari. "Well, not so great, really. It's called *We Were Strangers*, with Jenniffer Jones and James Garfield. TV listings usually give it only one star, which serves them right for trying to glorify terrorism." With that she disappeared into the pantry.

"Well, I never saw it, and don't intend to," Tia Babi put her hand on mine. "People said that Papá went on a rampage and had conspirators executed. If that were true, a lot of people we know, and probably more than one girl you've dated, would not be here today either."

"The greatest irony," José Emilio said as he readjusted his napkin over his chest, "is that quite a few of those men, who claimed to have been fighting a dictator, years later supported Fidel . . . the ultimate one."

"I don't mean to be insensitive," I observed after a moment, "but I do believe Jesus said, and I've heard Mari quote him, that the sins of the father should not visit the children—or something to that effect."

"Ah, yes!" Mari bounced back in with a refilled glass. "But so far as I know, Jesus never had anyone trying to bump off Mary and Joseph." Then she poked my chest with her forefinger. "I'd suggest you get yourself another date."

"DID YOU KNOW that your dad supposedly tried to bump off my great-grandfather?" I joked to my date, Cristina, when I picked her up.

"No." She laughed. "But I do know that your father and mine played golf together at the Country Club almost every Thursday."

With that, the subject was put to rest.

I had planned for us to go down to the Village and hear music somewhere, or maybe walk toward St. Marks and sit at a coffee house to watch the colorful hippie parade. But the moment my family's would-be assassin's daughter appeared in her dorm lobby, I sensed from her tailored suit and pearl earrings that the Village was not on her agenda.

"There's this great new club that my Cuban friends keep telling me about."

The Ginza was an Upper East Side version of sophisticated hip—stylized fruggers crammed onto a tiny dance floor, doing stiff rhythmic jerks with blank expressions. High above the crowd was a go-go dancer doing similar icy moves inside a gilded cage. There was a five-dollar minimum per person, and I also sensed that this would not be Dutch treat. As I watched the waitress who took our drinks order slip my ten-dollar bill into the cash register, I waved goodbye to half my weekend budget. I calculated that for what I'd just spent I could have seen three Broadway shows on standing room.

Cristina's friends were already there. I knew a couple of them myself. After some chitchat about our respective schools and exchanging tips on other popular places, we started comparing childhood memories of Cuba. Someone remembered eating *pirulís* and *mamoncillos* while wading in the waters of Varadero. I remembered the plates of *dulcecitos* that were a staple at every children's party, and how the reddish one, made of *mamey*, had been my favorite. Cristina remembered Mandrake the Magician, who frequently performed at those celebrations, and how he had once made a baby chick appear from her Flamenco costume.

"I threw a tantrum when my *tata* said I couldn't keep it. Then all the way home I kept searching my sleeves, hoping to find another *pollito*."

One of our friends, whose family had had some connection to the Batista regime, remembered being awakened in the middle of the night.

"My parents came home from a New Year's Eve party—not *the* famous one that everybody claims to have been at—just a family thing.

My mother was still in her ball gown and smelling of Gerlain." She drifted off into memory for a moment. "Anyway, Mami said we were leaving, and by noon we were in the Bahamas. Oh, I also remember that as she helped me get dressed, I asked if we had any money outside of Cuba."

This last detail startled me. "How old did you say you were?"

"Ten."

"And that's the first thing you thought of?"

"Well, yes. I wanted to make sure we weren't going to starve or anything."

I thought about my own first thoughts. I would be free to ride a bike anywhere, away from the turmoil of Havana . . . and be able to have an Ant Farm. Then another question came to my mind.

"You guys ever wonder whether our fathers were partly to blame for what happened?"

I became surrounded by blank stares. "No." "Not at all." "What could they have done?"

With that, couple by couple, we headed toward the dance floor and squeezed in among all the hip East Side fruggers.

When I got home I found Mari sitting alone at the kitchen table with an orange juice. I could see that she had been crying. She said that a dear friend had just been killed in a car accident.

"She left six children behind. *I* should have been the one in that car. Those poor kids needed her so much, and what use am I to anyone?" She began to cry again.

For the second time I found myself having to comfort an adult, so I reached for her hand. "What are you talking about? You're needed too, by all of us. Certainly by me."

"Thank you, darling." Still sobbing, she threw her arms around me and held on tightly.

It was difficult to see my godmother falling apart like this. I much preferred picturing her as my own crazy Auntie Mame. But unlike the one on Broadway, Mari could never seem to turn her low points into upbeat musical numbers. It was as if the songs fizzled and the band stopped playing, despite all her efforts to keep on singing.

While I had breakfast the following morning, Maria Regueros explained that Mari had had a miscarriage while living with Andres in that sugar mill. The country doctor who attended her had apparently botched things up, and she was never again able to get pregnant. "She had so looked forward to becoming a mother."

Before heading to Penn Station on Sunday afternoon, I stopped by to see Ramón Antonio. As usual, his apartment was crowded with an eclectic cast of friends, running the gamut from aging Cuban actors to young, supposedly recovered, drug addicts. He claimed to be living through one of those periods when everything falls magically into place.

"And I've certainly lived long enough to appreciate how quickly these moments can end again," he told me. "So I intend to enjoy every minute."

There was no special someone in his life, but he had made peace with his fate as a revolving door through which wounded souls passed, got some healing care, then moved on. Herving, rid of his addiction, at least for the time being, had left the city to attempt a clean start. But Rudy had made it back safely from Vietnam. He was now living in the apartment, doing assorted day jobs while taking some kind of technical course at night, which had been my uncle's pre-requisite for providing him with free room and board.

Contrary to what I had imagined from Ramón Antonio's stories about Rudy's troubled history, he seemed like a gentle soul, of very few words. I couldn't tell whether that might have been partly a result of his combat experiences, but he now gave off an aura of someone totally at peace with himself.

"Of course the negative side," Ramón Antonio pointed out, "is that he's become so damn placid you practically have to light a fire under his ass to get him moving."

But the one thing that Ramón Antonio was especially excited about was the little informal group of present or former caseload members, to whom he had started giving acting lessons.

"I begin each session with sensory exercises, to help them vent their rage. They're usually too macho to get into it right away, but little by little they discover that these exercises can bring back some crucial memories, sometimes tender ones, which make them start to bawl like babies." He seemed to be very proud that these classes were also making his pupils read, and even enjoy it. "I realize it may be just some lines of dialogue, but it's already expanded their vocabulary beyond shit, goddamn, and mudderfuck."

When I went to the bathroom I smelled the pungent scent emanating from Ramón's little bedroom. Four of his *pupils* were piled in there passing around a joint.

"*Tio!*" I found him at his turntable, putting on the incongruous background music of Schubert's Mass in A flat major. "You know what's going on back there?"

"I can imagine. So?"

"Aren't some of these guys supposed to be recovering?"

"I only allow them to smoke grass. I think knowing they can at least do that helps wean them from the heavy stuff."

"But people can probably smell it from way down the block. What if the police come?"

"You mean to raid us for a little marihuana? *Mi chino*, they'd have to arrest the entire Village."

• 35 •

The Mothers of Invention blasted away as I passed by Scheible's dorm room. He was squatted on the floor churning out posters, printing each letter with thick black magic marker, then adding an artsy shadow of bright Day-Glo red. I scanned the room, reading the signs already lining the walls: We do give a damn! Get our boys out of Nam! Hell no! We won't go! Make love, not war.

"What's all this for?"

"The peace march, next Saturday." He stood back so that I could admire his latest creation—Let's Lick Dick!

"I assume you don't mean giving Richard Nixon a blow job."

"Hmm," Scheible reconsidered. "Perhaps there's no place for clever nuance in anti-war slogans." He ripped it up and got back to work. "Oh, by the way. I signed you up."

"For what?"

"The bus to D.C. Space was filling up fast."

"Scheible, you know I go to New York on weekends."

"This is war, man. You can sacrifice one week of hot pussy."

His cheap remark infuriated me. "That's not what I go up there for."

"Then all the better!" He held up his new sign. Lyndon or Dick, same old schtick!

"Just get me off that list, okay?"

"You know, while you putz around up there each weekend, thousands more keep dying." He waved a suspicious finger, "You *are* against this war, aren't you?"

"Of course."

"And what have you ever done about it? Here's a chance to prove you mean it."

I started to walk out but then realized he had a point. I felt that this war made no sense, and I definitely didn't want to go fight it. But all I'd ever done was criticize within the safety of a college campus.

"How much would this trip cost?"

"Nothing. The S.D.S. bus is free. And I can find us a place to crash."

"Okay, let me think about it."

I hated giving in to him, but the more I thought about it, the more that taking part in this demonstration made sense. Before going to bed I decided that I'd better call Cristina. We had talked about maybe going to see *Hair* or *Promises, Promises* that same weekend.

"*Hola!*" She sounded very chipper when she came to the phone. That quickly changed the moment I said that I might not be coming up after all.

"How come?"

"There's this . . . peace march in Washington, and I've decided to go." It wasn't till I said it that I figured I'd made up my mind.

"You're kidding me, right?"

"Not at all. Why do you say that?"

"Because these anti-war things are being organized by a bunch of leftists."

I had always felt slightly to the left of most of my Cuban friends, which still placed me way to the right of my American ones. Cristina's words now threw me back into my internal tug-of-war.

"I wouldn't say they're *all* leftists."

"Well then, ninety percent of them. The rest are malcontent radicals."

"And how do you know I'm not one of them?"

"*Ay*, please. Just take a good look at yourself. You wear tweeds and wingtips."

"No, I don't. Well, except maybe in New York. Anyway, who cares what I wear? The point is I'm against this war, and I feel it's time I do something about it."

"So you want communism to overrun Southeast Asia like it did in Cuba?"

"God, now you sound like my father. At least *he* was traumatized by what he went through, but you're just parroting what you've been told without even questioning it."

There was dead silence.

"Well," Cristina finally said, "if that's how you feel then maybe you should stop dating a parrot."

I was too mule-headed to backtrack. "Maybe."

"You know, Luis, you're so damn inconsistent."

"Oh?"

"You question your family but then let yourself be brainwashed by fanatics."

"Brainwashed?" That got to me. "Look, let's not turn this into a whole big thing. I'm not coming up next weekend, that's all. Call you in a few days." With that I hung up.

When I went by Scheible's room again he was still crouched on the floor penning more brilliantly witty posters.

"Are you sure this trip will cost us nothing?"

Night had already fallen when the S.D.S. bus reached the capital. As our group of peace marchers got off outside Union Station, we were handed maps with directions to our meeting point the following morning. Within minutes everyone had dispersed, leaving Scheible and me alone and disoriented.

"So who's this friend of yours we're crashing with?"

"Well, he's not exactly a friend. He's a friend of a friend. Sort of."

"Scheible! I thought you said you'd worked this out."

"I did, man. My friend Brian told me this guy's opening his door to anyone who needs a place tonight. So relax. I'm sure it's cool."

Brian's friend's apartment was somewhere in Georgetown. Blaring rock music and the smell of marijuana led the way to his wide-open door. The place was crammed with anti-war demonstrators, all dressed in various shades of faded denim and olive green. Scheible zeroed in on a burly guy who seemed quite at home as he rummaged through the small railroad kitchen.

"Are you Wilford?"

"Me?" The guy chuckled, "Nah, Wil's my identical twin." He pointed across the room to a short professorial fellow with thinning hair and granny-glasses.

We headed over. "Wilford, hi. I'm Brian's friend, from Villanova."

"Brian who?"

"Brian Becker. You guys met last summer, at some encounter weekend thing."

"Oh, man. I was so wasted I barely remember being there." He scrunched up his face. "Brian, hmm?"

I suddenly saw myself sleeping in the streets of D.C.

"Yeah, Brian. Droopy moustache, black curly hair," Scheible persisted. "He said it'd be cool if we kinda . . . crashed here."

Wilford scanned the packed room and shrugged. "Hey. We're all in this together. If you can stake your claim on a piece of parquet, you're welcome to it."

It wasn't clear whether Wilford was also footing the bill for the endless supply of joints and beer, or for the piles of food that the crowd kept wolfing down under the effects of *cannabis sativa*. The stuff was strong too. After a few tokes, I was overcome by brotherly love and enveloped by the communal sensibility that had brought us all together. As I looked around, I wished that my parents, and friends like Cristina, could feel what I was feeling. They would realize that the only thing these "leftist liberals" wanted was to make a better world. Then I spotted a familiar face staring at me from the kitchen. It was Che Guevara, stenciled in eye-popping black upon the T-shirt of a short pixie-haired blond.

I headed over, feeling like a telephoto lens zooming in on my target. Then with an altered sense of depth perception I tripped on a tub of iced beer and fell right into Che's breast-cushioned face.

"Oops!" the little blonde said as I bounced off her.

"I'm sorry." Embarrassed, I reached down for a beer and started to walk away, but the image on the T-shirt drew me back like a magnet. "How come you're wearing that?"

"You mean Che?" She smiled. "He's my hero."

I snapped the flip-top can open and took a swig. "Why?"

"'Cause . . . he's *the* ideal revolutionary. And also . . ."

"Cute?"

She laughed. "Yeah. I guess that too."

I felt like telling her some of the less complimentary things I had always heard about her idol and thus prove to myself that I was not a brainwashed case. But then what was I? I believed in justice, equality, civil rights—all the things that I assumed those around me believed in too. Yet one T-shirt had suddenly set me apart from everyone. I wanted to talk about this and try to sort it out in my head. But by now I had also decided that the little blonde was pretty sexy—and flirting was much more fun than arguing politics.

"So do you find Fidel cute too?"

Her eyes tilted up, as if to double-check a thought-bubble with the bearded leader's image. "Yeah. Kinda."

"But not *as* cute, right?"

"No. But God, does he have charisma. I'd definitely . . ." She stopped.

"Come on. What where you going to say?"

Someone passed her a joint and she took a deep drag. "I'd definitely let him do me." She exhaled in a burst of giggles.

"You mean you fantasize about Fidel?"

"Well, it's not so much him in particular. It's . . . all of it." She took another toke.

"Marilyn! Stop being a hog and pass that damn thing!" hollered a guy enveloped in hair, like Cousin Itt from *The Addams Family*.

Marilyn passed it to me, but having had plenty, I passed it on to Cousin Itt.

"What do you mean by all of it?"

"You know . . . the ideals men like him stand for. I guess the way some people get into rock stars, I'm into revolutionaries."

I was wasted by now. "Wow."

"I mean, not that I've ever done any. But yeah . . . Fidel, Che, they could do me any time." She flashed a big stoned grin. "The two of them at once . . . now *that* would be nirvana!"

I suddenly realized that I had said nothing about myself. "You know, I'm Cuban too."

"Really? From where?"

"Havana originally. But I grew up in Miami."

"Oh. An exile." This seemed to lower me a few notches.

As she leaned down to get a beer, I started to feel competitive. "But I've seen both Che *and* Fidel."

"You have?" She popped up, eyes all aglimmer. "Where? How? What happened?"

"Well . . . Fidel I saw when he gave a speech, for the youth of Cuba. My whole class went to hear him. And Che . . . I was in old Havana with my mother, buying shoes. There was this big commotion and next thing we knew, his motorcade passed by."

She swooned. "Did you get a good look at him?"

"Sure. He must have been, oh, not more than five feet away. He even waved."

"Oh, my God. I would have wet my panties." She clasped my wrists. "I can't believe I'm touching someone who's actually been that close to my idols."

I didn't elaborate about having spent the whole of Fidel's long speech wandering around in search of water. Nor did I dare tell her that instead of waving back at Che, my mother had mumbled, "Wish he'd go back to Argentina."

In the course of countless rounds of marijuana, the gathering slowly mutated into a slumber party. Lights became dimmer, the music mellower. As if by magic, people began to conjure up sleeping bags or blankets and to take possession of their slivers of floor.

"Shit!" Scheible reappeared from wherever he'd been. "We forgot to bring something to sleep on."

"Forgot?" Even in my humanity-embracing state I was still furious with him. "I never knew we were supposed to."

"Listen, it's not like we're on a snorkeling trip to Bimini. We came here for a cause. If sleeping on the floor is part of that—so be it." His eyes scouted the room. "Look! There's no one under the dinner table. Take that spot. I'll go find another one."

Seeing no alternative, I got on my hands and knees and started crawling. The uncarpeted floor felt cold and hard, so I spread out my overcoat and molded my overnight bag into a makeshift pillow. But no matter how I shifted, some bone or other kept poking out uncomfortably. I was resigning myself to a long sleepless night when a little voice whispered . . .

"I found a great spot, and there's room for two of us." It was Marilyn, angel of mercy, come to my rescue. She led me across the obstacle course of sleeping bodies. As we stepped over them, still feeling a bit high, I fantasized that we were giants, crossing mountain ranges. Some of the mountains budged, as if our footfalls had caused tremors.

Marilyn's secret hideaway was a walk-in utility closet. It was filled with gadgets that she had piled up at one end. She had even lined the floor with towels, like a bird feathering her nest.

"If you squeeze your feet around that vacuum cleaner you can almost stretch out completely." She closed the door and pointed to the louvered slats, like a real-estate agent talking up a property. "And look! We have both privacy *and* ventilation."

Despite her claim, the space was barely wide enough for both of us. In a gentlemanly gesture, I lay down facing away from her, although our bodies could not avoid touching. This was not very sleep-conducive either. I closed my eyes and started listing the European capitals, which usually worked better for me than counting sheep. I had already gone through all of Western Europe and was making my way toward Budapest and Bucharest, when I felt Marilyn's little hand reach for my sweater.

"Aren't you hot in that thing?"

"Now that you mention it . . ." I sat up to take it off, then threw it on the pile at our feet. Encouraged by her overture, this time I lay back down facing her. My eyes had by now adjusted to the dark, and in the slits of light filtering through the louvers I could see Che Guevara's eyes bulging over Marilyn's breasts. Then I felt her hand again.

"I may never get anywhere near Che or Fidel," she started to undo my shirt buttons, "but I'd love to do it with somebody who has."

I pondered the irony that the very men who had dispossessed my family should now be the ones to help procure my first score.

"I'm yours, Ernesto," Marilyn whispered the Christian name of her Argentine icon.

Loosened by all the grass I'd smoked I recast myself as a horny revolutionary, coming down victorious from the *Sierra Maestra* mountains and encountering my first female.

"And what about me . . .?" I asked.

She stopped, thinking that I'd gotten offended. "Oh, I'm sorry. Uh . . . what's your name again?"

"Fidel," I whispered in her ear. "Your double fantasy's about to come true."

We proceeded to make fumbling but enthusiastic love.

"Oh, Ernesto . . . Oh, Fidel . . . Oh, Jesus, Mary and Joseph!"

During the brief time our session lasted, Marilyn uttered many names, none of which was my own.

The message taped to my dorm room door was written with a blood-red magic marker. *"Hey Cubano, your padres have been calling all weekend. Mucho lucko!"*

"Where the hell have you been? I was already picturing you dead somewhere." My parents were both furious. But still feeling high from my experience, I decided not to lie.

"In Washington. At a peace march."

Papi's volume shot way up. "You mean you were at that thing?"

They had seen the news coverage, which had focused on the worst of it: National Guards, tear gas, demonstrators being hauled off or treated for toxic inhalation.

"Did you breathe in any of that stuff?"

"No, no. I'm fine." I wanted to tell them about all the positive things, like the communal feeling and brotherly spirit. But the more I said, the more my father accused me of being a *tonto útil*—a useful fool being taken advantage of by the so-called *peaceniks*. What I had hoped might be a transformational exchange became a hotheaded shouting match.

"We took you out of Cuba so they wouldn't fill your head with all that nonsense, and now it's happening right here."

"But please explain to me what's wrong with being against an unjust war? I wish you could have felt the love that was in the air, everywhere."

"The love? *Mira*, I've heard enough *basura* for one night." Papi had had it. "Start worrying a little less about peace and love and worry about those two courses that you're getting C minus on." Then he threw in that favorite Cuban epithet. "I never thought that you could be such a *come mierda*."

Being called a shit eater by my own father made me lose it completely, and I went for the jugular. "Okay, so maybe I am a *come mierda*. I'm just trying to sort things out as best I can. But have you ever really wondered why the revolution triumphed . . . or if perhaps you were on the wrong side?"

There was total silence at the other end. Then the line went dead.

I regretted having said those words the instant they came out of my mouth. I wanted to call right back and apologize, but I didn't. Throughout the night I kept tossing and wallowing in guilt. By morning I was dead-tired and did not hear one word that the professors said in either of my C-minus courses. That evening my mother called again.

"You really hurt him, you know. After he hung up he just sat there, repeating what you said as if he still couldn't believe it . . . Luisma, they didn't just take away material things, they destroyed his whole world. Even you ended up suffering because of it. He cried reading every single one of those letters that you sent us from military school."

"I know, I know." It was painful to hear her spell it all out. "I didn't mean for things to come out like that. And I'm sorry. I really am."

"Then please call and tell him so."

"I will. I promise." I meant it. I truly did. But then I wasn't brave enough.

• 36 •

Posters with turkeys wearing Pilgrim hats were hanging all over campus, wishing everyone a happy Thanksgiving. By Wednesday afternoon the dorm was a ghost town, but feeling added guilt over those C-minus grades that my father had reminded me of, I decided to spend the day studying, then catch an early evening train to New York.

Ramón Antonio had called to say that Mari invited him to join us for Thanksgiving dinner, and he even sounded excited by the prospect. "Though I suppose they'll expect me to put on a coat and tie," he added with less enthusiasm.

On Thursday morning, the sound of marching bands could be heard from every stairwell landing. Every TV in the house was tuned to the Macy's Parade. Those typical Thanksgiving sounds had become an instant tradition from our very first year of exile. One November, I had actually ventured across the park to watch the parade live but was disappointed to find that the Rockettes and all those big numbers from Broadway shows only appeared in front of the cameras at Herald Square. It was far better to watch it all from the warm comfort of home.

MARIA REGUEROS HAD never been able to lift a turkey, and this one was so heavy she could barely pull out the oven rack to baste it. Mari had been helping her all morning, while basting herself in the pantry with magical orange juices. Andres was also home from Philadelphia for the long weekend. He had recently announced that he was through letting Fidel dampen his life, and couldn't care less if that *isla de mierda* sank into the Caribbean. Despite the claim, however, he still kept following every last development within that "shitty island." He too appeared to have been basting himself.

"Well, darling," Mari welcomed me to the kitchen, "here we are again . . . all set to give thanks for yet another blessing-filled year." She already knew about my unfortunate phone call, and she suggested that this would be the perfect day to make peace with my father. She also warned me to avoid the subject of Tia Berta, who was still stuck in Mexico and driving everyone crazy with her growing desperation.

"She apparently heard that Maria saw Papá Gerardito up on the fifth floor, and keeps begging us to ask him to help her."

Maria Regueros seemed regretful of ever having started that rumor.

When the doorbell rang in the late afternoon, I knew it had to be Ramón Antonio and rushed on down to let him in and escort him upstairs.

"Wait, *mi chino*." He stopped by the entrance hall mirror to fiddle with his tie.

"Will you quit that? You look great." I was impressed by the change that a blazer and tie had brought about. But in typical fashion, my uncle kept grumbling.

"I never understood this absurd need for formality. All it does is constrict one's sphincter."

The second-floor rooms were unrecognizable, softly lit by candlelight, which had become Mari's favorite tactic for disguising the deterioration. She had also put out a cinnamon-scented potpourri to cover up the mustiness. The long dinner table was beautifully set with whatever crystal and china remained from the first exile. In the center sat an artsy floral arrangement, which Mari had rescued from a discarded Metropolitan Museum display. Even the Greek slave girl statue was sporting a pilgrim hat with a big orange bow.

Mamá Elvira had had a light bite in the kitchen earlier, then retired to her room. But Tia Babi and José Emilio were already holding court in the library, both looking very elegant, as were the two female boarders, Margarita and Isabelita, and also Tony, José Emilio's nephew. Everyone had outdone themselves for the occasion, although the only fashion item that gave any hint of the cultural revolution taking place outside was the string of love beads that Andres wore over his Nehru jacket.

"Ramón Antonio, *corazón!*" Tia Babi's arms flew open to embrace him. "Shame on you that Luisma had to practically drag you up to come see us."

"Well, maybe next time he will drag you down to come see me."

The thought of Tia Babi being greeted by Min Ariza in his red and gold kimono made me break into giggles. The Scotch I had poured myself was already taking effect.

We were still in the midst of introductions when Mari made her grand entrance in a flowing pantsuit printed with giant eye-popping blossoms.

"Darling!" She swept across toward Ramón Antonio, "It's been far too long."

"*Muchacha!*" He matched her dramatics. "You look like Rockefeller Center at Easter."

She did a full spin for everyone's benefit. "Don't you love it? It's a Rudy Gernreich original. Don't ask how I'm paying for it. Some people consider these wearable art. I'm at the Metropolitan now, you know." She seemed bent on sounding cultural. "Has everyone got a drink? Luisma dear, you're in charge of the bar." She turned to Ramón Antonio again. "So tell me, have you seen any worthwhile theater lately?"

"Yes. Zoe Caldwell is magnificent in *The Prime of Miss Jean Brodie*."

"But depressing, no? I refuse to pay to get depressed when it's so easy to do it for free."

"I just saw *Mame*," Margarita chirped. "Have you seen that?"

Ramón Antonio winced. "I'd rather have rectal surgery."

"Luisma, *mi amor*." Mari held up her glass. "This is pure ice, and I'm not Sonja Henie."

Maria Regueros' clip-clops could be heard emerging from the elevator. Even though she had no intention of joining the festivities, she had put on an old black uniform that seemed more suited for a funeral.

"Caballero Andres, I'm going to need your help with the turkey."

As Andres headed downstairs with her, Ramón Antonio leaned over and whispered, "God, I wish I were directing *Bernarda Alba*. She'd be the perfect Poncia."

I whispered back, "Apparently she's been seeing my *bisabuelo*."

Tia Babi overheard me. "Luis Manuel, please."

Ramón Antonio tried to make light of it. "Oh, I would love to make contact with the other side, so I could ask if they have music up there. I don't mean little *putti* with harps, but Mozart or Beethoven. If I could have proof that they're still composing, death would be so much more appealing."

"Then again," said Mari, who had gone for a refill, picking up exactly where she had left off, "if you say *Miss Brodie* is so good, maybe I *will* go see it."

"What I would really love to see is *Hair*," said Isabelita.

"I bet what you *really* want to see is all those naked guys on stage," Mari shot back.

Isabelita turned beet red as everyone burst out in giggles, which then got drowned out by the shouting coming from the butler's pantry. Andres had tried to send the turkey up in the dumb waiter, and now it was stuck between floors.

"What ever possessed you?" Mari shouted at him through the dark shaft. "This thing hasn't worked in ages."

"Yes, it has!" Andres shouted back while tugging at ancient cables. "Last year."

"In your drunken dreams, darling!"

The stuck turkey had unleashed a marital squabble, but the rest of us found this a rather amusing distraction and voiced our opinions.

"Get a broom and push it back down!"

"No, no! We need something heavier."

"How about Maria Regueros?"

"What we need is to forget the damn thing and order pizzas."

I could see that Andres was making some progress, and I leaned into the shaft to help him tug. As we did, clumps of soot kept falling on our heads. By the time the turkey surfaced, our faces were as black as chimney sweeps. There was a round of applause as Andres carried the bird to the table, smiling like a proud fireman who had just rescued a fat baby.

Mari had placed José Emilio and Andres at opposite ends of the table, then sat as far as she could from her husband. After everyone had served themselves, she turned to Ramón Antonio.

"Now *you're* a man with a progressive mind. Where do you stand on free-love?"

"Mari, *por Dios!*" Tia Babi was mortified.

"Don't be so old fashioned, Mamá. It's *the* topic of the moment." She turned to my uncle again. "So?"

"I think whoever coined that phrase knows very little about the subject. Love is never free. In fact, you usually end up paying far more than it's worth."

"Bravo!" Tia Babi clapped softly. But Mari kept at it.

"Well, I think I'd still take my chances, if opportunity knocked."

"*Hija*, please!"

"So would I!" Andres matched his wife's boasting. "How about you girls?" he turned to Margarita and Isabelita, who blushed and giggled again.

"Tell me, Luis Manuel," José Emilio changed the subject, "what's happening with all that research you were doing at the public library?"

"Well, I came across this incredible pamphlet . . . it's a word-by-word record of the meetings that U.S. Ambassador Welles had with the leaders of the ABC . . . basically giving them carte blanche to do whatever it took to get rid of Papá Gerardito. But the more I find the more questions I have, and don't know where to turn next."

"How about our fifth floor?" said Andres. "Go straight to the horse's mouth."

Tia Babi's chair screeched as she pushed it back and stood. "I forbid you to joke about that. This is still my father's house, and the least you can do is have some respect."

"*Al carajo* with Thanksgiving!" Andres tossed his napkin aside and stormed out.

"You know," Ramón Antonio leaned toward Margarita, "I take back what I said about *Mame*. It's looking more appealing by the minute."

Maria Regueros had just clip-clopped back to see how everything was going.

"Now what do you suppose Papá Gerardito would say about all this?" Mari grinned.

"Don't look at me," Maria Regueros shrugged. "I am a sealed tomb."

"Well, thank God for small favors." Mari picked up her empty cocktail glass. "All right, who's ready for another round?"

Throughout Thanksgiving weekend, I hid my head in the sand to avoid calling my father, but when I opened my school post office box the following Monday, I found a familiar-looking envelope waiting for me, addressed in Papi's handwriting. It was neither a lecture nor a reproach, but rather a carefully thought out letter in which he did his very best to reach out and explain himself.

Dear Luis Manuel,

I much regret the way that our conversation ended the other day. I realize that there's an ongoing romance between liberal intellectuals everywhere and the Cuban Revolution, and apparently, even some people within more conservative institutions.

It is so simple for a false prophet to come along and paint a Utopia, in which all will be just and everyone sharing equally.

Unfortunately, we humans are much more complex, and in the process of achieving such Utopias, these prophets find themselves having to impose controls that end up enslaving everyone.

In a way I admire your trying to search for your own answers and not rely only on what you might have heard from us. I trust that in doing so, however, you will also try to look beyond the glamorization and remember all the people who have been executed simply for disagreeing with the revolution's ideas, and the ones we know who are still political prisoners, or those who have risked their lives crossing the Florida Strait on rickety makeshift boats because they can't live one more day under such a Utopia.

We lost everything, but even so, if the revolution had truly benefited everyone, perhaps I could have made my peace with it. Unfortunately, it has only created a new all-powerful ruling class that now owns everything.

It is easy to praise from afar what one perceives as ideal, without having to experience its realities. I wonder how most of these idealists who talk of the revolution's wonders would feel if a leader like Fidel appeared here tomorrow and took away everything they had, along with their right to express any dissenting opinions.

As to the Vietnam War, perhaps it would have been best for the Americans to stay out of it. As much as I hate communism, I would also hate to see you having to risk your life there.

Con todo mi cariño,

Papi

I finally got up the courage to call him that night and apologize, but he had already moved on from the subject. This time he just grilled me about making sure I had no more C grades by the end of the semester.

• 37 •

A few days after Christmas, Mamá Elvira died quietly in her bed, only months short of her hundredth birthday. Tia Babi had achieved what she wanted, to let her mother live out her final years without being uprooted again. Both Mari and Fifi, who had gone up from Philadelphia a few days prior, said that it had been a peaceful death, like a candle flickering away.

My great-grandmother's body was flown to Miami, so that she could be buried next to her husband, the ex-president, in Woodlawn Park Cemetery. The political passions that once raged around them had long since died down. The funeral was an intimate one, attended only by family members and loyal friends. During the funeral mass, two songs were played, both iconic symbols of our War of Independence: "El Mambí" and "La Bayamesa." Rafael Guas Inclán, who had been president of the House of Representatives during my *bisabuelo*'s administration, gave the eulogy. He spoke of Elvirita's youthful bravery, when she rode through the Cuban countryside bringing supplies to the rebel fighters and tending to their wounded. He called her the most modest and unaffected of our Cuban first ladies: "a woman who was content to live in the background shadows, but always within the majesty and greatness of her soul."

Once again, it was difficult for me to relate the sedate old lady that I had known, sitting on a rocking chair with her boxes of memorabilia, to the horse-riding freedom fighter being eulogized.

The news of her mother's death sent Tia Berta into a frenzy. She had still been unable to get entry visas, primarily because of Lugi's status.

But she was now tired of waiting and had become determined to take matters into her own hands. Tia Babi had no idea what her sister had in mind when she called to say, "You will be seeing me *very* shortly."

Another call awoke my parents early the following Saturday. It was collect, from Brownsville, Texas.

"I'm at a pay phone, in a gas station, but don't worry, we're fine. Let me give you the information of where to wire me money, for bus tickets."

By day's end, Tia Berta, Lugi, and Aurora, the still-shell-shocked companion, were on a Greyhound en route to New York. The story of their crossing, as told by Tia Berta, would soon become part of family lore.

"I had never broken a law in my life, except the revolution's, and was hoping to enter here legally, but it became obvious that the Americans had no intention of letting Lugi in . . . which I will never forgive them for because it kept me from seeing Mamá alive. But there was a man at our hotel who kept offering to sneak us across the border, and I knew people did it every day, so I finally said, 'All right. I guess that's what we'll have to do.'

"He put us on a rickety old bus that took a whole day to get to this awful dusty town, where we were to meet our guide. We had already paid plenty to the man in Mexico City, but this other one tells me I have to pay him more, and then walk from there to the border carrying our own bags. I said, 'No, no, no. I'm sorry, but that's not what I agreed to.' I will not repeat the words that came out of that mouth. Let me just say that he was no gentleman.

"Aurora got so scared she wanted to turn back. But I told her, 'Then what, stay in Mexico forever?' I didn't trust our guide either but could see no alternative. 'At least he's short,' I said to myself, 'and there are three of us.'

"After walking forever, with poor Lugi complaining that she was getting blisters, we got to the Rio Grande. I had heard that it wasn't really very *grande*, but it certainly looked that way in the spot where we were crossing. Our little man pulled out an old wooden raft that he had hidden in some bushes, and said 'Get on!' It didn't look very safe to me, but he assured us that he had crossed hundreds of times in it, with far more than three people, and that even in the worst case, the water was not too deep.

"We were about halfway across when Lugi got nervous because the current kept rocking us. So she tried to hold on to the guide, but he pushed her away. That made her really mad, and you know how Lugi can be when she gets that way. She grabbed him again and started shaking him like a rag doll, which made the raft rock even more. The man started yelling, 'Get this crazy woman off me!' But Aurora and I together couldn't pull Lugi away. She's a lot stronger than she looks. Aurora was afraid we'd all fall in. But I was more worried that border police would hear the man's shouts and send us back, after everything we had already been through.

"When the raft touched bottom at the American side, Lugi finally let go. But the instant he was free, the guide pushed us off into knee-deep water and took off as fast as he could. We had no idea where we were. Luckily we came to a road, and this very nice man with a truck, another Mexican, picked us up and drove us to the gas station from where I called Nenita. And here we are . . . but sadly too late to see Mamá once again."

Tia Berta and Lugi were now ensconced within Fifteen East, waiting for probate of Mamá Elvira's estate to be settled so that the house could be placed on the market. Lugi had put on a bit of weight since I had last seen her. She was spending most of her days sitting at the kitchen table, leafing through catalogues or fiddling with a needle and thread but not accomplishing much. She acted rather shy around me, perhaps because I had such a hard time understanding her language. But it was impressive to watch Mari chattering away with her.

"Tití Papá achoo?"

"No, Lugi. Tití Papá no achoo. He just *poofity* and go bed bye."

Lugi was far from dumb. She had her very own logic and could be quite sensitive to what people around her were feeling. Most of the family was in agreement that a lot more could have been achieved with her. Unfortunately, she had been the victim of too much sympathy. Whenever a teacher was brought in to work with her, if Lugi began to cry or threw a tantrum, both Tia Berta and Mamá Elvira would break into choruses of "*Pobrecita.* Poor Lugi," and the teacher would be instantly dismissed.

On more than one occasion, I had watched her suddenly stop whatever she was doing, then sit straight up and begin to speak as if to someone hovering over her. Other times she would swivel around to reprimand some other invisible being who appeared to be right behind her. Each time I had tried to act as if this was the most normal everyday occurrence, but then I couldn't wait to be alone with Maria Regueros.

"Why does she keep doing that?"

"*Ay, mijo.* You don't want to know." She kept shrugging me off.

Then one evening, just as I was drifting off to sleep in Mari and Fifi's old nursery, I began to hear strange sounds wafting in through the chimney. At first I thought it was a downdraft, then realized that it was a human sound, a mix of moans and whimperings, which kept growing louder. By now I was wide-awake and getting goose bumps. I couldn't quite make out what was being said, so I got up and went closer. There seemed to be two very different voices, one of them mournful, the other angry or perhaps scared. Then I realized that both of them were Lugi's. It was as if she was playing two separate roles, fighting against one another.

The very next chance I got to be alone with Maria again, I told her what I had heard and begged her to explain what was going on.

This time she caved in. "*Bueno,*" she sighed, "I might as well. Your Tia Berta found some woman up in Spanish Harlem . . . a *santera* or *espiritista*, and has been bringing her here at night after everyone else is in bed."

"But what for?"

"To contact your *bisabuelo*. I am already used to Señora Berta's eccentricities. What I don't like is that this time she's letting poor Lugi be used as the medium . . . for the spirit to speak through. That's why she has been acting like you saw. They have her so confused she's seeing shadows everywhere. And please, do not tell anyone about this. I don't even want to think what will happen if your Tia Babi finds out."

"You mean they haven't heard all those crazy sounds?"

"Luckily their fireplaces are on a different flue." Suddenly there was a devious glint in her eye. "You know, I can't sneak up there without their hearing me . . . but perhaps you could."

It was after midnight when I heard the elevator going up past my floor. Despite the splintered wooden planks I wore only socks as I tiptoed up to the little fifth-floor room where I had first stayed during our World's Fair visit. The dark narrow stairway that led to the next floor still looked intimidating, but I was much too curious, so I slowly crept my way up, step by step. The door at the top was ajar. By remaining flat against the landing and poking my head in slightly, I could get a pretty good view of the entire room. A little round end table had been set up beside the big billiards table. Lugi and Tia Berta were seated on either side, while a Black woman took her work tools out of a Klein's shopping bag. These consisted of two votive candles, a branch of some kind with dry leaves still clinging to it, a fat cigar, and a big bottle of cologne. She then took out a long strip of red cloth and wrapped it around the leg of Lugi's chair.

"This will tie *el santo* to *el caballo*," she said reverently, "the saint to the horse."

I assumed that *el santo* was the spirit they were hoping to conjure, and *el caballo*, the mount upon which *el santo* would perch—poor Lugi.

The woman lit the cigar then started puffing and exhaling smoke, fanning it toward Lugi with the branch. Although no expert on cigars, I could tell after one whiff that this was probably the cheapest *puro* that one could buy in a *bodega*. As the woman went around, Lugi coughed, and floorboards creaked under her weight.

"*Shh*. Softly, *por favor*," Tia Berta begged.

"*Ikú lo bi Ochá!*" she chanted in a language imported by her African ancestors to the Caribbean. I had read a little bit about Santería, and I knew that this was either Yoruba or Lukumí. "*Ikú lo bi Ochá!*" She kept repeating the words as the smoke formed mini-tornadoes around *el caballo*. Then she sprinkled Lugi with the cologne and, leaning closer, whispered into one of her ears, "*Orú ilé Olorun!*" then louder, "*Orú ilé Olorun!*"

"Please, not so loud." I could see Tia Berta getting nervous, but the woman was beyond hearing her. Then one of Lugi's feet went into spasm and started kicking the floor. "Lugi?" Tia Berta touched her, but now she too was beyond reach.

"*Siá!*" The *santera*'s torso stiffened, then went limp, as if something had passed through her. Then Lugi began to convulse and shake, making the old dry wood under her chair creak and squeak even more.

"Maybe we should stop," said Tia Berta, but the stare the other woman gave her implied that this was not a good idea. Lugi's head jerked, as if with a nervous tic, and she began to speak in a gravelly voice that was definitely not her own. The voice grew more forceful, then started ranting away like an angry politician—and just as incoherently.

"*Papá?*" Tia Berta's tone became hopeful. "*Papá*, I need to talk to you."

Lugi just kept mumbling replies to whatever her mother asked. By now my morbid curiosity had turned to sadness, and I decided that I'd seen enough. I carefully crept back down the winding steps and tried to go to sleep.

All throughout breakfast the next day, Lugi carried on another of her strange conversations. It appeared that *el santo* was still on *el caballo*, or rather, two of them. The one floating slightly above her she seemed to be in good terms with; it even made her smile. The one behind her, however, was making her very anxious and she kept shooing it away.

"*Titinini*, NO!"

From her usual spot across the kitchen, Maria Regueros kept exchanging glances with me and sighing.

When Tia Berta came down she was in high spirits. The moment Tia Babi returned from her eleven o'clock mass, she spread her arms in joyful welcome. "Angela Elvira, I have great news. Papá has promised that he's going to help us."

• 38 •

Cubans are supposed to be such extroverts, but for the most part it's only a surface act. With things that truly matter, they can be as unpriable as clams. My mother always felt that her family had raised avoidance into a high art. Their solution to problems had usually been to raise the volume of the music and dance more frenetically. But no one could keep dancing forever. The party always ends, and when the music stops, the problems one had tried to dance away from were still there waiting.

After nine years of holding on to the townhouse, it was finally put up for sale. Within twenty-four hours, a description of the property was being circulated through all the major Manhattan real-estate agencies.

> Magnificent private residence, former home of a Cuban President, on fine East Side street facing museum. Under one single ownership for many years. While somewhat neglected, the house is complete with elegant fireplaces and woodwork paneling. Elevator up to the sixth floor, which consists of a large suite and rooftop terrace.
>
> By appointment only. Price and terms upon request.

When Tia Babi read the notice she felt a pang of regret. She had never expected things to move so quickly, but there was no turning back. Everyone was calling to set up appointments, and Maria Regueros became the reluctant receptionist. She sat at her post keeping track of who was coming when, while continuing to dice onions and bell peppers for her daily *sofritos*. Mari, who had long been an advocate for the sale, along with Andres, was now all weepy and sentimental. She made it clear that she was much too busy at the museum to make herself available for the showings, and Tia Berta could certainly not be trusted with that, so the task fell upon Tia Babi.

She dressed up for each appointment as if she was back at the presidential palace helping her father receive some head of state. Most prospective buyers preferred taking the stairs in order to get a better view of everything, so Tia Babi kept going up and down those six flights, ending each day in exhaustion. People usually insisted on seeing every last nook and closet, some of which she had forgotten existed. The clutter inside these made her feel exposed, but still she smiled on, like Jackie Kennedy giving her tour of the White House. Plaster potholes, leak-stained walls, warped floors, and maimed statues: she convinced herself that all of it was merely a manifestation of laid-back gentility.

The kitchen never failed to impress. "My God, Mel! Look at that oven! My great-grandmother used to have one just like it on Essex Street."

Maria Regueros threw killer-glances at anyone who dared deride her beloved appliances. "But they still work perfectly," she defended them. "I'd like to see any of these modern ones last half as long."

As word spread about the time-warped property, celebrities looking for a substantial *pied* à *terre* also began to show interest. The first one passed by imperceptibly.

"I'm bringing a special client tomorrow, but he would like to keep this very low-key," one of the agents announced to Maria Regueros in reverential tones, and Maria jotted down the scheduled appointment without giving it a second thought. Tia Babi too was unimpressed by the encounter. She resented having gotten all dressed up for an albino mop-head who kept his dark glasses on and never said two words to her.

When Mari got home and saw his calling card she was livid. "You mean, Andy Warhol was here and you didn't tell me he was coming?"

"We had no idea who he was."

"We still don't."

From that moment on she made a point of finding out who was on the agenda. The night before the John Lennon and Yoko Ono appointment, she stayed up plucking her eyebrows and giving herself a facial—even though she was no Beatles fan. She seemed less interested in who the celebrities were than in letting them know that she had once been one herself, by association. As she later told me, "When John Lennon was still a baby crawling around Liverpool tenements in soiled diapers, I was in a presidential palace, enviable enough to have people bombing my nursery."

She waited for John and Yoko looking her most Audrey Hepburn glamorous. She even made Lugi presentable, and told her that under no circumstances was she to speak to the dead in the former Beatle's presence. But then more than one hour after the celebrity couple's appointed time, it was a mere minor assistant who showed up, charged with deciding whether it was worth John and Yoko's time to come see the property. She apparently decided it wasn't.

The day Barbra Streisand was scheduled to come, even Andres stayed around. He kept saying how sexy he found her, which cranked up Mari's jealousy.

Everyone sat around pretending to be having an endless breakfast and breaking into off-key renditions of "People." This time, it was Elliott Gould who showed up. He was charming and apologized for his wife not being able to make it. Mari got even with Andres by flirting with Elliott through six whole floors. Along the way, she mentioned how much she had loved *Funny Girl*, which she hadn't actually seen. Elliott smiled. "I'll tell Barbra." Then he became aloof. Realizing she had put her foot in her mouth, Mari tried to compliment him on his own work, but couldn't think of anything he had been in. After this failed experience, she lost all interest in meeting celebrities.

Everyone who saw the house claimed to love *its potential*, but the offers were all way below the asking price. When Tia Babi complained to realtors about this, she was reminded of the extremely poor condition the property was in and that whoever bought it would have to pour a fortune into it. She began to wonder whose side the realtors were on and pictured them telling their clients that the family was desperate to sell.

"If they think they can take advantage of us, they have a surprise coming," she told herself. One thing she had learned from all those years around Cuban politics was to sit tight while the bombs fell—and wear out the opposition.

The door to Ramón Antonio's apartment was slightly ajar. I found him sipping coffee at the kitchen table and reading a biography of John of Austria, illegitimate son of Charles V and leader of the Christian forces in the battle of Lepanto. He greeted me in a whisper. "Herving is taking a nap."

"Oh. He's back?"

"Just for the day. He's working at a hotel in Poughkeepsie and wanted to bring me a present." He pointed to a big basket of apples. "Picked them himself, right off a tree."

I could see Herving, sprawled face up, with an arm hanging over the edge of the sofa. I remembered the purple welts that I had once misread. Those were now gone, and his skin looked as smooth as polished marble.

Ramón Antonio read my thoughts. "Isn't that wonderful? No more *tattoos*." He lit a cigarette. "So what did you want to talk about?"

Despite having made peace with my father, I was still feeling guilty over our incident. At school, I kept being bombarded by pro-revolution sentiments, which were not helping me to clarify where I stood.

And now, adding to my political confusion, I was also questioning all the religious beliefs that I had been taught throughout my twelve years of Catholic schools.

"Come here, *mi chino*." He gestured for me to pull my chair closer. "You know I'm not religious, though I do believe there's some kind of cosmic plan . . ."

"Please, Tio. I'm up to my ass in mystic bullshit. I have this neighbor in my dorm who keeps playing Ravi Shankar and chanting Ommm all night long."

"Okay, then. No mystic bullshit today. Just don't worry too much about any of it. You'll find your way . . . in *every* respect." He looked into my eyes for a moment, as if he knew more about me than I myself did. Then quickly changing the subject he held up a beat-up manila envelope with lots of big colorful stamps on it, like those that Mimamá used to send us. "This arrived from Cuba today. I left some photo albums with a friend before I left—my dentist, of all people." Ramón Antonio slipped out a disorderly stack of old black-and-white prints. "Wait!" he pulled them away when I reached over. "There's one that I want you to see first." His fingers riffled through the pile searching for it. It was a family group, posing in front of an ornate altarpiece. Ramón Antonio and Mari were at the center, both looking terribly young and jointly carrying a baby who was the focus of the gathering.

"You know what this is, don't you?"

"Uh-huh. My baptism."

This particular photo had not been among the ones that Mimamá had sent, but I remembered having seen it years ago, before it got left behind along with so much else. Most images from my Havana life had by now become a fuzzy blend of childhood memories and romanticized family descriptions. It made the picture that I was holding feel like a precious artifact from some long-lost world. My parents seemed so young in it too, as if they had been almost children themselves when they had me. And there was Mimamá, with a long curving feather sticking out of her hat, creating a halo for Padre Llaguno, our family priest, who was standing beside her. Everyone was smiling for the camera, except for Lugi, whose eyes were looking up, as if seeing something that no one else could. But the biggest smile of all, even bigger than my parents', was the one on my godmother, Mari. She seemed transported by the new life she was holding in her arms, and perhaps also the promise of the children that she herself would bear one day. There were so many observations that could be made about the happy group, but I just made one.

"Tío, look how much more hair you used to have."

"*Ay, mijo*. Whenever we look back, we realize we had much more of everything." He rubbed out his cigarette, then when I handed back the picture, he waved his hands exhaling one last puff. "No, no. Keep it." Something else had occurred to him. "Maybe your Tia Mari would like to see it."

As I hugged him goodbye I said, "I so wish I could have been around you more all these years."

"No you don't. I might have *really* screwed you up."

"That's not true at all. Look what a great job you did with Herving and Rudy."

"That's because they were both screwed up to begin with. I couldn't possibly mess them up any further."

• 39 •

The good news was that there finally seemed to be a buyer for the house, an architect. His wife had already come by three times, but he had been out of town with a project so all that remained was for him to come and make a final decision.

The night before his appointment, Mari and Tia Babi spent hours making sure that the house looked as presentable as possible.

Up in her fifth-floor room, Margarita had been studying for a test but finding it hard to concentrate. The only reason she had even cracked a book was that her social plans for the evening had fallen through at the last minute. To make matters worse, her sister, Isabelita, was out on a date. Feeling sorry for herself, she decided that a little pampering was in order and started to prepare a bubble bath. She had just turned on the water when the phone rang.

Mari had dozed off while reading, and did not appreciate being startled. She was about to hang up on whoever it was, but then hearing that it was long distance—from Dartmouth—she decided to be merciful to poor dateless Margarita.

Thrilled to be getting a call from a man, Margarita threw on a robe and dashed over barefoot, splinters be damned! The young gentleman caller was someone she had met over Easter weekend while having drinks at Mike Malkan's, an Irish pub popular with the collegiate crowd. She sat there, reacting fawningly as she listened to his exploits on the debate team. By the time he asked her to tell him a little more about herself, Margarita had drawn her bare feet up on the telephone bench and was absentmindedly playing with her toes. Had her feet been more firmly planted, she would have surely felt the water gliding by beneath her.

Her conversation lasted almost half an hour, which was just about how long the bathtub had been overflowing. Margarita had been so transported that she never heard the trickle and gurgle or the gushing cascade beginning to roll down the stairs.

"So can we get together when I next come down?" the young man asked as his last dime ran out.

"Oh, yes. Definitely!" Margarita knew she had sounded over-eager, but for once in her life she told herself, "To hell with façades!" She hung up floating on a cloud, a perilous height from which she plummeted the moment her feet sank into the floor.

"*Ay-ay!*" She had forgotten where she was, but she knew that wetness was not what she should be feeling. When she looked down, her nerve endings went into spasm. The entire hallway was under water, and clusters of soap bubbles kept drifting by like ominous icebergs. A lone nylon stocking floated by too, with a cockroach trying to climb aboard.

"*Ay-ay-ay!*" Suddenly remembering what she had been about to do before the phone call, she splashed her way to the bathroom to turn off the faucets. Her heart was beating so fast that she had to sit down on the toilet. From there she contemplated the disaster, trying to decide whether to go get towels or just jump out a window.

I had awakened from an enchanted liquid dream, which had given me an intense need to pee. When my feet stepped onto the soggy area rug I wondered, *Did I do this?* Then I turned on the light and saw that the whole room had become a wading pool. There was no way that my bladder could have been the culprit.

What I encountered in the hallway was actually quite magnificent. Dozens of parallel rivulets were dripping between the banisters, glistening in the dim light like long nylon guitar strings. I walked further and saw that the stairway was a mini-Niagara, one that any child would have loved to have in their home. Curious to see how far down this was going, I leaned over the railing. The cascade lost itself in darkness, but the echoing sounds hinted that it was going far enough. I stood there, admiring the incongruous beauty and wishing it weren't something that was not supposed to be happening. After a moment I waded toward Mari and Andres' bedroom and gently knocked on the door.

"Sorry to wake you, but I think you should see this."

All peaceful dreams came to an end, as everyone got to work with the frantic energy of ants in a jiggled Ant Farm. Soon we had used every towel and sheet in the house, spread these over hallways and stairs to sop up the mess then wrung them out into buckets. But the water seemed endless. I thought of Mickey Mouse in *Fantasia* and wished that I could conjure up squads of living mops to come to our rescue.

For hours we all sponged and squeezed in dead silence, too shell-shocked to utter a single *"Ay!"* or *"Dios mio!"* Even Maria Regueros made herself useful, rolling around in an old desk chair while wielding a long-poled squeegee.

Margarita kept apologizing and feeling even worse for getting the silent treatment. "Somebody, please, say something."

"I hope you remain a spinster till the day you die!" Mari now regretted her moment of kindness.

Even the normally sedate Tia Babi had reached the end of her fuse. "I thought that Papá was going to help us," she snapped at Tia Berta. "Why didn't he warn us about this?"

By the time the first rays of dawn shone through the stained-glass skylight, the stairwell looked like a Neapolitan tenement on washday. There were five flights of railing draped with shriveled rugs, and the once-bone-dry floorboards had warped into rolling hills that made the whole place feel like a topsy-turvy carnival fun house. Then the ceilings began to attack.

The seepage had created bubbles under the remaining patches of paint. These were now popping like liquid grenades, sending chunks of plaster down like sudden hailstorms, drenching furniture, knocking over vases, and creating hazards for anyone standing beneath.

We were all still at it, wearing whatever we had been sleeping in, when the doorbell rang. Mari, who was mopping the entrance hall, stood demurely behind the door to hide her negligee.

"We're not too early, are we?" The realtor was standing there, looking perfectly groomed and cheery-faced, with the prospective buyers at her side. "Your housekeeper said that nine o'clock would be fine."

Overcome by a sense of total powerlessness, Mari emerged from behind her cover with an Audreyesque smile. "Yes, come in! Your timing is perfect." Three jaws dropped in unison, for even in the Age of Aquarius, a dripping wet negligee was not your standard guest-greeting garb. "But be careful!" she pointed to the glistening floor. "I'd hate for you to slip and break your necks."

After one quick look around, the architect stared at his wife wondering how she could have been so enthusiastic about what he was seeing.

"What happened?" The realtor's manicured hand flew to her lips.

"Oh, just a little leak." Mari kept smiling. "But don't worry, when you've lived through two exiles and multiple bombings, these things are way low on your Richter scale." She then turned to the bewildered couple, who seemed reluctant to step in further. "Go on! Inspect all you want. Would you like galoshes?"

Tia Babi could not find it within herself to be as jovial. She stood in embarrassed silence as the inopportune visitors wandered through drenched rooms trying to avoid ceiling grenades. She had no doubt that the sale would now fall through, but that very afternoon the realtor called, with an offer far below the previous one. Tia Babi felt insulted and told her that she would not even consider it. "We have had much better offers, and you know it."

"Yes, but I can assure you, none of them would still stand if those clients saw the house now."

"Fine. This offer is still unacceptable."

"Just sleep on it, all right? I'll call again tomorrow."

"Don't bother. Unless it's to make a higher one."

"As I said, sleep on it." The agent remained calm. "Or better yet, lie in bed staring at that ceiling. Let's be honest, I know you have no money to repair it . . . and before long you won't have a ceiling either. Just pray it doesn't cave in before we can close the deal."

Tia Babi hung up outraged. Then that evening, exhausted as she was, she lay in bed unable to sleep. The once moderate plaster hole above her head had now tripled in size. Whichever way she turned, her eyes kept seeing new damage.

In the morning, Tia Babi discussed the situation with all concerned, even calling my mother, the legal representative for Mimamá, who was still in Cuba. She then called the realtor and accepted the offer.

• 40 •

One month is a very short time to pack up a lifetime. My semester was over and I was heading down to Miami for the summer, but I wanted to spend one last weekend in the house and offered to help with whatever I could.

Tia Babi stared at the piles of trunks and mystery boxes that now lined the fifth-floor hallway. The flood had damaged most of them. Anything cardboard or paper was bulging and stained. Still, she saw it all as pieces of her identity and therefore held the bathtub flood as a disaster equal to the burning of the Alexandria library.

Mari had now become the voice of reason. "It's simply not possible to go through everything, Mamá. We'd be here for the next two years."

"Then we'll go over whatever we can and finish the rest in Miami."

"And pay a mint for shipping things just to throw them away there? Look at this!" she held up a mildewy log. "Financial records from nineteen thirty-five. Why the hell do we need that?"

"To prove Papá did not steal one penny." As Tia Babi reached for it, an old newspaper clipping fell out. I picked it up and read the bold headline:

"'*Machado Turns Himself In.*' You mean they finally caught him . . . with that dancer?"

"No, *corazón*. This was three years later, when . . ."

"Mamá! We won't even get through one floor if you also stop to explain everything."

"I do not intend to, *mija*. But maybe just this one thing." She shifted on her chair to get more comfortable, then began.

"The time you're referring to he did manage to get away, and somehow made it to Baltimore. There he had to bribe a ship captain who was sailing for the Bahamas, so he would take him. Then on the way down the captain blackmailed Papá, saying that if he did not give him more money he would pull into the next port and turn him in. Papá had to give him almost everything he had. Then after weeks of more hiding and stowing away he finally ended up in Paris, where the French welcomed him and even presented him with the Legion of Honor. Afraid to come back, he stayed there for over two years. We were all dying to go see him, but the money was simply too tight, so we never went. Our separation would have probably lasted even longer if Papá had not come down with cancer.

"We contacted everyone we could down in Washington, hoping to get him a permit to return, so he could get treatment. But we never succeeded. Papá was determined to spend with us whatever time he had left, so he decided to take his chances and come back anyway. When he showed up at that door I almost didn't recognize him. He looked so frail.

"We took him straight to Murray Hill Hospital, and word quickly got out that he was back. Within a matter of hours, two officers showed up and arrested him under the extradition warrant, which had never been revoked. He was allowed to remain in the hospital, but with guards posted outside his door twenty-four hours. Every time we went in or out they would check our coats and purses, as if we were criminals."

"Mamá," Mari went by dragging a stuffed trash bag. "*Must* we hear every detail?"

"Yes. I want him to know," Tia Babi continued.

"The extradition hearing was held before a commission. The presiding judge was outraged by the way that the authorities had treated Papá . . . and said that since the American Revolution this country had been a haven for political refugees. He pointed out that almost three years had already passed and the Cuban tribunal had still not been able to prove any of the charges. But the hearing went on anyway. Papá was transferred to an isolation unit, which was even more like a prison. Things dragged on for so long that I was sure he would die before it was over. Then the Cuban government, which had kept changing since Papá left, changed yet again. Someone in the new administration was an old colleague of his from the War of Independence. Not that they hadn't also had their political disagreements . . . but there's something about the friendships of one's youth that seem unbreakable. So Papá was granted amnesty and finally discharged from custody. Unfortunately, there wasn't much that the doctors could do for him otherwise, so he was released from the hospital too.

"When we stepped out of the building we were mobbed by reporters and photographers . . . all shouting out questions that Papá felt too weak answer. He asked me to say that he would give them a statement by morning."

Tia Babi handed the clipping back to me. "His words are all in there."

I read them aloud.

> I bear no complaints against this great country, which has offered shelter to my family. While I was still President of Cuba I was greatly honored with a visit by President Coolidge, and then again by his invitation to visit Washington. For that I shall always be grateful. Nor will I complain that in The United States, where every man is innocent until proven guilty, I was denied such treatment. However, I do hope that in the future, other political refugees, no matter where they may come from or how humble their station, will not have to endure the same experience that I did.

I felt proud to read those words, yet soon afterwards, my nagging doubts returned. It still bothered me that my *bisabuelo* should have brought up such a democratic principle when he himself had agreed to a change in the Cuban constitution, to extend his term of office, which had disrupted that very process in his own country. But those thoughts I kept to myself.

IT WAS WHILE clearing out items from the basement that Andres finally came across what he had been searching for all these years. From behind a bunch of old bedsprings and brass bedsteads that were being carted away by a metal scrap company, emerged a big bank-like safe.

"I knew it!" Andres was convinced he had unearthed the Machado treasure, the money that the ex-president had so often been accused of fleeing the country with.

This discovery reignited his old battle with Tia Babi. She assured him that she had no idea of the safe's existence, and was positive that Papá Gerardito couldn't have known about it either. But Andres was still not dissuaded.

"Don't you find it a little suspicious that out of all the basement walls those bedsprings could have been leaned against, someone strategically placed them hiding that safe?"

In the end it was he who convinced Tia Babi that even if her father had not hidden anything there, perhaps the previous owners had. After all, they *had* moved out in a hurry.

A company specializing in cracking open old safes was called in. For what seemed like an exorbitant fee, they placed some kind of explosive device around the combination lock, and the safe was blown open. The result was one of mixed feelings for Tia Babi. On the positive side, it proved once again that her father had not taken those reputed millions. On the other hand, they had incurred yet another big expense only to find a few bottles of overly aged wine that they could not even drink.

FOR TWO WHOLE days, a moving van partially blocked East Eighty-Second Street, as workmen emptied out the house. By the final night the place felt like a vast echoing cavern. I was to hear that story many times.

"Well, this is it!" Tia Babi said to herself, "At least for this chapter of my life." She could now look back and see the outcome of everything that had begun here. There were no past mysteries left to unravel or future ones yet to begin—at least not in this house. Her father had escaped, then come back to be arrested and to die. They had all returned to Cuba, then been forced into a second exile, and now here they were heading down to Miami, the Cuban exile Mecca. Tia Berta and Lugi had already left, as neither had been of much use during the packing process. But Tia Babi felt grateful for Maria Regueros, who had been so loyal and constant throughout all these years, like the North Star, or whatever it was that one could be guided by in the wilderness.

"This is it," she whispered to herself again as she stopped to take one last look at the deserted entrance hallway.

"*Por Dios*, Mamá! *Vamos!*" Mari called out from the sidewalk. She, Maria Regueros, and José Emilio were waiting for Andres and the two taxi drivers to finish loading their luggage.

"Don't worry, Señora," Maria whispered when Tia Babi finally stepped outside. "The General is coming with us."

"Oh, really?" Mari overheard. "Does he intend to keep following us around like the Fiddler on the Roof?"

Tia Babi and Maria, who were unfamiliar with that Broadway musical, looked at each other assuming that she had already been drinking.

The drivers grimaced too, commiserating over their misfortune to have been saddled with this bizarre group.

It took Maria Regueros more than five minutes to maneuver her rear end into the back seat. Whichever way she turned, one leg kept sticking out. The frustrated driver moved the front seat up as far as it would go. When that didn't help, he tried pushing at the bottom of

Maria's protruding foot, which only made her stiff knee creak and Maria cry out in pain. Andres had to go around and give her little heave-hoes from the other side until inch-by-inch all of her was at last inside the cab.

As the taxi pulled away, Tia Babi turned her head for a quick final glance.

Maria Regueros patted her hand and smiled. "*Ay*, Señora. Just think. No more coal shoveling."

• 41 •

Although my Cuban passport had long ago expired, I had originally entered the U.S. with a student visa, which somehow I was able to keep renewing throughout my high school and college years. It was only after graduation that I finally applied for my citizenship papers. It came as a total shock when I was informed that I had failed to register for the military and was therefore considered a draft dodger, subject to legal proceedings.

The God's-honest truth was that when I turned eighteen, I had gone to the foreign students office at Villanova and asked whether I needed to register. Perhaps my case was an unusual one, but without hesitating for a moment, the lady in charge had assured me, "Of course not, dear. You're still considered a foreign student." But when I told this to the immigration officer who broke the bad news, he stared back with a guilt-inflicting look that said, "You really expect me to believe that bullshit?"

It was already mid-December when, to dampen my holiday cheer, I received an official letter informing me of my impending trial and advising me to hire a lawyer. My father asked around and got me an appointment with an attorney who specialized in cases such as mine. Our meeting was on December twenty-third.

"Before we go any further," he said right away, "I should let you know that my base fee is four thousand dollars."

"Four thousand?" my heart started pounding. "I don't have that kind of money. I just graduated."

"I understand. But I assumed that your father would be taking care of it."

"My father is still paying for my college bills. He has two other kids who started last fall and two more not far behind them. I can't ask him to pay for this mess I got myself into."

The man remained silent for a moment. "Okay, tell you what. Here's the name of the immigration attorney who has your case. His office is downtown. I want you to go there today and explain your situation to him." Then as I was walking out he added, "But make sure not to show up till after three P.M."

At three P.M. sharp I entered my prosecuting attorney's office, with hands and feet soggy from fear. There was a pitiful-looking Christmas three on the reception desk, and two secretaries were rushing around setting food platters and liquor bottles on a long, festively decorated table. It appeared as if their holiday party was about to start.

After being asked to sign a waiver stating that I had no legal representation and was therefore undertaking my own defense, I was escorted into the attorney's office. He pulled out my file and after scanning it for two seconds gave me a grave look.

"I hate to tell you, but your case is an open-and-shut one. You didn't register, which plainly makes you a draft dodger, and as an immigrant, liable for extradition."

"Extradition to where? My family's all here." I pictured being sent back to Cuba to work on some pig farm or tomato field, never again able to see my parents or siblings. Despite realizing that I was making a total fool of myself, I began to sob like a little kid who's just been told that he'll be spending the rest of his life in detention. Tears flowed, shoulders heaved, my nose dripped, and I couldn't even find my handkerchief.

The attorney watched the spectacle in stern silence for a moment. "Yes. I could definitely get you extradited for this." Then he held up my file and smiled. "But it's Christmas," he said, "so I'm going to give you a present," and he ripped the file in half.

This time, crying from happiness, I sprang across the desk and embraced the startled man, who had to take out *his* handkerchief to wipe off the soggy mess that I was making on his jacket lapel.

"All right, all right. Enough. Now go home. And *Feliz Navidad*."

The citizenship ceremony was held at the Dade County Junior College's North Campus, all the way across town.

"I hope you won't mind my not going," my mother said, "but I have a million things to do."

My father had already left for work, which meant the only transportation available was our old Chevy Biscayne. The car, now a beat-up relic on which I had drawn a big peace sign, had been kept as a kind of totemic symbol. Its floor was full of precarious holes, through which more than one precious item had vanished onto the streets of Miami. I found it rather poetic that the vehicle that witnessed the first baby steps of my Americanization should be the one taking me to its climactic conclusion. I did not feel quite as sentimental when the beloved relic conked out in the middle of I-95 on my way there.

Mami had given me her Triple-A card, fearing exactly such a mishap. I was already running late, and by the time the tow truck arrived and gave me a jumpstart, I was afraid of not making it at all. I reached the auditorium with my nice citizenship outfit now a sweaty, grease-stained mess.

Everyone had already stood for the national anthem as I slipped into the last row. The recorded version was reaching "*O say, does tha-hat star-span-gled ba-ha-neh-her yeh-het weh-hayve*," and goose bumps sprang up all over my damp arms. I suddenly recalled that long-ago exile gathering in Pigeon Park. It was the Cuban anthem that had played back then, and even my father, who was tone-deaf, had sung along. They had all still believed that our stay here would be a brief one. But unlike that day, when I myself had remained stubbornly silent, I now burst into song. As I did, I noticed that this time I was the only one singing, then figured that perhaps it was because none of these new *Americans* knew the words.

Throughout the ceremony, people kept whispering to each other in Spanish. They were about to become citizens, but it appeared that they hadn't yet gone through the melting-pot process, and perhaps they never would.

A speaker talked about the great honor that was about to be bestowed upon us and about the responsibilities that came along with being a United States Citizen.

"*Que dijo?*" The old lady sitting next to me leaned over, not having understood a thing. I translated the gist of it, wondering how she had passed the citizenship exam, which was supposedly in English.

We were all then asked to stand again and raise our right hand.

"I am so nervous." The lady had decided to make me her confidant. As another speaker congratulated us for being new *Americanos* and welcomed us to the fold, she explained that her husband, who was somewhere in the balcony watching, had been against her doing this. He saw it as a betrayal of Cuba. "But all my children and grandchildren are Americans now," she said with a tear in one eye, "and I do not ever want to be separated from them again."

I calculated that she was probably about my own grandmother's age. And though I felt that I should be contemplating all-American thoughts at this crucial moment, I decided to ask her a Cuban question.

"Do you remember President Machado?"

"Of course. He was the best president we ever had. The only one who really tried to do something for our country. Well . . . our other country."

I felt myself swell with pride.

"But, please," she leaned over again, "if you meet my husband when we go out, don't tell him I said that. He thinks Machado was terrible."

I broke into a smile, realizing that some things would never change.

Her words made me think about the duality of my life. I had just sworn allegiance to the United States and was now unquestionably a part of it. For over nine years its culture had been remolding my thoughts, my rhythms, my vocabulary. Yet Cuba was still very much in me too, and always would be—perhaps differently from the way it was in my father, but present just as well. It was my roots, my earliest memories, and my heart.

My thoughts then returned to my great-grandfather. Maybe I would always feel a duality about him too. There was the General Machado of history books. The man both praised and reviled. The one I myself could rage against for having been seduced by power or adulation, and for not having known when to let go. Then there was Papá Gerardito, the man who had taught my mother to dance and gave her a kamikaze pigeon *piñata* . . . the one that Mamá Elvira and Tia Babi adored and defended, despite whatever the family had had to live through in his wake. He was the *bisabuelo* who supposedly sent cryptic messages from the other side, that never did Tia Berta and poor Lugi much good, the one still floating around somewhere keeping watch over his loved ones. Perhaps the time had come to make my peace with all the conflicting elements in my life, and let them coexist in quiet harmony.

• 42 •

My father was very proud of his new home. He himself had helped with the design of it. The ten-house cul-de-sac that he had developed was a mini-monument to invincibility, a symbol of his triumph over adversity—and in particular, over Fidel Castro. The saplings he had planted in our new yard were now growing too. They had started to give mangos, avocados, custard apples, and hopefully one day, if the one struggling sprig ever made it, perhaps *mameyes* too. It was still not La Finca, but life had not ended with the loss of it. My parents had forged another one in Miami and enjoyed wonderful times with old friends and new ones. They had been able to travel even farther away than they had before the revolution—to China and Patagonia, to Russia and South Africa, to Australia and New Zealand.

"I think we've had a good life, Luis," my mother would often say to my father.

"You *think*?" he would invariably reply, although he never did stop dreaming of one day returning to Cuba.

These days there was plenty of room for guests to stay over comfortably—no more *pin-pan-pun* cots being dragged in and out of the garage. There was also a full-time housekeeper to help out. But in a way, having part of the New York family staying with us until they got resettled reminded my mother of those early exile days, when our house had been a refugee way-station. The years had blurred the more unsettling aspects of that period. All she remembered now was the closeness and the pulling together to help each other. She loved seeing every inch of the house populated again and everyone sitting elbow-to-elbow at dinnertime. Having finally left behind the encumbrances of the townhouse, the New York group also seemed infused by the lighthearted sense of a new beginning.

There was only one development that my mother was not at all happy about. Our entire two-car garage was now piled up floor-to-ceiling with the boxes that had arrived from New York. As Mari had feared, Tia Babi's snail-paced weeding-out process had resulted in roomfuls of bric-à-brac being crated and shipped down, at an immense cost. Mami's unhappiness over this matter came to a head one morning after a windstorm. She stepped outside to find that a fallen branch from the avocado tree had dented the hood of her brand new Oldsmobile.

"That's it! I'm throwing it all out." She turned to my brothers and me. "Sunday night I want you to put everything out on the sidewalk for the garbage truck."

"You're insane!" I told her. "For all your talk of loving your grandfather, I can't believe you're so damn eager to get rid of whatever remaining records we have of him."

"All I want is to be able to park *my* car inside *my* garage." As the words came out she realized how petulant she had sounded. "All right. You may help your Tia Babi go through it all. But don't let her keep anything unless it's absolutely important. And I still want everything else gone by next week."

The following morning I carried a comfortable wicker chair into the garage for Tia Babi to sit on as we worked. But the determination she had shown back in New York to go through every scrap now seemed to have left her. She kept getting distracted and drifting off into thought. Then, after half a morning of my showing her things in order to elicit her opinion, she said, "You know, he realized that he was making a mistake."

"What do you mean?"

"The day they extended his term . . . he knew it then. He had spent hours with cabinet members and some other politicians. The amendment would also extend all their terms, so they had been pressing for it. Not that that excuses his going along. Your great-grandmother and I were sitting right outside when Papá came out of the meeting, with his hair and coat looking atypically disheveled. He turned to Mamá and said, 'Elvirita, I think I may have just ruined myself . . . as well as the rest of you.'"

With that, Tia Babi put down the batch of letters she was holding. "*Corazón*, I trust you to decide what's important." Then she went into the house and never set foot in the garage again.

Soon I began to wish that she hadn't been so trusting. There were too many things that I didn't feel qualified to pass judgment on, letters that seemed insignificant but might provide some important detail to a sharp-eyed historian. Still, each time I went inside to get her opinion, Tia Babi would wave dismissively and say, "Just follow your own instinct, *mijo*." I was also working against the clock, just one week to pare things down to a manageable set of boxes that could be stacked along the wall and leave room for my mother's Oldsmobile.

After long days of going through everything, much of what I saved were things that spoke of the family's financial straits: overdue bills, letters from creditors, SOS notes to Papá Gerardito in Paris. Many of these were written by one of his daughters, always starting by assuring him that all was fine, then adding some subtle hint that a little extra money would certainly come in handy. His replies were invariably regretful, for he was barely making ends meet himself. Those letters were interspersed with ones from former supporters who, ignoring the family's true situation, asked for loans or handouts in their own moment of need.

I was disappointed by the lack of more intimate writings. While the financial side had been fastidiously recorded in yearly logs, there were no diaries or letters that expressed inner feelings. On that regard they had subscribed to an old-fashioned propriety that now left too many things open to conjecture. My initial enthusiasm had begun to flag also. Then, as I haphazardly leafed through another financial log from yet another troubled year, a carbon copy of a letter slipped out. It had been written by my *bisabuelo* in the last year of his life, and was addressed to a Mr. McAndrews, in Miami.

The message was brief, and typically cryptic: "Thank you for granting me the impossible."

I instantly rushed back into the house. And this time, when Tia Babi began to wave me off, I persisted. "Do you remember a Mr. McAndrews?"

The name rang a bell, but she had to repeat it a few times before she could place it. "Oh, yes. He was a diplomat. An attaché at the American embassy."

"You mean, in Cuba?"

"Yes. He and Papá had gone fishing together a few times . . . before relations with the Americans started to sour. I think McAndrews always felt a little bit guilty about that."

"Did Papá Gerardito ever see him again?"

"*Ay*, Luisma. You're asking me to remember things from so far back."

"Please. This could be important."

"Why?"

"I'll tell you in a minute." I sat next to her. "Did he ever see this guy again?"

Tia Babi thought for a moment. "Yes. He came to visit us once. Toward the end."

"In New York?"

"No. Right here. We knew that it was probably Papá's last winter, and he had always hated the cold. So we rented a little house near the beach. If I remember correctly, McAndrews was already retired and also living somewhere in Florida."

"And . . .?"

"And what?"

"What happened when he came?"

"Nothing."

"Come on, Tia Babi. Think."

"But I'm telling you, Luisma. Nothing happened. Mamá and I left them alone so they could talk. That was all. And now please leave me alone too."

I was heading back to the garage when she turned to me again.

"Oh, wait! There *was* something else."

I made a U-turn.

"After McAndrews left, Papá told us that he had said he would like to do something for him, and he asked Papá if there was anything at all he wanted."

"And . . .?"

"He said he answered that what he wanted was something no one could give him."

"What was that?"

Tia Babi's eyes misted over. "A chance to see Cuba one last time."

I broke into a smile. "Maybe Papá Gerardito was wrong about that." I handed her the carbon copy.

"No, no. It couldn't be what you're thinking."

"How do you know?"

"Because he would have told me."

"Not necessarily."

"Luisma, what reason could he have had for keeping something like that from us?"

"Who knows? This guy was a diplomat. Maybe he felt compromised and asked him not to say anything. Or maybe Papá Gerardito couldn't believe it had really happened, and was afraid to say something then find out that it had only been a dream."

Tia Babi still found the possibility very remote, but she picked up the letter and read it again. *Thank you for granting me the impossible.* Then she remembered another thing. "You know . . . He did take Papá on one last fishing trip."

"Oh?"

Her fingers furrowed the armrest of her chair as she recalled details. "We were worried about his health and didn't want him to go.

But he was determined. I never understood why people have to get up so early to go fishing. They left practically in the middle of the night, and didn't return until late the next evening. By then we were all hysterical. But when Papá walked in, he looked the best that I had seen him look in months."

"There it is!" I said in triumph. "What more proof do you need? I think Papá Gerardito got his wish after all."

Tía Babi smiled. "*Ay, corazón* . . . I certainly hope so."

Since my *bisabuelo* had left no record of the trip, I gave my imagination license to run free.

• • •

It's a moonless night in nineteen thirty-nine. A small biplane carrying General Machado and his old friend McAndrews flies over the Everglades and lands on a tiny key somewhere south of Cayo Hueso. McAndrews's yacht is already waiting for them. The captain welcomes them aboard with a pot of coffee. *Café Cubano*, in honor of the guest. He's offered a comfortable seat inside the cabin, but not wanting to miss a single moment of the excursion, the General prefers to remain on the deck. A light blanket is brought out for him to throw over his frail shoulders, then they set sail into the blinding darkness.

By dawn, an island can be seen in the distance, silhouetted against a pink-orange sky. There's no need for anyone to identify it. The General recognizes it with the unwavering instinct that enables so many beings to intuit the place of their birth. He leans forward into the railing, impatient to draw as close as possible. The captain apologizes for not being able to go any closer, but he must adhere to the twelve-mile territorial limit. They give the General a set of binoculars. His hands shake as he raises them to his eyes and adjusts the lenses. The island comes into perfect focus. It seems so near now that by reflex he reaches out, trying to sustain the illusion that he can touch it. He imagines himself bathing in its translucent waters, being lulled by the waves to a slow Afro-Cuban tempo. He feels the fine white sand crackling as it wedges itself between his toes. Then, as the early morning sun of his beloved Caribbean starts beaming down upon his shoulders, he's young again. A whole life still lies ahead. He has a chance to do things over—and this time to make all the right choices.

His eyes strain, trying to absorb every detail. A small fishing village pops into his circular viewfinder. Fishermen are tugging at their nets. He wonders whether they're setting off or returning. He aims the binoculars higher. Farther inland, just above the rickety wooden houses, is a gently sloping hill crowned by a tiara of majestic royal palms. He thinks about his childhood in a town not unlike this one. Not by the sea but yet so similar. He stands up, remembering how everything used to feel back then, and for an instant, the distance between the two ends of his existence evaporates like a dewdrop.

But then all too soon reality returns. There are no second chances. He isn't young anymore. And this is his very last glimpse.

Inside the cabin, one of the sailors picks up a local radio station. It's playing an old Cuban *son*, a tune that by coincidence had been popular during the General's own presidency. How many times had he danced to that melody, sung those words, celebrated and rejoiced to them.

Softly, very softly, for he did not want anyone else to know he was doing so, he began to sing along once more.

> *"Se fué para no volver. Se fué sin decir adiós.*
> *Se fué por la madrugada—matando mi sueño de amor."*
> "He left never to return. He left without saying goodbye.
> He left at the break of daylight—ending my dreams of love."

This time, he did not dance.

• 43 •

It was our housekeeper's day off, and my mother wanted to astonish everyone with her own culinary strides. She had come a long way from her days of pouring Campbell soup over boneless chicken breasts.

Seeing ten chairs crowded around the dinner table and four more at a small one set up in a corner, made her heart leap with joy. Mequi, Gerardo, Lourdes, and I were at the card table. At the main one, Mami had placed Papi at one end and José Emilio at the other. The rest all sat elbow to elbow on either side, with Mari squeezed in between my two younger brothers.

"Darlings, I'm wearing a brand new pantsuit, so don't you dare spill any ketchup on me,"

Mari had started to study for a real estate license and was already spending part of her future commissions.

We were fourteen Cubans, carrying on ten different conversations all at once, none of them in a moderate volume. Andres was asking my father for his opinion on a Key Biscayne condo that he was thinking of buying. My mother was telling Tia Babi about her volunteer work at the Liga Contra el Cancer and the wonderful things that organization was doing to help newly arrived immigrants without medical insurance. José Emilio was reprimanding Tia Berta for having turned over most of the money that she got from the sale of the house to a total stranger, a man with apparent ties to a Santería church in Hialeah. A delighted Lugi kept thanking Mequi in her special language for the Eiffel Tower snow globe that she had brought her from a recent trip to Europe. Gerardo was telling me about the frat he was pledging for at

Georgia Tech. Lourdes was railing at all of us for having read a batch of love letters that her Puerto Rican fiancé had sent her. Francisco and Carlos were comparing notes on their respective summer lifeguard jobs. And I kept waiting for the proper moment to announce to my father that I had realized my B.A. in Sociology was pretty much worthless and had applied to Syracuse University to get a Master's in Television and Film.

My mother interrupted everyone, raising her water glass. "I want to make a toast . . . To all of us being together again."

"And to a free Cuba," my father added.

Afterwards, in a reenactment of early exile days, Mami rinsed the dirty dishes while I stacked them in the washer. Following an undying habit, she still insisted on their being spotless before entrusting them to the machine. Then, after drying every last inch of the counter and straightening everything upon it, she made herself a cup of Sanka.

"Would you like one, Luisma?"

"No, thanks."

A brew that she had once referred to as disgusting dirty water had now become part of an almost nightly ritual—Sanka and a cigarette, one quiet moment of introspection at the end of another busy day. Tonight I decided to join her at the breakfast nook.

I could tell there were many things on her mind, but she seemed too tired to share any of them. So it was I who broke the silence.

"Tell me one of your stories about when you lived in the presidential palace."

Surprised by my request she stared at me. "What for, so you can question my memories or make fun of things like my pigeon piñata?"

"No at all. I'd just like to hear one. It's been so long."

She sipped her Sanka, still trying to evaluate my motives. "I've already told you every single one of them. More than once."

"Then tell me one again." I meant it sincerely. "Please." For some reason I wanted to feel like a little kid once more, being told an old bedtime story for the hundredth time. So I sat there, staring back at her, waiting, until my mother finally dug into her attic full of stored-away remembrances. After taking one last puff, she put out her cigarette and began.

"The day your great-grandfather became president, the people of Havana poured out into the streets to celebrate"

THE END

Epilogue

I have often wondered how my paternal grandmother, who in the early sixties spent so many hours listening to radio reports of Fidel's imminent doom, would have reacted if some farsighted Nostradamus had told her that in 2017, as I write this, the totalitarian system imposed by the Castro brothers would still be very much in place.

All the main characters in my memoir are now gone, along with most of their generation. Even many members of my own age group who left Cuba as children, including my brother Gerardo, have now gone too.

I used to cherish hearing stories of the past that older family members would tell me. Then one day, I realized that I had become the sole repository of those stories, the only one still able to pass them on. Any recollections that they might not have shared with me, or answers to questions that I forgot to ask, were now gone along with all of them.

Since leaving Cuba in 1960, I have returned twice. My first trip was in 1979, when for the first time the Castro government allowed Cuban exiles back to visit their families. Mimamá, my maternal grandmother, was still living there, and we hadn't seen her in almost twenty years. My mother was reluctant to return, so I decided to book a ticket.

A trip that had once been a quick hop away had become an ordeal, entailing long flight delays and an evening stopover in Jamaica. As the plane finally landed in Havana, I was overcome with feelings that I never suspected I'd have. These emotions only intensified as I walked up Mimamá's weed-overgrown driveway, then knocked at her iron grill door. Her words of greeting, "*Ay*, you're shorter than I thought you would be!" startled me a little, but probably also kept me from breaking down completely. That was fortunate, as she had never been a fan of emotional outbursts.

My week there was like a time-machine trip to the past. Her ceilings leaked, and the paint was peeling. She had also sold most of her furniture on the black market, and the one remaining chandelier was whisked away during my visit. But what did remain was exactly as I remembered. There was the same shower curtain, the same clothes hamper in which we would deposit our dirty clothes before Mimamá sent us back home, squeaky clean, after a weekend visit. She also had the same curtains, bedspreads, and embroidered sheets, all of which would tear at the merest tug.

My visit caused quite a stir among the people we had known who still remained, and I made a point of seeing every one of them. There was Mercedes, our *manejadora*, and José, our chauffeur; Carmen, our laundress, and Machito, Abuela's factotum, with whom she had so often quarreled over his erratic work habits. Even *he* now looked back upon those days with fond affection. I also saw Padre Llaguno, our family priest, who had married my parents and baptized all of us. Every single one of these encounters was full of emotion and questions. Everyone seemed so much older, but the past was very much alive in them, and they were all eager for me to show them photos and see how *we* had changed.

Mimamá finally left Cuba in 1984, when the house was about to fall on her head and the government was ready to move her to an old-age institution. She was a strong-willed woman, and her arrival in Miami caused many buttings of heads with my mother over their different approaches to life. But coming to the U.S. also gave her the chance to get to know her grandchildren as adults, and to be loved by us, as well as by her eleven great-grandchildren. She lived with great gusto until the age of a hundred and one.

My second trip to Cuba was in 2012. My mother, who had dragged her feet when my father, near the end of his life, expressed a desire to go back once more, suddenly announced that she wanted to return. She explained that she had feared how such a trip might affect him, since he was already growing frail. But now she seemed determined to go and share her memories with whoever would accompany her, before she herself was gone.

Children and grandchildren, along with some husbands and wives, all jumped at the opportunity to join my mother on the adventure. There ended up being fourteen of us. This time, not a single relative or friend still remained on the island. Our visa application required that we name a family member that we were visiting. My mother put down the name of a distant cousin, who she was certain had long ago died.

During our week's visit, we went to every single site that had once been meaningful to our family, as if we were on a pilgrimage, following the Stations of the Cross. My childhood home, La Calle Ene, no longer existed. In its place was an undistinguished exposition building called Pabellón Cuba. Although I left this out of my story to avoid complicating it, my father had finally built my mother's longed-for dream house, in what was then called the Country Club district, along with another house next door for Abuela. But we only got to live in those houses for about ten months. My parents' house was now the Saudi Arabian embassy. Their national emblem, two crossed scimitars with a palm tree between the blades, was now embedded on the main pediment, high above the front door. Abuela's house had been given by Fidel to the writer Gabriel Garcia Marquez. It was said that the two of them spent many evenings together there, discussing world events while smoking fine cigars. Both houses were now protectively enclosed by an ornate iron fence. My mother glanced at her former dream house from inside one of our tour bus windows. "It feels like I never really lived there," she said "And anyway, those were the most miserable ten months of my life." She never even got off the bus.

We also went by La Finca, which was barely recognizable. The main house was now painted bright green and stripped of all the flower vines. With all of my father's trees also now gone, it stood in the middle of a barren weed field. We were told that it was a police headquarters, and our driver wouldn't even slow down long enough for us to take pictures, afraid that he might be arrested for doing so. It annoyed me that fifty-two years after having had it taken away from us, we couldn't even photograph it from inside a bus. Another thing that angered me during this visit was finding that total strangers had been buried in our paternal family's tombs. It was my mother who calmed me down. "It's not worth getting upset over this, Luisma," she said. "There's nothing in there but ashes." We then walked over to her father's grave, which she was visiting for the first time. As she bowed her head and stood in prayerful silence, I wondered about the emotions that must have been going through her mind. But whatever they were, she neither shared them nor let them show.

Our family's return trip was a rollercoaster of emotions. There were some joyful moments as we all sat together in one of the beautiful restored plazas, feeling proud of our native city and listening to an evocative song being played by a trio, one of the many now catering to the reborn tourist industry. There were also many sad moments, as we contacted people for whom friends or colleagues had sent money or medicines and we listened to accounts of their harsh realities. But the unquestionable highlight was my mother's visit to the presidential palace, now the Museum of the Revolution, which had been her childhood home.

We were told that we could not use the elevator, so at age ninety, my mother led us through three flights of the elaborate building, sharing memories of the eight years that she had spent there. She pointed out her room, which was right next to her grandfather's. She showed us the breezy dining room where the family ate their private meals, the ornate little chapel where she used to pray, and the grand salon where each Christmas they would set up a big *nacimiento*, or nativity, for her. She also took us to her grandfather's office and pointed out the little stairway that led up to the family's quarters. It had a grill gate with a lock on it. She said she would often listen for the jiggling of Papá Gerardito's keychain, then wait to greet him at the top. Finally she took us to the hall of mirrors, where her pigeon piñata had once hung. She pointed to one of the little balconies that faced the huge hall and recalled how she would sit behind the balustrade to watch the presentation of credentials ceremonies held for arriving foreign dignitaries. I stood behind her, watching as she stared at the room in silence. It was only here that I noticed that, for a brief moment, her eyes had become tearful.

I have many wonderful memories of Cuba; it is an integral part of my soul and of my beginnings, and yet, I don't really belong there anymore. Unexpected events changed our lives completely. Who would have thought prior to 1959 that one day we would not even know a single soul on the island where the family had lived for generations. But as my mother often reminded my father, life does go on. Their decision to bring us out of Cuba, difficult as it may have been, resulted in a different life for all of us, yet a happy and rewarding one. For that, and for so many other things they passed on to us, I will forever be grateful to my parents.

Luis Santeiro
New York
June 2017

Mami's return to the presidential palace at age 90.

Made in the USA
Middletown, DE
15 September 2017